CW00793739

"KLEARWELL"

RED SQUILL RAT BAITS

GUARANTEED TOXICITY

SAFE, SIMPLE and ATTRACTIVE.

Used and recommended by Medical Officers, Rat Officers, Sanitary Inspectors, &c.

SPECIALITIES:

Liquid Extract of Red Squill—Red Squill Rat Biscuits, &c. Barium Baits in great variety, Phosphorus Bait, Ratlime, &c.

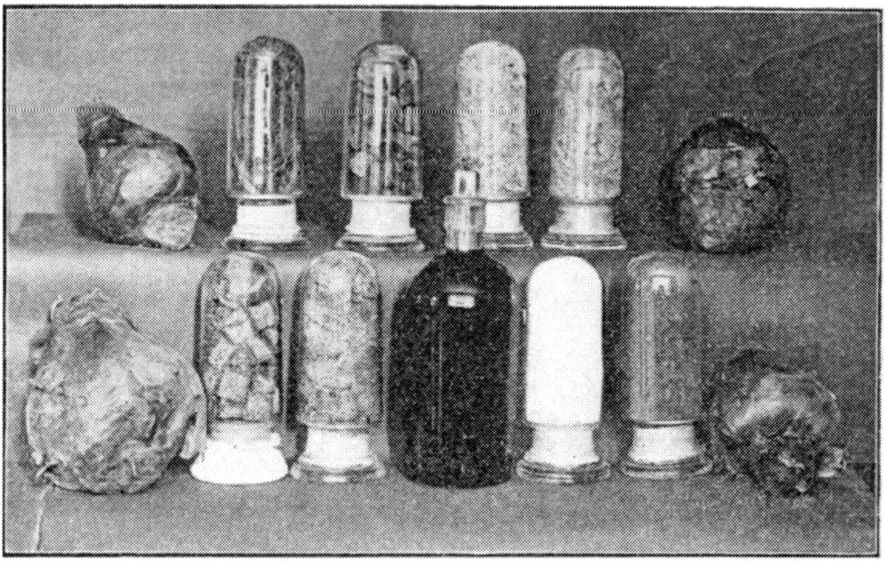

Red Squill Bulbs and typical Klearwell Baits.
Part of an Exhibit for Wembley.

Full details and Price List on application to

THE RODENT & INSECT PEST DESTRUCTION CO. LTD.,

69a, SANCROFT STREET, KENNINGTON, LONDON, S.E. 11,

who also offer a contract

SERVICE OF SCIENTIFIC RAT DESTRUCTION

unique in its reliability and thoroughness.

Managing Director:

C. L. CLAREMONT, B.Sc., F.I.C.,

Late Research Chemist on Rat Destruction,
Ministry of Agriculture.

PHONE:
HOP 6678.

"TERRIER" DEATH RUN RAT TRAP

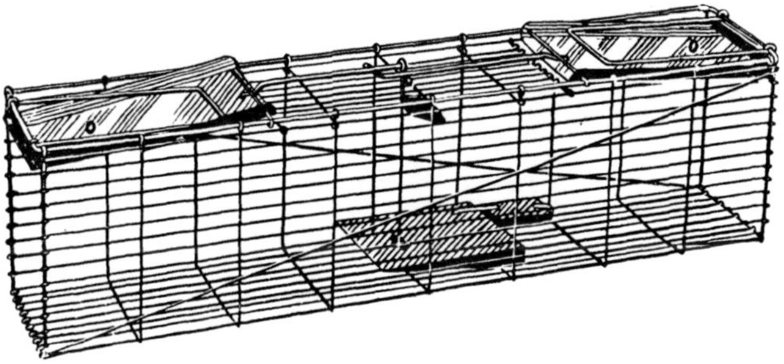

30″ long. 8″ high. 6″ wide.

Designed by the author of this book. Strongly made and galvanized after manufacture. No baiting required; cannot be sprung by vibration. Nothing to break or get out of order. **19s. 6d.** each.

THE "WONDER" RAT TRAP

No. 196

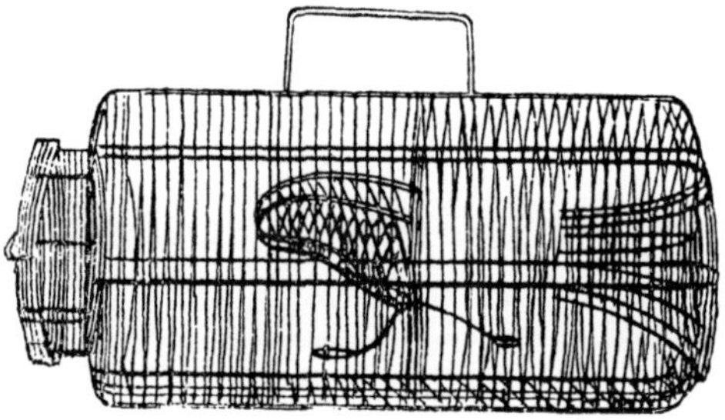

17″ long. 8″ high. 9″ wide.

The most successful cheap trap yet invented. Always set for business. **4s. 3d.** each.

THE COLIN PULLINGER MOUSE AND VOLE TRAP

12″ long. 3½″ wide. 3″ high.

A very useful trap. Balance action. Continuous trapping, no resetting required. **4s.** each.

For further particulars apply to the Manufacturers;

DUKE, WARING, CRISP & CO.,

SOHO WIRE WORKS,

139, WARDOUR STREET, LONDON, W.1.

Telegrams: "TRANSPECTUS, OX, LONDON." **Telephone: GERRARD 8798,**

MAKERS OF ALL DESCRIPTIONS OF TRAPS.

DESTROY RATS in
The "Londovus" Way

in a perfectly **CLEAN AND HEALTHY** manner without objection of any kind.

Consumes flesh and bone quickly **WITHOUT ODOUR.**

To kill by poison which creates contagious disease is dangerous.

THE "LONDOVUS" WAY IS THE SURE WAY.

HAS PROVED ITS EFFICIENCY FOR MORE THAN 10 YEARS.

Safe and saleable outside the Poisons Act.

Sold in tins at 1/1, 2/8, 5/4 10/-, & 18/- post free.

MANUFACTURED BY

LONDOVUS LIMITED.

WANSEY STREET WORKS, LONDON, S.E. 17.

ESTABLISHED 1810 **MAGIC PASTE**

For effectually destroying **Black Beetles, Cockroaches, Crickets, Ants, Rats, Mice, &c.,** in an incredible short time, let them be ever SO numerous, without leaving the least smell, as they immediately become dried up.

For over a Century we have relied entirely on the recommendations of our customers, without advertising. A large number of unsolicited Testimonials received. **(Clean and Simple to use.**

Prepared only by the Widow of the Late

CHARLES PENNY (SON OF THE INVENTOR)

83, GRAFTON STREET, MILE END, LONDON, E. 1

(Late of DALSTON, N.E., and REEDHAM, S.O. NORFOLK.)

SOLD IN POTS with directions for use **at 1/9, 2/3 & 3/3** POST FREE.
N. B.—The Paste to be had Genuine, only at the above address. No connection with any other house trading in the same name.

W. & G. SIDEBOTHAM,

Graisley Works, WEDNESFIELD, STAFFS.

ESTABLISHED 1865.

Makers of Steel Rat, Vermin, Rabbit And Large Animal Traps for Home and Export Trade.

Kills Rats

AND MICE.

"RATSTICKER," the non-poisonous rat and mouse catching compound, supplies a long felt want. It is a pest destroyer that is perfectly harmless to use and handle.

SAFE. CERTAIN. CONTINUOUS.

Dr. Howarth, the City of London Medical Officer, has experimented with **"RATSTICKER"** and has been successful in catching as many as 80 Rats at a time. He affirms that the Rats die quickly, death being caused by shock.

"RATSTICKER" is now being used by:—

County Municipal Authorities. Well-known Caterers.
London Borough Councils. Leading Hotels.
Port Authorities, &c., &c.

IN TINS

Small . 1/-
Medium . 1/9
Ex. Large 2/6

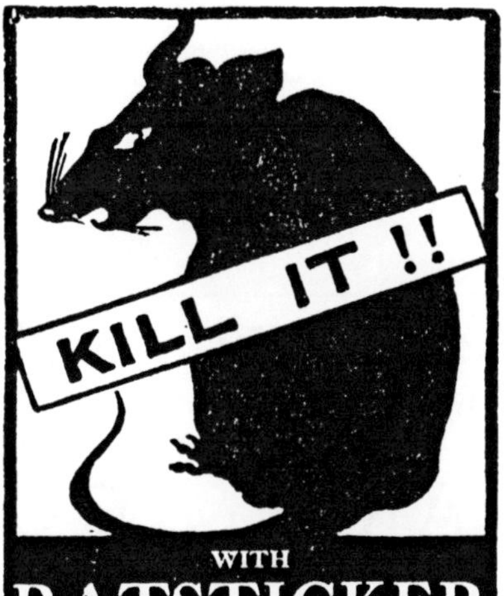

IN TINS

Small . 1/-
Medium . 1/9
Ex. Large 2/6

DIRECTIONS FOR USE.

Place tbe tin in boiling water, and when warm pour the contents (or part) on to the centre of a piece of thick cardboard, size 15-in. by 10-in. The **"RATSTICKER"** will slowly spread and cover the board.

Place a piece of cheese or other bait in the centre of the Board. The trap is now complete and should be placed near rat or mouse holes and runs.

CAUTION. Do not continuously boil **"RATSTICKER"**—merely place the tin in boiling water for a few moments.

Sole Proprietors and Manufacturers:—

B. WINSTONE & SONS, LTD.,
100/1, Shoe Lane, London, E.C. 4.

141 Collected in One Place.

Mr. Widdess, Chemist, Limerick, writes :—"A customer having a Skin and Hide Store laid 'RODINE' in various places. As a result in one morning 141 rats were collected, and thinks as many more probably died elsewhere. He is satisfied with

'RODINE' RAT POISON."

"RODINE" is the "clean sweep" Rat Poison. Fascinating and Fatal. It quickly brings to a dead stop the Rat nuisance. It is the sure and speedy Rat Remover as well as the most economical. Get a tin now. Tins, **7½d., 1/3, 2/6**, post **3d., 5/-,** post **6d.**

Sole maker and proprietor,

T. HARLEY, Manufacturing Chemist, PERTH.

RAT-CATCHING VARNISH

as used by all the leading authorities

Manufactured by

DANE & CO.

ESTBD. 1853

3, East Register St., Edinburgh. —AND— **91/2, Shoe Lane, London.**

"RATINOL."

The Well-known Rat Exterminator.

Harmless to Everything except Rats and Mice.

Used by the Zoological Society, L.C.C., most of the Scotch Municipal Bodies, Borough Councils, etc. Recommended by the Ministry of Health and other Medical Authorities. Lately had great success in clearing badly infested premises. **Estates Cleared. Contracts undertaken.**

In Bottles, 1/-, 2/6 and **4/6. In Jars, 16/9** Qt., **32/6** Half-Gal., **£3** Gal.

TO BE HAD OF ALL CHEMISTS OR FROM

THE RATINOL CO., LTD., 80, Coleman Street, London, E.C.2

Tel.—9011 LONDON WALL.

BOOKS ON RAT DESTRUCTION.

The Rat Problem. By W. R. Boelter. Illustrated. **3s. 6d.** net, post free **4s.**

Household Pests and Household Remedies. By the same Author. Illustrated. **3s. 6d.** net, post free **4s.**

The Prevention and Destruction of Rats. By Sergt.-Major Elliot B. Dewberry, R.A.M.C. With a Preface by Sir Arthur Shipley, G.B.E., F.R.S., Sc.D., Master of Christ's College, Cambridge. With 19 illustrations. **2s.** net, post free **2s. 3d.**

The Rat and How to Kill Him. By Alfred E. Moore. With an Introduction by the Right Hon. Lord Aberconway, K.C. Official Handbook of the International Vermin Repression Society. With frontispiece and plates. **6d.** net, post free **8d.**

RAT POSTERS.

Sample copy **1s.** post free. Per 50 copies **25s.** Per 100 copies **40s.**

JOHN BALE, SONS & DANIELSSON, Ltd.
83-91, Gt. Titchfield Street, Oxford Street, London, W. 1.

This book was written before my "**Nomorats**" was placed on the market. Nomorats has been quickly and enthusiastically adopted by many great wharves, warehouses, furriers, caterers, hotels, town councils, farmers, etc., partly on recommendation from high quarters whose tests have shown that its use means what its name implies.

"NOMORATS"

Fatally attractive, infallibly fatal.

Rats (and mice) die in the open. Uninjurious to domestic animals aud human beings. Liquid, easy and clean to handle (bread-bait). Cheap: A **2/3** tin contains enough to kill 100 rats. Discard your dangerous poisons and cultures. Do away with dead rats under your boards. Nomorats is an epoch-making rat-poison.

Full particulars from Sole Maker—

W. BREDT, 41, GREAT TOWER STREET, LONDON, E.C.3

BUY IT and TRY IT.

RATMOUSINE NEVER FAILS.

A Specimen.

For the Speedy Destruction of

RATS, MICE & BEETLES use

RATMOUSINE

Sold everywhere in Tubes and Jars. 7½d. & 1/3 each.

DRIES UP THE CARCASE.

Sole Proprietors: **F. FARMER & Co., 1a, College Lane, Homerton.**

ON OFFICIAL LIST OF MINISTRY OF AGRICULTURE.

Laid by the heels!

Cunning must be met by cunning. Rats, unless hunger-driven, are far too wary to venture the unaccustomed bait, poison-smeared and human-tainted; and too wily to enter the weird contraptions of wires and springs. Only the sticky trap of DAK is a match for the cunning of rats. Laid across the rat-run, it is unperceived until touched by a forefoot. The panicky struggle to free the imprisoned paw promptly lands the victim in the glutinous DAK, securely "laid by the heels." DAK clears premises and keeps them cleared for the traps retain their stickiness for many weeks. DAK catches mice literally by the dozen.

Messrs. Bookless Bros. (Aberdeen) Ltd., Aberdeen, write— The first night fifteen rats and mice were got, and the same DAK was used again for the next two nights. Since then we have not seen a sign of a mouse or a rat, the whole seem to have been cleared out of the premises, and it is certainly highly satisfactory to be in a position to have the dead rats removed rather than die in holes as with other preparations.

Major D. Heyland, Ballintemple, Garvagh, writes.—The 2lb. tin caught 32 rats. Many more with fresh supply.

D. Gray, Esq., Inverness, writes— In a large hotel here the first trial tin caught over 30 rats. A poison previously used necessitated lifting large amount of flooring.

Fred. Griffiths, Esq., Lockhill Hall, Ashcott, writes.—The results are wonderful . . . . nearly a hundred rats with two tins. Neighbouring farmers are sending for supplies.

"DAK" Ratlime

No poison. *No germs.* *No danger.*

DAK is sold in tins at 1/- (Mice only); 2/6 (3 traps for Rats or Mice); 4/6 (6 traps); 14/6 (24 traps). Of Chemists, Ironmongers or post free at same prices from KAY BROTHERS Ltd., Manufacturing Chemists, Stockport. FREE.—Illustrated descriptive leaflet with reports by users post free on request.

RATS

AND

HOW TO DESTROY THEM

DEALING WITH

Rats in a House, Shop, Warehouse, Outbuilding, Yard, Stable, Cow-house, Fowl-house, Pig-sty, Garden, Greenhouse or Vinery; by a River, Stream or Ornamental Water; on a Ship, Shooting Estate, or Farm; and in Sewers

BY

MARK HOVELL, F.R.C.S.

With Introduction by S. L. Bensusan

LONDON:

JOHN BALE, SONS & DANIELSSON, LTD.

83-91, GREAT TITCHFIELD STREET, OXFORD STREET, W.1

1924

All rights reserved.

MADE AND PRINTED IN GREAT BRITAIN

DEDICATED TO

THE RT. HONBLE. LORD ABERCONWAY, U.K.,

AND

SIR JAMES CRICHTON-BROWNE, M.D., F.R.S.,
LL.D., D.Sc., J.P.

THE TWO MEN WHO HAVE DONE MOST IN THE PAST FEW YEARS TO DIRECT PUBLIC ATTENTION TO THE REAL SIGNIFICANCE OF THE RAT MENACE.

PREFACE.

MANY years ago, circumstances arose which induced the author to superintend the destruction of a large colony of rats that had frequented certain premises for a very long time. In the house entrusted to his care, the rats were in large numbers on the ground floor, and occasionally they were seen in the bedrooms. In stables, cow-houses and outbuildings they were to be found in large numbers at all seasons. They invaded the fowl-house and carried off the eggs. They destroyed young poultry in early spring, and in the autumn they would establish themselves in the fruit-rooms. The hedgerows were full of their holes, and they had undermined banks around the ponds. They gave the gardener no peace, and dug up the peas and beans as soon as they had been sown. They burrowed under the lights, and ate their way into the green-house, and, wherever they went they left a trail of destruction. Whatever the owner of the house and those who worked there may have thought of them they appeared quite satisfied with themselves, and their quarters must have been all they desired, since they made no attempt to leave them.

Needless to say, they had been attacked in spasmodic fashion. Ferrets were employed from time to time, and traps set with very little skill ; those who had charge of them thinking that any place where a rat had been seen, or whence young pullets had been carried off, was suitable for a trap. Somctimes the mangled body of a pullet or duckling was used as bait. Unfortunately, even those who were responsible for the attacks on the rats, were in the habit of handling the traps so freely that they left the taint of their hands upon them, and, in spite of all that may be said to the contrary, rats recognize the smell of a human being and it suffices to put them on their guard. Time out of mind the traps were carefully set and as carefully avoided.

The thresholds of stables and outbuildings were worn away here and there, for the place was old and the rats could pass freely under the doors. In parts, where the thresholds were sound, the rats had gnawed a hole large enough for their purposes in the doorways. Such holes were to be found in the fowl-houses and in many of the other buildings, and in fact, it may be said that the whole of the premises was open to rats. There was no part of house or buildings that could be regarded as secure. It was to this condition of affairs, that it was found necessary to apply a drastic remedy.

Before going into details, it may be stated that for very many years now no rats have been seen in the buildings or in the house, and although there is still a steady movement of rats from adjoining properties towards the premises described they have almost, without exception, been trapped as they entered them. Now and again, on a rare occasion a rat has found its way into one of the outbuildings, probably because a door has been left open. Right through the year, from January to December, traps are kept set, traps with covers and signals which will be described hereafter. The first intimation that a rat or rats have approached the premises is seen in the signal that tells of a rat captured. The method by which the premises were cleared was not an expensive one, although it involved a certain amount of trouble and expenditure. But had it cost thrice what it did, the profit would still have been out of all proportion to the outlay. In the first place, the thresholds were repaired and all the holes that had been gnawed by the sharp teeth of rats were closed up. Then the rats were driven from their holes and places of concealment, either by ferrets or by the use of the water-cart, and the few that escaped from the slaughter were trapped. Gradually, as the buildings were cleared, all other rats on the premises were driven out and the holes they had made were filled in. As far as the house was concerned, the holes in the basement were carefully followed and found to communicate both at the back and the front with old brick drains of which the existence had been quite unknown. When they were stopped up and the premises cleared, Run-traps were set in all the paths along which vermin were likely to approach from outside, whether in search of food or shelter. Needless to say, perhaps, that a certain amount of practical knowledge was necessary to set the traps in the right places. It is not suggested that anybody can dispense with experience if he would be a successful trapper, but experience is not hard to gain, and the change on the premises written about here was so marked, that friends and neighbours began to inquire how they too could get rid of the rats that were troubling them. Some help was given, but the question of rat-destruction has many aspects as will soon be apparent to the reader. The means by which a large and old-established colony was entirely destroyed will serve to get rid of rats elsewhere, and the author, yielding to the repeated request of many friends, has written this book from his experience and notes which he has made.

A further inducement to the writing of this book is the knowledge of the enormous loss that rats inflict upon Great Britain. It is impossible to present accurate statistics but, with values as they are at the time of writing, it would not be surprising if the damage sustained by Great Britain, say in last year, approached one million pounds sterling per week, taking rural as well as urban districts and considering the docks and warehouses in which food is stored in bulk. In spite of all that has been said, the public do not realize the loss occasioned by the consumption of grain in the stack, granary, and mill or the damage and pollution caused to the grain that rats do not eat. People would be surprised if they knew how our food suffered while in transit in ships, or if they could get a true estimate of the damage done by rats in any year to buildings. There is yet another and more serious indictment against rats. We have in the county of Suffolk, between the rivers Orwell and Stour, an area in which bubonic plague appears to be more or less epizootic among rats, and the plague has on more than one occasion shown itself in the deadly pneumonic form. The grave significance of plague-infected rats in British seaports is not generally grasped, though almost yearly the Medical Officer of Health for the Port of London and the Medical Officers of Health for other ports also find several rats suffering from plague. Reports all over the country show that the black rat (*Rattus rattus*), which has never been exterminated in London and several seaport towns, is largely on the increase on this island, probably as the result of immigration, the rats landing most likely with their fleas already impregnated with plague germs. When we remember that we have millions of brown rats (*Rattus norvegicus*) in this country, whose flea can spread plague as readily as the flea of the black rat, and that as these rats still exist in spite of the "Rats and Mice (Destruction) Act" it must be clear that if plague-infected rats were introduced among them, disease would be spread with great rapidity. As will be seen in a later section, the plague would affect not only rats but also other living creatures including man, in consequence of the bite of their flea.

The recent outbreak of infectious jaundice calls attention to another disease transmitted from rats to mankind which probably has caused many deaths, but as in the case of pneumonic plague at Shotley, its origin and real nature have been unrecognized.

For some time past the Ministry of Agriculture has been spreading information as to some of the means of rat-destruction, but the knowledge is not sufficiently comprehensive or widespread at present, and in many parts of England the measures that should be employed to keep premises free from vermin are not known. That this proposition is sound, and admits no denial, is shown by the universal distribution of rats. Nobody wishes to harbour them, most people try to get rid of them, but they persist. It is quite clear that, while the Act will do much to improve conditions, a determined and sustained public effort must be made and maintained to reduce the number of rats as far as possible; and general organization is required to disseminate knowledge of the very best and most practical methods and to see that they are carried out. Above all, in consequence of the rapidity with which rats multiply, the best methods must be of universal application; that is why legislation should be welcome, because it imposes, or should impose, penalties upon those who will not render voluntary help. All those who are doing their best to free their premises from rats, require the largest possible measure of help; while those who are neglecting their duty, require the largest possible measure of compulsion. Whatever penalties are necessary to make the last named do their duty to their neighbours should be rigorously imposed. Some years ago, details set out here might have been deemed not only superfluous but almost impertinent, in so far as they give insufficient credit to the average standard of common sense. Unfortunately, experience has shown that mistakes will be made by all who have not a natural instinct for trapping, or for pitting their intelligence against that of a very clever and cunning enemy, and consequently, the attempt has been made in the following sections to obviate the possibility of error. While some of the explanations will be found unnecessary to those who have had the advantage of a complete education, it must be pointed out that this book is written to help all classes, and there should be nothing in what is set out that should not be clear to every reader. The repetition, which in ordinary circumstances one would endeavour to avoid, has been employed with a twofold object in many parts of the book. In the first place to make each section complete in itself, and secondly to impress all details that are of practical importance. Inasmuch as the use of dogs and ferrets must be considered, it has been thought well to introduce special sections on the management of both, in the hope that they will prove not only of interest but of value. Thanks are due to Mr. John Murray for permission to make quotations which are duly indicated from the late Mr. H. C. Barkley's interesting and very practical book "Studies in the Art of Rat-Catching."

If the directions and suggestions given in the succeeding sections assist those who are troubled with rats to clear their premises and do something to save the country's foodstuffs, and prevent the general damage done by these destructive animals, the full object of a considerable effort, extending over some years and over much of the scanty leisure of a busy man, will have been attained.

THE AUTHOR.

SECTIONS.

PART I.

PART II.

CONTENTS.

PAGE

the rats have been destroyed which frequent the place where it will be kept set always in the future—Necessity for keeping traps set all the year round—Reasons why at the present time traps are not usually kept set continually—Unnecessary to bait Run-traps—Necessity for signals—The reason why traps must never be handled—Cause of the erroneous belief that it is difficult to trap a rat—Methods for preparing the hands for setting a trap—Gloves not recommended—Treatment required for a newly-purchased trap before it is fit to be set—Precautions which should be taken when a trap has to be handled—The habits of rats which should influence the selection of the place in which a trap is set—The reason why it is advantageous to conceal a trap in a Run, or cover—Reason why it is advisable, when trapping rats in a place which they have frequented for sometime, to prop open for several nights the doors of a trap which cannot be concealed —The manner in which a trap should be baited—Formula for bait—Advisability of making the floor of a trap which cannot be concealed harmonize with the surrounding ground —Good plan to darken place where trap is set—Methods for concealing a wire-work trap—Advantage of keeping a live rat for some hours in a trap which cannot be concealed, before the trap is set or placed in position—Probable reason why rats avoid a trap in which several have been caught—Collection in a cage of the rats which have been caught alive in a trap—Desirability for removing as soon as possible a rat which has been caught, and not leaving a trap set throughout the night unless it is believed that only a small number of rats remain—Blood should always be removed from a trap—Setting a steel trap inside a building for the rats that frequent it—Burying a trap out-of-doors—Useful trapping accessories—Precautions to be taken when burying a trap in earth—Useless to leave in position a trap which has been discovered—Position in which a steel trap should be set—Best to remove traps for two or three nights after rats have been caught—Usually advisable to lightly cover steel traps—Care must be taken to prevent a steel trap from rocking—Methods for occasional trapping—Break-back traps—Method for setting break-back traps—Preventing the risk of a finger being caught in a break-back trap—Dead rats ought to be burnt or buried —Rules for successful trapping.

SNARING 79

Use of a snare—Selection of place for setting snare—Making a snare—Treatment of "snare-shy" rats.

LIST OF ILLUSTRATIONS.

INTRODUCTION.

It is a condition preliminary to the destruction of rats that we should know all that can be taught about their life story and their habits. We have learned by costly experience to expect them in every place used for the storage, preparation or distribution of food; we must find out how they seek and obtain access to such places.

In the first instance we have to understand that the millions of rats in our midst look to man for food and shelter; they could not endure the British climate if left unprotected from its scanty mercies. Rats follow man into the palace, the cottage, the warehouse, the farm-building and the garden; they travel by his trains, they are stowaways on his ships. They have been detected of late in the upper air making a meal or attempting to make one off the more delicate economy of an aeroplane, and in one case recorded, the pilot was compelled to rise to sublime heights. These were extremely cold; the intruder, not dressed for flying, experienced something akin to petrifaction; a numbed rat went hurtling through space and a satisfied pilot sought lower levels in his wake. On ships equipped for the transport of frozen meat the rat adopts Arctic costume, a long grey-white coat replaces the ordinary dress, but this needs time, and time is at a discount on aeroplanes.

Suffice it to remember that the rat is ubiquitous, growing more and more cunning as enemies multiply, menacing the health as well as the good of mankind, not because it is really dirty but because it acts as the host of unclean things, increasing so rapidly that Nature threatens plague and the Ministry of Agriculture has been forced to take action. Years ago the old Board launched a pamphlet against rats much as the Pope might have launched a Bull of Excommunication against heretics, or as high dignitaries of the Church in mediæval times issued edicts against destructive insects. Unfortunately rats are made of sterner stuff than Keats, who, if Byron had been correct, which he was not, allowed himself to be "snuffed out by an article." Whether because the pamphlet was more inaccurate than most of those fathered by the august authority or whether it is that rats, for all the fleas they carry and anathemas they endure, find life merry as well as exciting, none can say. Only these facts remain, the Board published and the rats persisted. In later years when the public hat in hand approached the Board and prayed to be redeemed from the rule of rats, the Board waxed wroth. "Have we not issued a pamphlet?" it inquired indignantly. "Do you suppose that if rats persist after that any power on earth can move them? Hence! You stand between us and our meditations."

Happily even a Board can be moved, public opinion is potent to shape it, and to-day, when the Board has become a Ministry we have a Rats Branch with an expert in charge and, until Sir Eric Geddes intervened, there was a factory for the manufacture of poison too. In the interests of economy (?) the Rats Branch ceased to function effectively in April of 1922. So it is still more important, from the viewpoint of those who really wish to learn how to be free of rats by their own exertions, that we have a book here by one who is, in the opinion of most of us, the greatest living expert on the subject. The writer is a man who knows every aspect of country life, and every trick practised by the oldest and most cunning buck rat that ever defied trap, snare, ferret, dog, poison, water or gun. Moreover, he has a trained mind and writes with complete authority.

Five and twenty years have passed since first I began to wage war on rats, learning all that many gamekeepers, professional rat-catchers, and a collection of clever dogs could teach me, and even becoming passably expert in trapping. From time to time I endeavoured to rouse general or local interest in the subject with very modest success and it was necessary to admit that certain difficulties of the question lay beyond any solution I could propose. Perusal of the following pages made all things clear. The author has not left a difficulty unfaced or a coil unravelled. No detective high up in the Councils of the Criminal Investigation Department has followed criminals with greater concentration of thought or intensity of observation than Mr. Mark Hovell has brought to the pursuit of the rat. He has considered every problem in the first instance from the rat's own side and having seen how the sly, furtive animal proceeds, he destroys his quarry by the use of an ingenuity greater than its own. The rat is encouraged to follow its own method unchecked, to find them facilitated to the end where swift death, often in a merciful form, is waiting. I have learned from this book, as it is to be hoped very many thousands will learn, that there is no such thing as an impregnable position for any rat. There is not any form of rat attack against which defence cannot be perfected, no means of entry however cleverly contrived that cannot be dealt with.

Whether the rat comes to the stable, the granary, the hot-house, the pig-sty, the ship's hold, the station yard, the wheat-stack or the cellar, it must meet the same end if the lessons taught in the following pages are mastered.

The author is not a practised writer, he is no maker of books. Years ago, at the earnest request of his father, he undertook to superintend the destruction of rats in the country home, and he made it his business to master his job with the thoroughness that was to bring him distinction in wider spheres of activity. Since then, for forty years or more, he has been quietly taking notes, making experiments, inventing traps and covers for traps, devising signal systems, analysing poisons, mixing his own and testing their worth. Now all these notes and illustrations come together in book form and make what is probably the most complete and reliable work on rat-destruction ever printed, whether in English or any other language. There is not a direction missing; there is not a trap or a run or shelter for the trap mentioned that the author has not made with his own hands, tried on his own property, and found worthy of public acceptance and use. If there is a point of criticism, it is that he has been almost nervously careful not to be misunderstood. He describes traps, runs, and every sort of ledge, platform, post and cover with meticulous care, occasionally in dealing with his essentials he repeats himself, of set purpose. The Conclusion is largely recapitulation, he has not left a nail out of its place or scantling unaccounted for, and he is wholly unrepentant. "Better be too explicit," he will tell you, "than not explicit enough. I have written for learned folk and simple, for experts who can handle tools with certainty and precision and for amateurs who will go wrong if I leave them as much as a loophole for mistakes. Rats must be destroyed." This, as the wise author of Ecclesiastes remarked, is the conclusion of the whole matter. We must destroy these worst of all vermin, for if we fail to do so, they will destroy us. Not only will they add very many million pounds a year to our national losses but they will thrive so upon our negligence that Nature, the divinity that shapes our rough-hewn ends, will become alarmed at their numbers and send the plague among them. This plague is communicable to man in bubonic or pneumonic form as most people know and as Mr. Mark Hovell sets out with details that form no part of the common knowledge.

If every reader of this book will recognize his duty as a citizen and will set to work without any delay, to follow out on his premises the instructions given or, if he has no personal need, to tell those of his friends who have, the passing of the rat menace is in sight. The first national onslaught will account for millions and then the steady, careful trapping will waste the remainder. Hitherto the harbourer of rats has had many excuses. He did not know, and those he employed to destroy vermin for him were only moderately well informed; sometimes they were crafty and dishonest knowing that if they did their work thoroughly their occupation would be gone. That is the crux of the problem. If you train men to kill rats and they kill them all they lose their job, their grave is self dug. Our author has not overcome this difficulty but he has reduced it to a minimum. We shall always have the rat with us and nothing less than ceaseless vigilance will keep it within bounds. The trouble at present is that the rat has multiplied and increased and replenished the earth it threatens to subdue. The Ministry of Agriculture's Rat Branch will doubtless do good work if only it is allowed to ; I do not agree with many of the criticisms directed against it, but if those actively employed in rat-destruction are to succeed, they must master the lessons unfolded in the following pages. Then there is not in these islands, or on the ships approaching them, a rat whose life is worth a week's purchase.

S. L. Bensusan.

Rats and How to Destroy Them.

THE HABITS OF RATS—SOME FACTS OF GENERAL INTEREST.

IN establishing themselves on any spot that takes their fancy, rats are bound by no other law than that of their own convenience. If not molested or not seriously troubled, they regard their habitat as a permanent home, and their numbers are only limited by the capacity of the place chosen to supply their needs. When the full limits of support have been reached they throw out colonies much as bees throw out swarms.

While the company of intruders is small and the visible damage appears to be inconsiderable, little or nothing is done by the rightful owner or tenant of the places seized. When his visitors become too numerous or too destructive, it is his habit to wage brief war against them, and then, after a few weeks, to leave them undisturbed. The chief cause of indifference and of irregular reprisals is that rats are seldom seen. A new rat-hole or a fresh run frequently passes unnoticed, while, as far as the rats' footprints are concerned, they are not often recognized by the casual passer, though the trained eye can see them in very large numbers. Even when the hole, the run and the footprints are seen, the impression made is small because the rats themselves are invisible. If people could only see, day by day, the number of rats that over-run their land and buildings night after night, they would take very prompt action without the aid of any Act of Parliament. Another fact that helps the rat is that few people who handle traps are experts at setting them, while most of the other methods by which vermin may be destroyed are to them a sealed book.

It is not common knowledge that to destroy a large colony, traps should not be used, unless a very large number are set simultaneously, until the number has been considerably reduced by either blocking, flooding, ferreting, or poisoning, or by a combination of these means, the trapping being reserved to deal with the few survivors. As far as the first two methods mentioned here are concerned, although they are most effective, they are not generally known, and, as a consequence, are but seldom practised.

As a rule any man or boy who may chance to work on rat-infested premises is considered fully competent to deal with them. Frequently he is told to buy a trap and set it, and this is supposed to be the beginning and end of rat destruction. The lad, or the shopkeeper, will select the trap ; it is freely handled, not only in the shop but when it is brought home ; when all who have any curiosity have satisfied it, the trap is baited and is, of course, handled further in the process. Whatever the bait, it is tied or fastened to the hook or treadle of the trap and the hands that conduct the operation are quite unprepared. The trap is then taken to where it is to be set—generally a rat-hole—and instead of being placed several yards from the hole, it is set directly opposite it where, in spite of the fact that the trap is reeking with the odour of humanity—an odour that the rat fears and detests—and in spite, too, of the fact that an entirely wrong position has been selected for it, the trapper is surprised when he returns on the following morning to find that things are just as he left them. It follows, in these circumstances, that the trap arouses no great enthusiasm. After a few weeks the particular trap is probably thrown aside as useless, and the opinion is expressed that the rats are too artful. If anybody were to suggest that the trapper is too ignorant, it is probable that the man or boy concerned would feel hurt.

A full-grown rat weighs from 9 to 14 oz., but both bucks and does, the former chiefly, attain a greater weight, from 14 oz. to 1 lb. being not uncommon. Under the heading "Notes and Queries on Natural History," in *The Field* of November 12, 1904, it is stated that in that month a buck rat was killed and found to weigh 1¼ lb. The editor's comment is: "A heavy rat no doubt, but the weight is not unprecedented." Recently a neighbour told the author that a few days previously he had trapped a buck rat which turned the scale at 20 oz. John Jarvis, official rat-catcher to the London County Council, stated that on one occasion when he was groping his way through the old Gaiety Theatre he was attacked by a rat. He killed it and, rather astonished at its size, put it on the scale. It weighed 1 lb. 9 oz.

The average length of a full-grown brown rat (*Mus decumanus*), measured from the tip of the nose to the root of the tail, is from 9 to 11 in., the variation in length as compared with weight probably depending upon the condition of the animal as much as upon its natural size. Some rats are larger than others irrespective of the amount of food they have eaten: this variation is common to most kinds of animals; it is found amongst those of any litter, and, of course, with human beings of the same family.

Length from tip of nose to root of tail		Length of tail		Weight		Sex
9 in.	...	6 in.	...	8 oz.	...	Doe
9 ,,	...	6½ ,,	...	8 ,,	...	Doe
9½ ,,	...	6 ,,	...	9 ,,	...	Doe
8½ ,,	...	7 ,,	...	9⅛ ,,	...	Buck
10 ,,	...	5 ,,	...	9¼ ,,	...	Buck
10 ,,	...	7 ,,	...	10¼ ,,	...	Buck
10½ ,,	...	7½ ,,	...	10¼ ,,	...	Buck
10 ,,	...	6½ ,,	...	10½ ,,	...	Buck
10 ,,	...	7 ,,	...	11 ,,	...	Buck
11 ,,	...	7 ,,	...	11½ ,,	...	Buck
10 ,,	...	6 ,,	...	11½ ,,	...	Buck
10 ,,	...	7½ ,,	...	11½ ,,	...	Buck
11 ,,	...	7 ,,	...	11½ ,,	...	Buck
9 ,,	...	7½ ,,	...	12 ,,	...	Doe
10 ,,	...	7 ,,	...	12¼ ,,	...	Buck
11 ,,	...	7 ,,	...	12½ ,,	...	Doe
11 ,,	...	6¾ ,,	...	12¾ ,,	...	Buck
9½ ,,	...	7 ,,	...	13 ,,	...	Doe
9½ ,,	...	7½ ,,	...	13¼ ,,	...	Doe
11 ,,	...	7½ ,,	...	14¼ ,,	...	Buck
10 ,,	...	7¾ ,,	...	14½ ,,	...	Buck
11 ,,	...	7¼ ,,	...	14½ ,,	...	Doe
9½ ,,	...	7 ,,	...	14¾ ,,	...	Buck
11 ,,	...	8 ,,	...	16 ,,	...	Buck
11 ,,	...	8 ,,	...	17 ,,	..	Buck

In moving from place to place a rat carries its tail about an inch or more from the ground, and consequently its trail is seldom seen, save when there is snow sufficiently deep to prevent the tail from being lifted clear. In snow the rat generally progresses by a series of jumps, the tail making a more or less continuous trail. But when snow is deep, a rat plunges through it and those who follow the trail will see the impression of its body as well as of feet and tail. By night rats travel a considerable distance to obtain food, buck rats being the more venturesome, and, by following their tracks in snow, much useful information as to their haunts and the routes they follow may be obtained. The length of the tail appears to bear no direct relation to the length of the body, as will be seen by the foregoing measurements. All rats on the list given here were trapped consecutively on the premises referred to in the preface, but they have been grouped according to their weight. As there were no rat-holes in the place where these rats were trapped, it is evident that they all came from adjoining property, and, as may be gathered from their weight, they were adults. This list gives a fair idea of the average length of body of the adult rat in relation to its weight. It will be noticed that the bucks preponderate.

Most people know that rats are very prolific, but few are aware of the rapidity with which their numbers increase. The usual litter varies from five to fourteen, the smaller number, when present, being found as a rule in the first litter, though even in these circumstances it is frequently exceeded. Mr. Frank Buckland, in his "Curiosities of Natural History," speaks of a white rat in his possession which, when eight weeks old, had a litter of eleven and brought them up successfully. Adult rats frequently have from eight to fourteen—the larger end of the scale is more usually met with, and sixteen is not an uncommon number. An instance is mentioned of twenty-one being taken from a doe rat which had been killed, and several other instances of a similar or even larger litter have been recorded. The number of bucks and does in a litter varies considerably. Neither sex can be said definitely to predominate.

Rats breed throughout the year, although most young ones are stated to be born between January and June. Female rats, when not paired, come in season about every ten days for a considerable part of the year, perhaps about nine months, but the season only remains for a few hours and, in the absence of pairing, returns in another ten days. The period of gestation is about twenty-one days, and impregnation may be renewed within a few hours of the birth of a litter. Female rats have twelve teats, three pairs on the chest and three pairs on the abdomen, thus showing that a large number of young ones in a litter is usual. They begin to breed when only three or four months old, and continue to breed five or six times in a year. It is stated that seven and even eight litters in a year are not uncommon, and this number may be repeated for several years in succession. The number of litters probably depends largely upon food supply and the age and condition of the doe. The young are born with their eyes closed and without fur. The eyes open at about the end of the second week, and at four weeks the young begin freely to leave the nest. Their weight is then about 1 oz., and this increases at the rate of about $\frac{1}{4}$ oz. a week until they are about three or four months old. The rate and degree of development vary, not only with the conditions under which litters are reared, but as already noted with different members of the same litter; only an approximate rate of development can be given, but the preceding table gives a fair idea of the weight of adult rats. We should not have so many in existence in this island to-day but for the prevailing idea that no trouble need be taken to get rid of them when there are "only a few."

Perhaps the following pages will show the necessity of killing every rat as soon as possible, if the numbers are to be kept in check. With the object of making the enormous rate of increase clear, even when litters are not many and the numbers are comparatively small, the pair of adult rats in the following table are given only ten young ones in each litter and only six litters in the course of the year. Moreover, the young ones are equally divided as to sex, and are not credited with a litter until they are four months old. Only eight young ones are allowed in the first and second litters and yet, as will be seen, the number produced in the year by the original pair and their descendants is 1,130.

Date of litters			Number of litters	Number of young produced		Total number of rats produced
January	...	—	1	10	...	10
February	...	—	—	—	...	—
March	...	—	1	10	...	20
April	...	—	—	—	...	—
May	...	6	1 Original pair 10 5 Born in Jan. 40	50	...	70
June	...	—		—	...	—
July	...	11	1 Original pair 10 5 Born in Jan. 40 5 Born in March 40	90	...	160
August	...	—		—	...	—
September	...	36	1 Original pair 10 5 Born in Jan. 50 5 Born in March 40 25 Born in May 200	300	...	460
October	...	—		—	...	—
November	...	81	1 Original pair 10 5 Born in Jan. 50 5 Born in March 50 25 Born in May 200 45 Born in July 360	670	...	1,130
December	...	—		—	...	—

If the calculation is extended to only two months more the number will have reached 3,050.

January	...	231	1 Original pair 10 5 Born in Jan. 50 5 Born in March 50 25 Born in May 250 45 Born in July 360 150 Born in Sept. 1200	1,920	...	3,050

Mr. James Rodwell,[1] in his book "The Rat," published many years ago, made calculations on a much smaller basis than the above to demonstrate the fecundity of rats, and yet he showed that a pair of rats and their descendants, even under these conditions, could produce in three years 253,762.

As will be seen in the following calculations, the rats are allowed only four litters in a year and eight young ones in each litter. Of these only four are does, and the young does are not given their first litter until they are six months old.

First Year.

Date of litters		Number of litters	Number of young produced	Total number of rats
Christmas Day	1855	—	—	2
Lady Day	1856	1	8	10
Midsummer Day	1856	1	8	18
Michaelmas Day	1856	5	40	58
Christmas Day	1856	9	72	130
Second Year.				
Lady Day	1857	29	232	362
Midsummer Day	1857	65	520	882
Michaelmas Day	1857	181	1,448	2,330
Christmas Day	1857	441	3,528	5,858
Third Year.				
Lady Day	1858	1,165	9,320	15,178
Midsummer Day	1858	2,929	23,432	38,610
Michaelmas Day	1858	7,589	60,712	99,322
Christmas Day	1858	19,305	154,440	253,762

[1] "The Rat," by James Rodwell. Routledge and Co.

Mr. Rodwell's calculation, which is here inserted, has been somewhat amplified to render still more clear the manner in which the result is obtained.

And if the calculation is continued for one year longer the result is as follows .—

Lady Day	1859	... 49,661	... 397,288	... 651,050
Midsummer Day	1859	... 126,881	... 1,015,048	... 1,666,098
Michaelmas Day	1859	... 325,525	... 2,604,200	... 4,270,298
Christmas Day	1859	... 833,049	... 6,664,392	... 10,934,690

As before stated, the above calculation under-estimates very considerably the number which probably would be produced. Yet taking the figures as they stand, they ought to help people to realize that, if premises are to be kept free from rats, not one must be allowed to live longer than the day on which it is possible for it to be killed.

People who live in the country and have school-boy sons should not leave the rats for the boys to kill during their holidays; they should destroy them at once. If the lads want some ratting, let them search for holes that have been overlooked or for other holes on the adjoining premises. Let them trap and let them go ratting, but let them hunt newcomers; do not keep the old inhabitants for them. One of the reasons why most premises are scarcely ever free from rats is the almost universal custom of only setting traps for rats that are known to exist. The proper way is to keep traps set all the year round to intercept any arrivals. Only by this means can premises be kept rat free. As a colony increases, many are driven out in search of fresh quarters, and on this account the enormous additions to the normal number are seldom understood. Buck rats are always on the move from place to place, while in the country both sexes leave houses, barns, stacks and buildings in the spring to migrate to the hedgerows or the banks of rivers and streams. In the autumn they return again to the stacks and buildings. While in the hedgerows, where some remain all the winter, they eat young rabbits, young birds, mangel-wurzel, swedes, and other roots that the farmer has placed in the "clamp" or "pit" and has covered with straw and earth to protect them from frost. In times of shortage rats will even eat earthworms, and they are particularly partial to any growing corn, most of their depredations in this quarter being laid to the charge of rabbits.

The precise date of departure to the hedgerows depends upon the spring. If it is open and mild they will leave early, if it is hard or backward they delay their departure. Their return to winter quarters is decided in part by the state of the weather and in part by the supply of acorns, beechmast, sweet chestnuts and berries of all sort. In an acorn year, as it is sometimes called, rats remain out very much later. As long as the doorways or walls of barns that admit of entrance and exit remain defective, and while stacks containing cereal or other seeds are built on the ground, rats will stay near home. They ask for little more than undisturbed and well-stocked feeding grounds and a convenient water supply. While some rats will enter out-buildings and stacks as early as September, they are known to remain until the end of April or beginning of May, and if a stack is left unthreshed, rats will remain until they have eaten it out.

In eating food, a rat sits on its hind feet, holds a grain between its forepaws, and bites it through the middle.

If he likes the flavour, he eats the greater part of it but always leaves the piece at each end. If he does not like the flavour, he drops it after biting and takes up another grain. Mr. James Rodwell, in his book already referred to, tells how, in order to ascertain the amount of grain wasted by rats, he watched some closely, and found that in some cases they merely bite through as many as eight grains out of ten and then drop them. Unless there is a shortage of food, a rat eats only the best. Mr. Rodwell also filled a measure, holding $\frac{1}{8}$ pint, with the best wheat he could procure and found that it contained 1,220 gr. of which 420 were small, shrivelled, or unsound. It goes without saying that the rat would waste all this, and if this is the proportion of waste in the best grain it is clear that a much larger proportion of the inferior would be wasted or spoilt.

From the indifference shown by the farmers to the presence of rats in their stacks and barns, it is evident that they do not realize how much good food is eaten and spoilt. Therefore, in order to enable their loss to be better understood, the amounts in the following tables are given by measure and by weight. So that those who are unacquainted with farming may realize the measure of grain eaten and wasted, the equivalent of the quantities is given in the weight of flour and the number of loaves of bread which the flour would make. To this must be added the milling offals known as sharps or middlings (used largely for feeding pigs and poultry) and the bran that the wheat would also produce.

Although 8 bushels or 256 quarts equal a quarter of wheat, it is well known that the weight varies considerably from several causes. If 60 lb. is taken as the weight of a bushel, a quarter will weigh only 480 lb., but it is a common practice for corn dealers, when buying from farmers by the quarter, to stipulate that the quarter should be a certain weight, often fixed at 504 lb. or 18 stone per sack. However, for the purpose of the following calculation 496 lb. is reckoned as the weight of a quarter of wheat, and the percentage of flour, sharps, bran, in corn of the best, medium, and inferior quality as follows :—

		Best		Medium		Inferior
		lb.		lb.		lb.
Flour	...	75	...	70	...	66
Sharps	...	14	...	18	...	19
Bran	...	11	...	12	...	15
		100		100		100

This represents per quarter :—

		Best			Medium			Inferior	
		lb.	oz.		lb.	oz.		lb.	oz.
Flour	...	372	0	...	347	$3\frac{5}{25}$	...	327	$5\frac{19}{25}$
Sharps	...	69	$7\frac{1}{25}$	...	89	$4\frac{14}{25}$	...	94	$3\frac{21}{25}$
Bran	...	54	$8\frac{24}{25}$	...	59	$8\frac{8}{25}$	...	74	$6\frac{10}{25}$
		496			496			496	

A sack of flour weighs 280 lb., and is supposed to yield 96 quartern (4 lb.) loaves, but the general yield is probably between 92 and 94, so that for the purposes of this calculation 93 loaves will be taken as the number produced, i.e., one loaf for about each 3 lb. of flour.

A quarter of wheat yields 372 lb. of flour, so that the additional 92 lb. of flour with the above allowance may be fairly taken to represent an additional 31 loaves, making 124 quartern loaves produced from each quarter of wheat.

Sharps and bran are usually sold by weight, but the quantity of these will be given by measure as well. Their weight varies considerably, according to the quality and care taken in the milling, but for the purpose of this calculation sharps will be reckoned at 42 lb. and bran at 14 lb. a bushel.

It is generally agreed that a full-grown rat, or ten full-grown mice, will eat and waste half a pint of wheat in twenty-four hours, and, taking this quantity as a basis of calculation, we find that

A pair of rats will eat and waste—

In seven days	Wheat, $3\frac{1}{2}$ qt., or 6 lb. 12 oz. 8 dr.; or Flour, 5 lb. 1 oz. 6 dr.; or Quartern loaves, more than $1\frac{1}{2}$, as well as sharps and bran.
In one lunar month ...	Wheat, 14 qt., or 27 lb. 2 oz., or $1\frac{3}{4}$ pecks; or Flour, 20 lb. $5\frac{1}{2}$ oz.; or Quartern loaves, more than $6\frac{3}{4}$, as well as sharps and bran.
In six lunar months ...	Wheat, 84 qt., or $162\frac{3}{4}$ lb., or 2 bushels $2\frac{1}{2}$ pecks; or Flour, 122 lb. 1 oz.; or Quartern loaves, more than $40\frac{1}{2}$, and Sharps, 22 lb., $12\frac{1}{2}$ oz.; or more than 2 pecks, and Bran, 17 lb. 14 oz., or more than $1\frac{1}{4}$ bushels.

100 rats will eat and waste—

Daily	Wheat, 25 qt., or nearly $48\frac{1}{2}$ lb., or 3 pecks 1 qt.; or Flour, 36 lb. $5\frac{1}{4}$ oz.; or Quartern loaves, more than 12, also sharps and bran.
In seven days	Wheat, 175 qt., or 339 lb. 1 oz., or 5 bushels 1 peck 7 qt.; or Flour, 254 lb. $4\frac{3}{4}$ oz.; or Quartern loaves, more than $84\frac{3}{4}$, and Sharps, 47 lb. $7\frac{1}{4}$ oz., or more than 1 bushel $\frac{1}{2}$ peck, and Bran, 37 lb. 4 oz., or more than 2 bushels $2\frac{1}{2}$ pecks.
In one lunar month ...	Wheat, 700 qt., or $1,356\frac{1}{4}$ lb., or 2 quarters 5 bushels $3\frac{1}{2}$ pecks; or Flour, 1,017 lb. 3 oz.; or Quartern loaves, more than 339; and Sharps, $189\frac{3}{4}$ lb., or more than 4 bushels 2 pecks, and Bran, 149 lb., or 10 bushels $2\frac{1}{2}$ pecks.

In six lunar months ...	Wheat, 4,200 qt., or 8,137½ lb., or 16 quarters 3 bushels 1 peck ; or Flour, 6,103 lb. 2 oz. ; or Quartern loaves, more than 2,034⅓, and Sharps, more than 1,139 lb., or more than 27 bushels, and Bran, nearly 894 lb., or more than 63 bushels, 1 peck.

It must, however, be remembered that many stacks contain not only one hundred, but several hundred rats, that a farmer has many stacks on his farm, and that there are rats in most, even if not in all of them. Consequently the farmer's annual pecuniary loss in wheat, barley, oats, peas, beans, or some at least of these seed foods, must be very considerable. Moreover, every stack and barn is a breeding establishment.

Although the loss affects the farmer personally, it must not be forgotten that this shocking waste represents a corresponding loss of grain and seed food to the country. It is contended that it is a waste that would be entirely prevented if stacks were built on suitable staddles (see Section "Rats on a Shooting Estate and on a Farm") and if the walls and doorways of barns and granaries as well as of other places where seed foods are stored or placed were made rat-proof and the floors concreted.

It has been previously mentioned that indifference to the presence of rats on premises is generally due to the belief that their number is but few. More fully to illustrate the loss and waste incurred by leaving even a pair of rats alive, the following tables are given, showing the amount of corn eaten and wasted by the offspring and descendants of one pair of rats, all of them (1,130) born in one year (see previous calculation).

From the foregoing tables dealing with the fecundity

of rats, it is evident that in six lunar months their number will have increased enormously, but, nevertheless, this increase will be ignored and the calculation made as if there had been no addition to their number. The original pair are included.

1,132 rats will eat and waste—

Daily	Wheat, 283 qt., or 548 lb. 5 oz., or 1 quarter 3 pecks 3 qt.; or Flour, 411 lb. 3¾ oz.; or Quartern loaves, more than 137, and Sharps, 76¾ lb., or more than 1 bushel 3¼ pecks, and Bran, more than 60 lb., or more than 4 bushels.
In seven days	Wheat, 1,981 qt., or 3,838 lb. 3 oz., or 7 quarters 5 bushels 3 pecks; or Flour, 2,878 lb. 10¼ oz.; or Quartern loaves, more than 959½, and Sharps, more than 537¼ lb., or more than 12 bushels 3 pecks 1 qt., and Bran, 422 lb., or more than 30 bushels 1 peck.
In one lunar month ...	Wheat, 7,924 qt., or 15,352¾ lb. or 30 quarters 7 bushels 2½ pecks; or Flour, 11,514 lb.; or Quartern loaves, more than 3,838⅕, and Sharps, more than 2,149¼ lb., or 51 bushels 4 qt., and Bran, 1,687 lb., or nearly 120 bushels 2 pecks.
In six lunar months ...	Wheat, 47,544 qt., or 92,116½ lb., or 185 quarters 5 bushels 3 pecks; or Flour, 69,087 lb. 6 oz.; or Quartern loaves, more than 23,029, and Sharps, more than 12,895½ lb., or more than 306 bushels, and Bran, 10,122 lb., or 723 bushels.

In connection with this table, it may be mentioned that Professor A. E. Shipley, in "More Minor Horrors," published during the Great War, gives 40,000,000 as a moderate estimate of the number of rats in Great Britain and Ireland, but in all probability this number is very far below the real figure.

However, loss through rats is not confined to the consumption and destruction of foodstuffs, to the damage they cause to property or even to the illnesses and deaths which result from their conveyance of plague and Weil's disease (infectious jaundice), both of which subjects will be referred to later; plague under a separate section, and Weil's disease in "Conclusion." They are the carriers and transmitters of other diseases and contaminate food and water supplies. They act as the primary host of the tapeworm, which, when conveyed from the rat to the pig, and—by eating uncooked or imperfectly cooked infected pork—from pig to man, causes severe and very fatal epidemics, and helps to enforce the expenditure of large annual sums on meat inspection. They also carry foot-and-mouth disease, as was pointed out long ago by Professor A. E. Shipley of Cambridge. They convey rat-bite fever and a virulent form of equine influenza from one stable to another, and also mange and ringworm, not only to different parts of the same stable but to other stables. Distemper is also spread by rats from one part of a kennel to another, and from kennel to kennel.

The widespread belief that weasels and stoats destroy a large number of rats for food may be dismissed. They kill a few, but not many, compared with the other animals on which they prey, and the rat can hardly be said to be persecuted by them. Weasels very rarely attack a full-grown rat, they prefer mice or bank and field voles; they feed also on moles, young poultry and half-fledged game. They will even climb bushes to reach young birds in the nest. If in the course of their hunting they meet a young rat, they will certainly destroy it, but young rats are very plentiful and weasels are comparatively few. Stoats prefer rabbits and any bird they can find on the ground. They will attack poultry, leverets, mice, young rats and frogs. Like weasels they will climb after their prey, but they hesitate to attack a full-grown rat, unless they are so hungry that they have no choice. If stoats were in the habit of attacking adult rats, many would get killed, just as ratting ferrets are killed from time to time. The best ferrets die from the wounds inflicted by rats, because they will attack a rat that is standing at bay while a cowardly ferret would not continue to fight. Although stoats and weasels often make their nest at the bottom of a stack that is infested with rats, there is no noticeable diminution in the number of the rats, nor are skins or tails found in the stack, as would be the case if the stoats or weasels had attacked rats and eaten them. This suggests that the nesting-place has been chosen because it was warm and convenient, and not on account of the rats. Indeed, it will be noticed that although a nest of stoats or weasels may remain for some time, because the eyes of the young ones do not begin to open until after the third week, the litter is withdrawn from the stack before the young are old and venturesome enough to attack the rats and provoke reprisals. If weasels or stoats attempt to interfere with the young of rats the parents will stand and fight. It is often said that stoats and weasels hunt in packs, but the writer's observation suggests that what is called a "pack" is merely a gill with her young. They remain with the mother for some time after they are grown up, and when to all appearance they are quite able to look after themselves.

Rats usually come out to feed from about half an hour

to an hour after the premises they frequent are quiet in the evening; the young rats are the first to leave the hole. Sometimes it happens that rats have their home in holes or under buildings on one side of the road, and feed on rubbish heaps or in fowl-yard or pig-sty on the other side, often at some little distance from their nest. People who keep fowls for amusement, but do not understand the principles of managing them, often throw food down in the runs late in the evening with the idea that the early birds will find in it a substitute for the first worm. Such people generally succeed in feeding quite a large number of rats, and they are seldom up in the morning early enough to discover that whatever they have put down has disappeared long before the fowls have left their perches. There are many premises to be found on which rats may be seen throughout the year, and on which they have been living for at least as long a time as the memory of the tenant can travel. In cases like this it happens generally that only sporadic efforts are made to get rid of the nuisance. Traps have been put down from time to time now and again, when opportunity has occurred, ferrets have been employed, or poison has been used, but there has never been a system or sustained plan for destroying the horde, and making the place safe from further disturbance. There will always be a proportion of rats that will escape from poisoning or ferreting, and will continue to rear their families, while from time to time the colony will be augmented by rats driven out or migrating from adjoining premises. The question then arises, what is to be done to clear the ground. The first measure, of course, is to destroy the entire colony, but it is idle to imagine that this step will avail to keep any suitable harbourage rat-free. Where rats have been rats will continue to be, if the old conditions that encouraged them are maintained. It follows, then, that as soon as the colony has been destroyed, the houses and buildings must be put in order so that the rats from other parts will find no facilities awaiting them. In the first place all holes leading into the buildings, and all holes in the buildings themselves, should be stopped. Thresholds, doors and door-posts must receive attention, so that there are no opportunities for rats to make an entry. Openings through walls made for gutter drains, whether from stable, dairy or laundry, must have a grating on the outside, and no corner into which a rat can retreat and lie concealed should be left, after ferreting and flooding. (This last-named method is dealt with at length in another section.) When all this has been done, fill up all the holes. Stray rats will not be able to escape into them, and no fresh ones can get on to the premises without showing the road by which they have entered. It should go without saying that it is useless to fill up holes with broken glass or any other material without killing the rats first, because if the old apertures are closed rats will make others, and they will continue in this fashion to attack the buildings in which they seek to find a home. It is a waste of time and money to pour tar down rat-holes, and there is another practice equally futile and at the same time very cruel that should be discontinued. Sometimes people have caught a rat, covered it with tar, and allowed it to run away in the belief that some of the tar will be left about the runs and will keep other rats from frequenting them. This method is as ugly as it is foolish. When using poison, do not fill in rat-holes until at least a week has passed. Not only the rats who frequent the hole, but their friends and neighbours from other places, will then be able to get some of the poison. Every hedge adjoining a farm building or passing from a stream near by should have traps in it throughout the year, and if there is a well-defined track that rats use, several traps may be kept set, so that, in the event of more than one visitor arriving, there may be accommodation. Traps should also be kept around houses and outbuildings in all places that rats may be expected to pass in search of shelter or food. There is no animal more persistent than the rat, and it will make repeated attempts to reach its goal so that the presence of traps properly set is a perennial safeguard to the householder.

The individual who is chiefly concerned in the destruction of rats should personally undertake the active supervision of the work or, failing the ability to do this, should depute some really capable and conscientious person to do so. It is useless, if success is to be obtained, to be contented with giving instructions and assuming that they will be carried out. Where trapping is concerned and the trap and signal runs, described in a later section in this book, are used, it should be one man's duty to see that the traps are kept oiled and set and that signals are working properly. The same individual should be responsible for stopping up rat-holes as soon as they are discovered, after destroying any rats that may be within and, above all, the duty and responsibility should not be delegated. The work of rat destruction is not a long one, and as soon as it has been carried out and the premises have been set in order in the fashion described later on, there will be no living rats to cause trouble, and the whole duty of the man responsible for rat destruction will be to see that the traps are kept set and in proper order. It must be remembered that, once buildings are rat-free, traps provide the proper medium for securing immunity.

Run-traps being used, and placed wherever possible against a wall, will not require to be baited. A rat reaching a run-trap will prefer to pass through it rather than to go outside, because all rats welcome concealment if it is only for a few yards of their journey. The value of the cover to the trap is three-fold. In the first place, it protects the trap from the weather. Secondly, it prevents all accidents to domestic animals and poultry. Thirdly, the cover attracts the rat for the reason just given. As it is not necessary to bury a steel trap that is in a cover, such a trap has merely to be re-set and the signal to be re-adjusted after the capture. On large premises it may be found difficult to entrust trapping to one hand, however experienced. Where the signal runs are used, they should be in charge of a man who passes the traps or goes within sight of the signal while engaged in his daily work. Trapping around a house and in gardens and stable yard may be left in the hands of the gardener or any capable assistant. It is important that whoever is entrusted with the work should be given to understand that it is to be taken seriously. The gardener or groom deputed to look after trapping should be told that it is as considerable a part of his duty as attention to the garden or horses. Above all, the master's eyes should remain wide open, and from time to time he should go over the ground and should assure himself that the signals have not been left down or the traps unoiled or unset.

In a part of the country where rats thrive in large numbers—and it is to be feared that such parts are not difficult to find—great care is required to find the situations in which traps are most effective. The haphazard method is, as usual, useless. The only way to find out the facts is to investigate them, and the simplest method of investigation is to give each trap a definite position and a number. Just as the poultry-keeper trap-nests his birds and keeps a record to show what each hen or pullet has achieved, so the man who is engaged in rat destruction should keep his trap record and be able to say at the end of the year where rats have been caught and where traps have not been wanted. In this way it is possible to learn where additional traps may be placed with advantage and where they are not worth keeping. It is advisable, too, to know the sex of the rat caught, though it will be found that as far as traps are concerned the captures are chiefly the males. Buck rats are bold and venturesome, and they will travel a long way in the search of food and adventure, while the does are more timorous and prefer to remain at home, or as near home as possible. Where poison is used doe rats would appear to be the foremost victims, and where traps are kept set bucks are the chief sufferers. During the National Rat Weeks of 1919, and the following year, this fact was commented upon by several of the medical officers of health who took a particularly intelligent interest in their work and were anxious, not only to destroy rats, but to learn something of their habits.

For record purposes a small book, ruled for single cash entries, is the simplest and best. The spaces can be used for the date and place of the catch, while the cash columns serve for classifying the sex of the rat and entering the full number captured. The entry of the date and number of the trap and the figure in the column kept to record the sex will take little time in the making, but will afford valuable information at the end of the year.

SOME GOLDEN RULES.

The following rules for ensuring the destruction of rats, and keeping the premises free after the colony that infested them has been destroyed, might be printed and given into the hands of all whose duty it is to keep buildings free. They are very safe rules, and if every owner or occupier would adopt them for a year or two, it might be possible to make the rat as rare as the dotterel or the fire-crested wren.

(1) Never attempt to clear rats from infested premises by trapping. Begin by blocking, flooding, ferreting, or poisoning, or all these methods in combination. This will serve to reduce the numbers to insignificance, and traps may then be used.

(2) Keep run-traps set throughout the year against the outside of every house and building that rats are likely to approach, and in any other place where runs indicate their presence.

(3) Keep all doors leading into buildings closed throughout the night, and stop or protect every hole or aperture through which rats may possibly obtain entrance into a house or building. Close all holes as soon as the rats that occupy them have been killed.

(4) Never allow a rat that can be killed to-day to live till to-morrow.

TRAPS.

ALTHOUGH there are many kinds of traps sold for rat-catching, there are only two of practical utility for permanent use ; the steel trap—sometimes called a gin—and the different forms of run-traps which open at both ends, with doors that close when the catch holding them open is disengaged by the weight of the animal passing over the bridge or treadle.

As shown in this Section and also in the Sections " Rats in the Outbuilding" and "Rats in the Pigsty," a steel trap can be kept set throughout the year in an open passage way through which a rat will attempt to pass on his way to obtain food or when seeking new quarters. Though in constant use, the trap can be thoroughly protected from interference by domestic animals and poultry.

For a trap to be efficient throughout the year, it is obvious that a kind must be selected that does not require baiting as an inducement for rats to enter. It is essential therefore that it should be a trap that can either be placed in a passage-way or form a run or passage-way itself.

Hitherto the trap most sought after has naturally been the one that will catch the largest number in a night. Of late years the " Wonder" trap has become very popular and has done good work, its manufacture in French prisons enabling it to be sold in this country at a low price.

The " Wonder" trap has a permanent opening, on the eel-trap principle, into the outer compartment, the inner compartment being reached through a balanced horizontal door which rises after being depressed by a rat passing through. The trap is worked by fastening open the door of the inner compartment through which caught rats are removed, and also fastening open the door between the two compartments so that rats can pass through the trap. Bait is then laid in both compartments and renewed for several days until the rats feed regularly in the trap. The door of the inner compartment is then closed and the balanced door freed.

The days of the "Wonder" trap however are over, for if the directions followed in this book are carried out, rats will not exist anywhere in large numbers; indeed, if they do so, it is evidence that their nests have been left undisturbed and that the attempt to get rid of them has not been conducted on sound principles. Moreover, when there is efficient legislation, the owners of premises on which a number of rats are to be found will be heavily fined for harbouring them.

When rats have been driven from their holes and no places are left in which they can lie concealed, traps open at one end only and requiring bait to induce a rat to enter them, will only be wanted for occasional use. They will serve to catch a stray rat that has got into a building through an open door or other entrance, or has taken up his abode recently on the premises. Even then a trap open at both ends would cause less trouble and probably effect a catch more quickly.

A trap, open so as to form a run, is more expensive than one opening at one end only, on account of its larger size and the greater amount of work entailed in its manufacture. When, however, it is remembered that a trap will last for very many years, the original outlay will not seem so great, especially when it is realized that it will need very little attention. Although always set, it will require no baiting and yet remain far more efficient than a trap opening at one end only, and therefore requiring bait.

It must be remembered that rats move from place to place singly or in pairs and therefore a trap which catches only one at a time is all that is required to keep premises free from them. When several traps are kept set permanently, the pair are usually caught the same night.

For trapping rats, two kinds of steel trap are in use, viz., the rat-trap and the rabbit-trap.

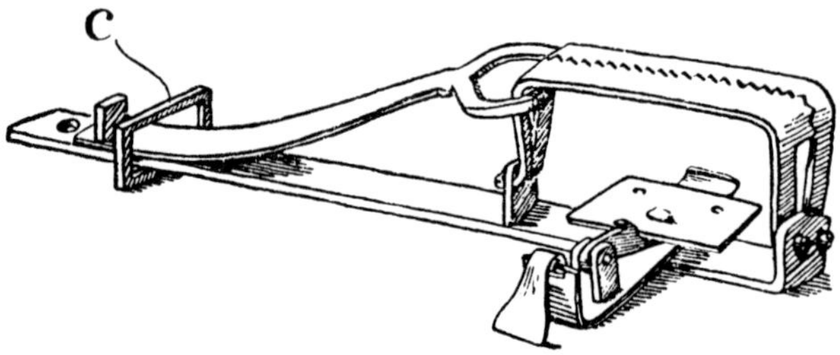

FIG. 1.—Rat-trap.

The rat-trap, as may be seen, has sharp teeth which meet closely, and the spring starts from the frame at an angle; whereas the rabbit-trap has blunt teeth which strike into large semi-circular notches on the opposite jaw, the spring starting from the frame in a curve. In other respects the arrangement of both is practically the same.

The rat-trap, whilst possessing several disadvantages, is in no way better adapted for catching rats than a rabbit-trap ; therefore the latter is recommended for use.

The disadvantages of a rat-trap are :—

(1) The teeth are unnecessarily sharp and meet closely, and as a consequence sometimes cut off one of the rat's feet and allow the rat, badly mutilated, to escape.

(2) The spring rising at an angle does not retain its strength as long as the rounded spring of a rabbit-trap.

(3) The sliding catch C, which is at the base of the spring, is apt, unless fastened back, to slip over the spring and prevent it from properly closing the jaws or holding them firmly together.

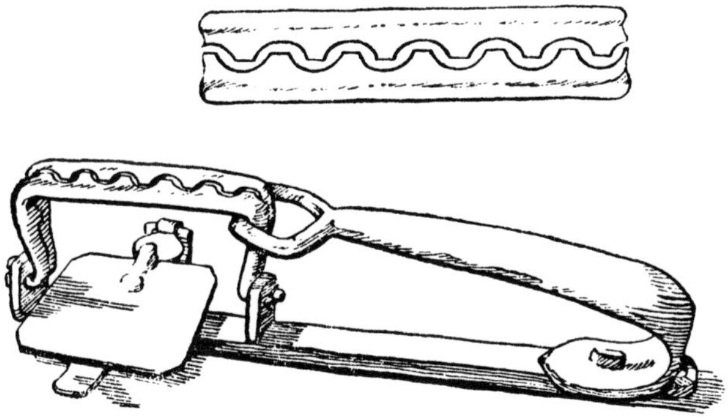

FIG. 2.—Rabbit-trap.

With regard to the sliding catch, this is not only useless, but a drawback to the trap. Nevertheless, it is still made, probably because it has been the custom to attach it to this kind of trap, and no thought has been given as to whether it is required or not. To prevent the sliding catch slipping along the spring, it should be fastened back with wire or cut off with a hack-saw.

It is most important to keep a steel trap oiled in the

hinge of the treadle, the notch and end of the catch, and the pivots of the jaws. Unless this is done, the hinge of the treadle is apt to work stiffly, and the catch to become either rusted to the notch or to fail to slip quickly. Either of these conditions prevents the trap from being sprung directly the treadle is pressed, and a rat, therefore, has time to get partially across a 5-in. trap; consequently it is caught by the hind legs and is not killed. In the case of a smaller trap, a rat may have got entirely across and thus escape. The quick working of a trap may be prevented by the oil becoming frozen. The pivots of the jaws and the surface they work against should be kept well oiled to prevent rust and to ensure smooth working. For this purpose any oil other than paraffin lamp oil is suitable.

As before mentioned, a steel rabbit-trap is recommended for catching rats, but so general has the custom become of using 4-in. traps for rabbits that only a few ironmongers or gunmakers stock any other size for this purpose. Some keep 4½-in. traps in case anyone should ask for them; but traps of a larger size than 4 in. have usually to be specially ordered.

By a 4-in. trap is meant a trap with jaws 4 in. long. This when set forms a square about 4 in. across. A 5-in. trap is measured in like manner.

Strange as it may seem to those who are unaccustomed to trapping rats, a 4-in. trap is too small. A 5-in. trap, therefore, should always be used, not only because it is more humane, but also because it is more efficient.

A rat caught in a 5-in. trap which is kept properly oiled and set lightly is usually found dead with the teeth across the body and the head and fore legs beneath the jaws, or it is caught along the body. In either case it is killed, whereas a rat caught in a 4-in. trap is merely held a prisoner by a leg or foot, and is very rarely found dead, as the jaws do not reach sufficiently high to seize the body. While thus held by a leg or foot, the rat frequently gnaws the contiguous woodwork or other soft material within reach, and sometimes escapes, leaving a foot in the trap.

Rats are more frightened by seeing another held prisoner by a trap than if they saw the dead body. In the latter case, if hungry, they would eat it.

Many persons who are unaccustomed to the use of 5-in. traps imagine that they are too large to set for rats, and that the jaws would meet over a young rat and leave him unharmed. This, however, is not the case, and as a matter of fact long-tailed field-mice and bank and field voles are often caught in 5-in. rabbit-traps.

It must not be forgotten that a young rat does not begin to leave the nest until about a month old, and then weighs about 1 oz., in another week about 1¼ oz., thus continuing to increase rapidly in weight and size. A full-grown mouse weighs rather less than 1 oz., and is much smaller.

It is true that a 5-in. trap costs a little more than a 4-in. trap, but the greater efficiency due to size more than compensates for the difference in price.

Time is saved by the rat being found dead in the trap, and there is much less likelihood of blood being on the trap than when it is killed while held by the trap. When blood is on the trap it should be carefully washed off and the trap boiled before being re-set. For like reason a first quality trap should always be procured, and if it is kept oiled in the hinge of the treadle and the pivot of the jaws, it will last for many years. The older it gets the better will it become, because although the spring remains good and brings the jaws firmly together, yet it is less strong than when new, and consequently allows the trap to be sprung more easily.

The author has first quality 5-in. rabbit-traps which have been continually kept set for rats during twenty years or more on the premises referred to in the preface; they are still in thoroughly good working order.

When the notch on the treadle becomes so much worn that it will not retain the catch sufficiently to enable the trap to be set easily, the end of the notch should be deepened horizontally with a thin, flat, warding key-file.

A first quality trap will wear out several second and third quality ones and be much more efficient during the time. The spring of one of second or third quality, becoming too weak after a while to bring the jaws properly together, will allow a rat to escape, a little fur on the teeth being all that is left to show the kind of animal the trap should have held.

For trapping rats a first quality "ordinary" rabbit-trap is quite good enough. It is therefore unnecessary, in the writer's opinion, to get a "Dorset" trap, which has a brass catch and galvanized treadle and is consequently more expensive. When ordering, therefore, it is advisable to state definitely "ordinary" (not Dorset) unless otherwise wished.

The terms "plain" and "grooved" applied to a rabbit-trap refer only to the shape of the outer or top surface of the closed jaws, the former being flat, whilst the latter has a raised rounded outer edge. The quality and efficiency are the same. In price lists "ordinary" traps are often quoted as "plain."

Some rabbit-traps are made with merely a wavy edge to the jaws and not with teeth, as shown in fig. 2. Traps of this description should not be used for rats.

For the last forty years the author has used traps manufactured by

Messrs. W. and G. Sidebotham,
Graisley Works,
Wednesfield, Staffordshire,

and as he likes a strong trap, he has bought their "Shave" brand; but there is a lighter trap known as their No. 6, which is less expensive, and does very well for rats, but probably is less durable.

The price of steel traps varies somewhat with the price of iron, and for this reason they now cost more than formerly; but the following prices taken from a recent list of Messrs. Sidebotham show the comparison between the sizes and qualities.

ORDINARY RABBIT-TRAPS.
"Shave" brand without chains.

	5-inch	4-inch
1st quality	29s. per dozen	24s. per dozen
2nd ,,	25s. ,,	21s. ,,
3rd ,,	21s. ,,	18s. ,,

CHAINS.
Heavy ... 3s. per dozen Medium ... 2s. per dozen

SIDEBOTHAM'S NO. 6. SHAM DORSET.
Without chains.

5-inch ...	19s. per dozen
4-inch ...	16s. ,,

The same rate of prices applies to single traps and chains as per dozen.

If a dozen or more traps are required they may be obtained with the purchaser's initials stamped on them;

the makers will attend to this without additional charge.

Steel traps are made usually with the catch to fix the right-hand jaw from the spring end. As will be seen from the construction of the trap, it is just as easy to turn and rivet the cross piece to the frame the reverse way, so that the catch secures the left-hand jaw. The price is the same either way.

Before ordering steel traps, it is well to consider the positions around the house and buildings in which it will be best to place them, and the direction the jaws will face, so that they may be made with either the right or left jaw from the spring end fixed as required. It is more convenient to have the fixed jaw next to the wall, for the attachment of the hook of the signal, which is described later.

On account of 5-in. rabbit-traps not being usually kept in stock, a reliable person should make the purchase. If a stupid or ignorant individual is sent, he may return, probably feeling very pleased with himself, and report that he has brought 4-in. traps, because the shopkeeper told him "that 4-in. traps are the best for rats and he always sells them for this purpose."

When a steel trap is set in a Signal Run—to be hereafter described—a chain is unnecessary, as the trap is too large to be taken through the entrance to the Signal Run, and is too heavy to be carried away by any animal sufficiently small to enter the Signal Run. Moreover, the animal caught is usually killed by the trap if the 5-in. size is used. When ordering traps for Signal Runs, therefore, it should be stated that chains are not required.

As mentioned already, 4-in. traps merely hold a rat,

but rarely kill him. It is obvious, therefore, that it is still more cruel to set a 3-in. or even smaller sizes; these often catch a rat by a foot or only just above it.

The author has used traps with jaws 5 in. long, that is, with 5 in. between the two pairs of pivot-holes, and nearly 3 in. wide, so that when set the teeth are 6 in. apart. These traps seize a rat ½ in. higher than a 5-in. trap, and therefore take a still more secure hold. For ordinary work the author considers a 5-in. trap preferable, as it holds full-grown rats securely and is more suitable for young rats. The grip of a 6-in. trap, which is 3 in. above the level of the treadle, is a little too high to make a catch of the latter certain.

If a trap has become rusty, it may be scraped and oiled, or even painted, provided it is not used when a trap has to be buried. In that case the smell of the paint might disclose its presence. There is no objection to a trap being painted when it is to be exposed and kept set throughout the year.

All traps should be sprung at least once a month to ease the spring, and whilst unset the opportunity should be taken to oil the notch and end of the catch, the hinge of the treadle and the pivots of the jaws.

Blood should always be carefully removed from a trap, and it is best, after this has been done, to boil the trap. If the trap has not to be buried, a drop of oil of aniseed or other essential oil may be put on the place which the blood covered.

Setting a Steel Trap.

A steel trap should be set as follows: Take two pieces of stick about 12 in. long and about the thickness of a finger, each cut on opposite sides at one end to form flat surfaces. Hold one in each hand. The catch which keeps the jaw down when the trap is set having been thrown back, and care being taken that it does not get forced into the ground, the spring should be pressed down by placing a foot on it. The jaw to be held down should then be turned outwards by the flat end of one of the pieces of stick, and the catch thrown over it. If necessary, it is then pressed down by one piece of stick while the treadle is raised by the flat end of the other stick, which has been passed under the free jaw until the notch on the treadle is caught by the catch over the jaw which is to be fixed. The free jaw should then be lowered gently to the level of the fixed jaw. When this has been done, the trap is set.

The object of placing the stick raising the treadle outside the free jaw, is to prevent it being caught if the jaws spring together by accident.

When set, the trap should be lifted with several thicknesses of paper intervening between the hand and the trap, or, if out-of-doors, a leaf may be used instead of paper. Care must be taken that the paper or leaf is not left in the vicinity of the trap.

When moving a trap from one place to another, paper, leaves, or some other material, should always intervene between the trap and the hand.

As before mentioned, when premises have been cleared of the rats which have long frequented them, there is no longer any necessity for a steel trap to be concealed. A rat coming to it, in a place visited for the first time, will run as fearlessly across it as over a piece of iron or any other substance, provided of course that the trap has not been touched by a hand, even in the slightest degree.

If this has been done, suspicion will be aroused at once by the smell of the hand, and the rat will not go near it.

Although many rats will be caught in a trap which is set quite bare, yet in some cases it is advisable lightly to cover a trap with grass or leaves according to the nature of the ground near by.

The trap, however, must be protected, for it is illegal to set uncovered a steel trap above the ground, and failing protection, poultry and domestic animals may be caught, and the trap will be liable to be knocked or trodden on by accident.

THE "TERRIER" SIGNAL RUN.
(Patent.)

The Signal Run is a box about 2 ft. in length, 9 in. high, and 7 in. wide across the inside, for a 5-in. trap, with a movable top and without a bottom. It is made to conceal a steel trap and so protect domestic animals and poultry. It has an entrance 3½ in. high at each end and is fitted with buttresses to compel vermin to pass over the treadle of the trap. The top is narrower than the inside measurement of the run, so that light may be admitted on each side of it.

An upright is attached to the side of the Run on which a movable arm is pivoted, the arm being held in a horizontal position, when the trap is set, by a wire attached to it, and caught by its hook under the fixed jaw of the trap. As soon as the hook is released, on the trap being sprung, the arm falls, and thus shows from a distance what has taken place. For details with regard to the Signal Run, see Part II.

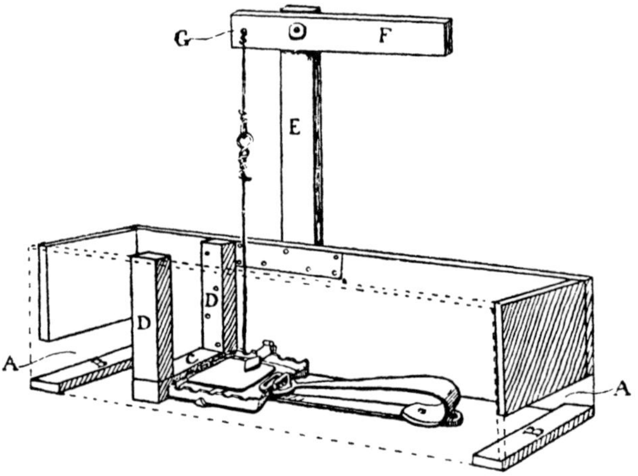

FIG. 3.—The "Terrier" Signal Run[1] (Patent). The cover and one side have been removed to show the interior of the run more clearly. A, entrance; B, threshold; C, transverse block below buttresses; D, buttresses; E, Upright to support signal arm; F, signal arm; G, screw to engage wire.

RUN-TRAPS.

Five-inch rabbit-traps are the most convenient for keeping set all the year round for catching rats, because a rat caught is usually found dead, and therefore no time has to be spent in killing it. Where there are children, run-traps may be thought to be preferable to steel traps, for fear lest a child should touch a steel trap and be hurt. In such cases run-traps, by which is meant traps which open at both ends, should be used, but it must be understood that they cost more than a smaller trap. However, the initial cost should not prevent the purchase of a trap,

[1] Manufactured by Messrs. Boulton and Paul, Norwich, and Messrs. Charles Orfeur and Co., Colne Bank Works, Colchester.

for it must be remembered that a trap, if properly treated and its bottom kept dry, will last for twenty years or more. The price should be divided by twenty, and the annual expenditure thus arrived at set against the pecuniary loss due to the rats which the trap will catch during each year, even excluding the number of descendants (1,130, see table) which each doe rat will create in the twelve months, and the additional damage which they will do.

For a trap to remain efficient for many years without requiring repair, a kind must be selected with doors that close by their own weight, and are made sufficiently heavy, or provided with a catch to prevent them being lifted by a rat. If a spring has to be used to close the doors, it will become weak in course of time, and if not renewed the rat caught may escape.

When set, the doors of a run-trap should be raised not less than 4 in., as this height prevents the doors being pressed against and lifted by a rat entering the trap, but it is best for them to be held open nearly to the full height of the run.

A run-trap should be selected for preference with the treadle pivoted across the width of the trap, and not at one side as usually made. Obviously in the former case the leverage is the same on whichever side of the trap vermin are running through it. In this respect the "Terrier" Death Run trap which is about to be described is preferable to other run traps now procurable, as well as having the very great advantage of its treadle being counter-weighted.

The trap is about 8 to 9 in. in height, and it has a door at each end, so that when set there is a clear passage through it. The doors are kept open, when the trap is set, by a series of levers which are released when the treadle is depressed.

The special features in connection with the trap are :—

(1) The treadle is counter-weighted, so that the trap is not sprung if accidentally knocked. It cannot be affected

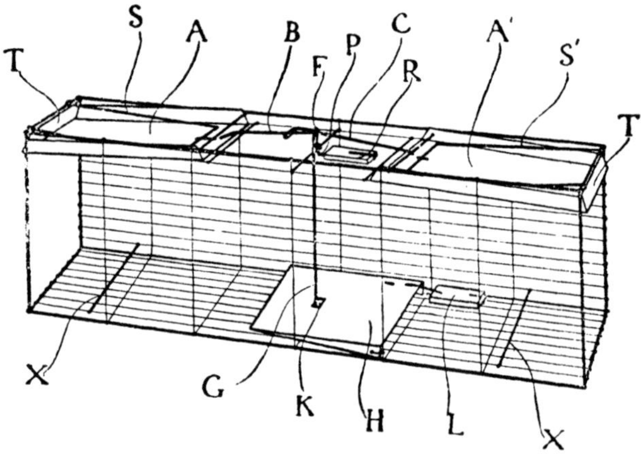

FIG. 4.—The "Terrier" Death Run Trap[1] (Patent). Trap set. The top and one side have been removed to show the interior of the trap more clearly. A, A[1], door; B, lever attached to door A; C, lever attached to door A[1]; F, loop at upper part of three-armed lever F, G, P; G, vertical arm of lever F, G, P; H, treadle; K, aperture in treadle; L, counter-weight to treadle; P, horizontal arm of lever F, G, P; R, weight at end of arm P; S, S[1], pivoted catch to prevent door from being raised when the trap has been sprung; T, turned up end of door to prevent the catch S, S[1], from swinging beyond it; X, baulking bar to prevent a small rat escaping under the door.

by vibration, if set in proximity to machinery, heavy traffic, &c., as may occur to ordinary treadle-traps. It is sprung only when the treadle is depressed by a weight on its upper surface, as happens when an animal passes over it. The trap, therefore, should be of especial use on board ship, where it would be unaffected by the vibration

[1] Manufactured by Messrs. Duke, Waring, Crisp and Co., 139, Wardour Street, London, W. 1. "Terrier" is the trade mark.

caused by the engines or the movement of the vessel. The counter-weight rests on the floor of the trap, and thus keeps the treadle at a constant level until it is depressed.

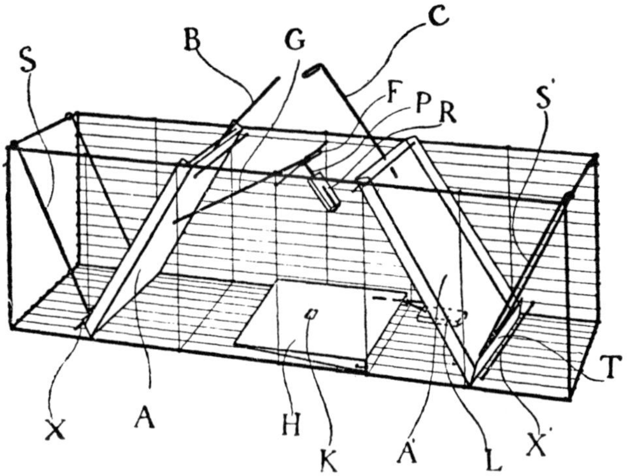

FIG. 5.—The "Terrier" Death Run Trap (Patent). Trap unset. The top and one side have been removed to show the interior of the trap more clearly. A, A^1, door; B, lever attached to door A; C, lever attached to door A^1; F, loop at upper part of three-armed lever F, G, P; G, vertical arm of lever F, G, P; N, treadle; K, aperture in treadle; L, counter-weight to treadle; P, horizontal arm of lever F, G, P; R, weight at end of arm P; S, S^1, pivoted catch to prevent door from being raised when trap has been sprung; T, turned up end of door to prevent the catch S, S^1, from swinging beyond it; X, baulking bar to prevent a small rat escaping under the door.

(2) The treadle is placed parallel with the length of the trap and pivoted across the trap, i.e., from side to side, so that the leverage is the same on whichever side of the trap vermin are running. This is a distinct advantage in trapping young animals.

(3) The doors close by their own weight, and therefore, as there are no springs to get out of order, the trap always remains as efficient as when new.

(4) Being a run-trap it is unnecessary for it to be baited.

Run-traps are less suitable than steel traps for clearing premises of rats, for the latter can be concealed by burying them in sawdust, earth, &c. If run-traps are used for this purpose, it is best to fix them open so that they cannot be sprung, and place food in them and at each end of them until the bait is taken freely, and then to set and visit them at short intervals, so that a captured rat may be removed quickly. (See Section "Trapping.")

The "Terrier" Death Run is an ideal trap to be kept set throughout the year in places to which children may go. Its efficiency is increased by being kept in a cover (fig. 6), and trouble is saved by attaching a signal to it.

The trap may be made of wire or metal.

Wooden Traps.

Wooden traps have the advantage of being much darker than wire-work traps, and for this reason are more readily entered; in fact a rat prefers to pass through such a trap rather than go outside it, on account of the shelter afforded. Wooden traps, however, are usually only made to order, as they cost more to make. Consequently, the price is considered prohibitive by the general public, who compare it with the price of wire-work or sheet metal traps which answer the purpose. The inside edges of wooden traps, moreover, require to be protected with sheet metal, and these must be renewed from time to time.

The author has two Hutch-traps which have been in use for more than fifty years and are still in good working order and kept constantly set. Each has been in a cover out of doors for the last thirty years or more. He has several other Hutch-traps, which have been out of doors in covers for nearly as long a time, that are still in thorough good order. A trap made of galvanized sheet metal or wire-work, however, will last as long if kept in a cover to protect it from injury and weather.

Wooden traps are best made of yellow deal, unless elm, oak or another of the harder woods is used.

The "Hutch" Trap.

The "Hutch" trap, frequently referred to in old books on rat-catching, and figured in the "Universal Directory for Destroying Rats," &c., by Robert Smith, Rat-catcher to Princess Amelia, 1768, is a wooden run-trap worked by a treadle, hinged to one side of the trap, the doors closing by gravity. Each door is formed by the end and part of the top of the trap being fixed together at a right angle, and hinged to the central part of the top. When the trap is set, the doors are held open by a cord tied in a small loop in the centre, each end passing from the loop through a deep notch in the top of an upright, fixed in the centre of the top of the trap to its door. To the loop is fastened a piece of thin cord, at the end of which a wooden catch is attached. The upper end of the catch, when the trap is set, is placed against a block fixed to the side of the trap while its lower end is engaged by a hook fastened to the treadle. This passes through a slit in the centre of the side of the trap, this part of the arrangement being similar to that of the Combined Rabbit and Vermin trap (fig. 8). The outside measurements of the trap are: length about 2 ft., height and width about 9 in.

The author noticed many years ago that for outdoor work the smooth working of the trap was interfered with by the cord becoming tightened in wet weather. He therefore removed the cord and central upright, and held the doors open by levers pivoted to uprights attached to the catch side of the trap, and arranged so that they lifted the doors about 4 in.—the inner ends of the levers being held down when the trap was set by a lever passing across the centre of the trap. This lever is pivoted to an upright fixed to the opposite side of the trap to the door lever uprights, and has the thin cord and catch already referred to attached to its free end. This arrangement has been used with complete success. The author also pivoted the treadle transversely to the length of the trap, and counter-weighted it so that the treadle always rests in a horizontal position at the same level, and is not affected by vibration. This uniform position makes pressure by the catch unnecessary to hold it in position and allows the catch to rest almost vertically when the trap is set, and thus enables the trap to be sprung by a light weight on the treadle.

Obviously, Hutch-traps must be lined with sheet-iron around all the edges of the doors and the surfaces with which they are in contact, special care being taken with regard to the slit in the side through which the hook passes, as mentioned in connection with the Combined Rabbit and Vermin trap.

All wooden run-traps, as well as steel traps, should be sprung at least once a month to ease the catch and move the hinges, and these parts should be oiled before the trap is reset. If there is a day fixed for doing this, such as the first Monday in the month, it is more likely to be done regularly. With proper attention the traps will last for many years and work more efficiently. Any oil other than paraffin lamp-oil is suitable.

COVERS.[1]

When a run-trap is kept set out of doors, it is advisable to place it under a cover, not only to protect it from the weather, and thus ensure it working properly year after year, but also to prevent it being injured by a dog while trying to get at a captive rat.

A cover also increases greatly the efficiency of the trap, as it darkens it somewhat, and thus causes it to be more readily entered. A rat on coming to a trap under a cover would prefer to pass through it rather than outside it, on account of the passage-way being darkened and shelter being afforded in consequence. This habit of rats does not appear to be generally known.

For ordinary purposes, when a "Terrier" Death Run trap is kept against a wall, it is sufficient to have the cover made in one piece, the front and top being 6 in. or more wider than the length of the trap, with ends reaching to $3\frac{1}{2}$ in. of the ground. The cover thus formed must be securely fastened to the wall by a hook on each end. There should be a space about half an inch wide from the top to the bottom of the ends in the centre to admit light—a transverse piece of wood or stout wire being fastened across the inside of the signal end at the level of the top of the trap for the pin which holds the signal in position to rest against. A space should be

[1] Manufactured by Messrs. Charles Orfeur and Co., Colne Bank Works, Colchester.

left also between the boards forming the front to admit light.

The cover must be high enough inside to allow the door-levers space to rise when the trap is sprung. For preference the top should be sloped sufficiently to carry off rain quickly, but a flat top will last for many years. The trap may be kept off the ground, and dry underneath, by being placed on pieces of slate, tile, &c.

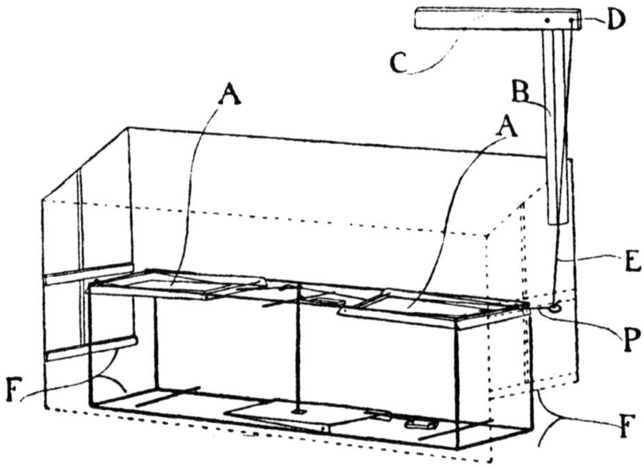

FIG. 6.—The "Terrier" Death Run Trap under a cover. The front and right end of the cover have been removed and are shown only in outline, so that the position of the trap in the cover may be more clearly seen. A, door; B, support for signal; C, signal arm; D, screw for attachment of wire; E, wire holding the signal arm transversely while the trap is set; P, pin passed through the aperture in the end of the cover and resting against the top of the nearer door; F, entrance to the cover.

The signal connected with a run-trap in a cover (fig. 6) must be supported on an upright (B) fastened to the cover or wall, or to a stake placed against it in a position which will allow the end of the arm to which the wire is attached to project beyond the end of the cover, and the pin (P) to pass horizontally through the aperture the whole height of the end, and rest on the top of the door under the cross-wire of the frame of the trap.

A cover is so easily constructed that it may be made by an intelligent lad, and if painted, black varnished or otherwise coloured, does not look unsightly

THE "TERRIER" BLOCKING TRAP.
(Patent.)

This trap is intended for all places to which rats are drawn by the smell of food. Among these may be mentioned quays, markets, slaughter-houses, knackers' yards, hotels, restaurants, provision stores ; shops, such as butchers, bakers, fishmongers, grocers, fruiterers, &c., also warehouses, granaries, flour-mills, factories, glue and chemical manure works, barns and outbuildings of every description.

The trap consists of a trough about 9 in. wide, and not less than 8 in. deep, covered with wire-netting and having at each end a door (A) working in vertical grooves. This can be raised and kept in position by a cord with a ring at its free end, through which a pin (C) is passed to take the weight of the doors, thus allowing a free run through the trap. The lower corners of the doors are slightly rounded, to lessen the chance of their catching in the grooves while falling.

At each end of the trap and on each side is an upright joined at the top by a transverse piece (B), on the under surface of which is fixed the screw-eye through which the cord passes which suspends the corresponding door. The pin (C) is held in position by two screw-eyes (D) fixed about an inch apart, one on each side of the medial line of the trough to a transverse support in the centre of the top of the trough.

A partition (E) is placed diagonally across the trap at one end, so that the width of the entrance is narrowed to about 4 in., and no corner is left in which the rats can congregate. The object being to enable the rats caught

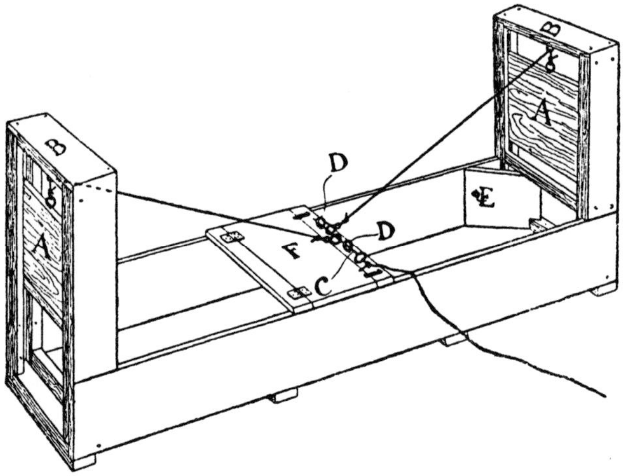

FIG. 7.—"Terrier" Blocking Trap[1] (Patent). The top of the trap has been removed to make its arrangement more clear. A, door; B, transverse brace to which is affixed the screw-eye on which the door is hung; C, pin which holds the doors suspended when the trap is set; D, screw-eye to hold the pin in position; E, partition placed diagonally, to ensure that the captured rats pass at once into the drowning box.

to be driven immediately into the drowning box which will be described.

Rats are very timid animals, and when driven in an enclosure such as a trough, will run backwards and forwards along the same side, congregating again and again

[1] Manufactured by Messrs. Boulton and Paul, Norwich, and Messrs. Charles E. Orfeur and Co., Colne Bank Works, Colchester.

in the corner opposite to the one which they have left. The diagonal partition is to prevent this.

The trap is placed against a wall with that side next to it on which the narrow doorway is situated. This allows a rat approaching the trap and running by the wall, as he is sure to do, to see the opposite doorway through the trap. In these circumstances he will enter the trap fearlessly, for rats always like to see another opening for escape in case of need.

The drowning box, which is covered with wire netting, is about 2 ft. in length, and in breadth about ½ in. smaller than the interior measurements of the trough, so that it can be slipped inside the small exit end of the trap as far as the door. At this end of the drowning box is an entrance about 4 in. in height and width, closed by a wire-work door sloping towards the interior of the box, and similar in construction to the small door at one end of an ordinary cage rat-trap. This entrance can be securely fastened by a door external to the sloping door, sliding in vertical grooves and secured by a button on the top of the box, or by a pin passed horizontally above the sloping door. At the other end is a door the whole width of the box, for removing the drowned rats. This door also works in vertical grooves and is secured by a button at the top. A hinged flap at the end of the top fastened with a button does very well.

The trap is worked as follows: Food is kept in the trap from one year's end to the other, so that any rats that are about may go to it to feed. When it is seen that the bait is being taken, arrangements are made for springing the trap, which is done by pulling the pin out of the screw-eyes, and thereby releasing the cords supporting the doors. While the rats are being driven into the drowning box, it is as well to darken it by throwing a cloth over it. The small door may be held up by a piece of string, to allow them to pass in more quickly.

When the trap is first placed in position, food should be kept in it for a week or ten days before the trap is sprung, and then only if it is seen that the rats are going to it regularly to feed. It is the rats which have been some time on the premises that are most difficult to catch. Bait should always be laid for a few feet at each end of the trap, as well as inside it, and the outside bait renewed each time it is taken, especially if that inside the trap is untouched. When rats are to be caught, a bait which cannot be carried away, such as meal, should be placed in the centre of the trap, so that they may congregate away from the doors. It is well to use some of this bait for a day or so previous to the actual trapping.

For convenience while placing bait and for cleaning, there may be a door at the top of the trap.

Rats come out to feed in the evening, from about half an hour to an hour after the premises are quiet, the younger rats usually venturing first from their hole, so that an interval of about an hour is best given before springing the trap ; afterwards the trap may be sprung about every hour until midnight, by which time most rats have had their meal.

The trap may be sprung from any distance and from any angle, provided the screw-eye, through which the cord passes on its way to the pin, is fixed on a level with the pin at a continuation of its longitudinal axis. When the position from which the trap will be sprung is in a line with the longitudinal axis of the pin, the intervention of the screw-eye is unnecessary.

The trap is made in three sizes, viz., 6, 5 and 4 ft. in length respectively. The largest size is recommended for quays, markets, slaughter-houses, knackers' yards, warehouses in which edibles are stored, granaries, flour mills, factories and glue and chemical manure works, barns, and all other places to which rats resort in large numbers. The smaller sizes are for shops, and places in which rats are generally to be found, but not in large numbers. If shopkeepers were to combine and spring their traps in a pre-arranged manner, the area occupied would soon be freed from rats. (See Section "Blocking.")

In places where a watchman is employed, it might be made part of his duty to spring the trap at stated intervals. One of the 6-ft. traps in three months caught 947 rats, thirty-nine being caught on one occasion by one drop of the doors, and frequently fifteen to twenty were captured at a time. It was admitted that the total would have been larger if the watchman had been more energetic.

A trap which stands out of doors may have a cover made of boards fixed in a sloping position away from the wall against which the trap is placed, the angle creating a space on the wall side 3 to 4 in. high, between the top of the side of the trap and the cover. This arrangement will not only keep the interior of the trap dry, but partially darken it, and thus make it more attractive to rats.

The trap is not lined with metal, for as a rule the rats captured are driven immediately into the drowning box and therefore have no time to gnaw, but when ordered galvanized sheet-iron can be affixed.

To preserve the trap it may be tarred or painted.

It is easy to arrange for the trap to be sprung automatically at a given time by means of a clock weight, electric current, or sand balance.

A sand balance is arranged by having a deep trough, with a transverse partition, pivoted transversely below the partition, and having a sufficient cover to both ends of the trough to prevent the sand falling out when the trough tips. To the end of the trough, which is empty when the trap is to be set, a string is attached connected with the pin of the trap, arranged so that it will jerk it out when this end falls to a vertical position. The proper weight of sand must be placed in the other end of the trough, which remains filled permanently to form the counter-weight, to enable it to be kept in the set position for the required time. Over the other end arrange a large funnel or box, with funnel-shaped bottom fitted with an aperture which will allow a given quantity of fine dry sand to pass through in an hour or other required time, the quantity placed in the funnel being rather more than that in the permanently filled portion of the trough. A shoot must be arranged on the top of the part of the trough which has to be filled, so that it still catches any sand which falls after the trough has tipped, and adds it to that which has previously fallen. A slide, at the end of the trough which falls, will enable it to be quickly emptied and the funnel refilled, if the trap is to be reset. The trough must be screened, so that the movement caused by the trough tipping is not seen by the rats feeding in the trap.

The remarks made with regard to the price of a "Terrier" Death Run trap apply equally to this trap, which will last a lifetime if properly looked after, as there is nothing which can get out of order.

COMBINED RABBIT AND VERMIN TRAP.

As mentioned in the Section "Rats in the Garden, Greenhouse or Vinery," it is very difficult to keep rabbits out of a garden by merely placing wire netting around it, but they may be effectually excluded by the use of the above-mentioned trap when set as described in that Section.

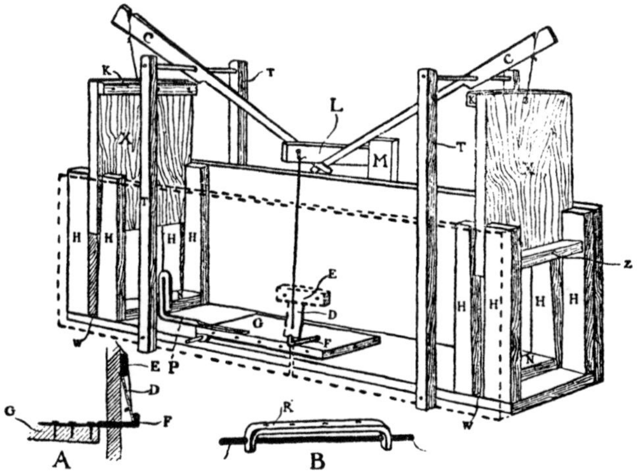

FIG. 8.—Combined Rabbit and Vermin Trap.[1] One side and top have been removed to show interior. C, pivoted lever; D, catch; E, block for catch to rest against; F, iron hook fastened to treadle; G, treadle; H, sides of groove; K, piece of wood to close aperture between door and top of trap; L, cross lever to secure door levers when trap is set; M, upright for cross lever; N, block across trap immediately inside door; P, counter-weight; R, iron for hinging treadle; S, pivoting bar of treadle; T, uprights to support pivoting bar of lever; W, groove in which door works; X, door; Z, block attached to door to close space between outer sides of groove when the door is raised.

As shown in the illustration it is a run-trap with a counter-balanced treadle, and arranged with vertical doors dropping in grooves.

[1] Manufactured by Messrs. Charles Orfeur and Co., Colne Bank Works, Colchester.

The treadle and the bottom of the trap may be sprinkled with dry leaves, or dry grass, &c., but the author has used these traps successfully for many years with the bottom quite bare.

A signal (see Section "Signals") may be attached to the trap, so that one can see from a distance whether the trap is set or sprung.

Occasionally the trap is found sprung and without a prisoner. This presumably has been done by mice or bank or field voles, their escape having been effected through the aperture in which the treadle hook works. When this occurs a balance mouse-trap (see Section "Mice") will soon secure the culprits.

It is well to have several traps for a large garden. The author has used these traps for many years, and has caught annually, not only the rabbits that were determined to enter the garden, but also a considerable number of rats, as well as hedgehogs, stoats, &c. For details regarding the construction of the trap see Part II.

Traps for Occasional Use.

The ordinary wire cage trap does very well for occasional use when a better trap is not at hand, but it is unsuitable for constant work. Not only has it to be baited, because having only one open entrance a rat would not enter it unless an inducement were offered for doing so, but when set it is easily sprung by an accidental jar.

The necessity to bait is a serious disadvantage in itself, as this gives additional trouble, and the bait has frequently to be renewed to keep it inviting, while, if mice are present, they remove the bait soon after it is placed in the trap.

In order to save two or three wires and the very short additional time in fixing them, some wire-work cage traps are made with the space between the wires so wide that a young rat can escape between any two. In any case, the space between two wires should not be more than $\frac{7}{16}$ of an inch ; and if the public would refuse to buy traps which are made with the wires wider apart, the manufacture of such useless traps would soon cease.

The various forms of break-back trap are of use for occasional work.

The best kinds of these are those made with a treadle. They can be concealed when buried in sawdust, sand, or other material, so that they may be placed across a run. (See Section " Trapping ").

Pitfall traps are useful where rats are not numerous, or where a trap is wanted for other animals besides rats, but they are more trouble than a run trap with falling doors, although they possess the advantage of being always set and therefore able to make more than one capture.

FIGURE 4 TRAP.

The figure 4 trap is useful when manufactured traps are not available, or when a trap is required in a situation from which a manufactured trap might be stolen. By its arrangement a heavy flat surface is supported until the trap is sprung, when the weight falls and crushes the creature which has caused it to be unset.

Any heavy substance with a large flat surface will do to create the crushing force, but what can always be obtained is a box, the necessary weight being produced by filling it with bricks or stones, or by nailing boards across what will be its lower half when set. The box is then filled with earth, the boards nailed across preventing the earth falling out of the box when tilted into the necessary slanting position to enable the trap to be set. When a large box cannot be obtained, boards may be fastened together to form a crushing surface of the required size, and a weighted box fixed to it to give the crushing weight.

It is sometimes advisable to place the trap with one side close to a wall, as this position facilitates several rats being killed by one fall of the crushing surface, especially if they have congregated beneath it on the wall side.

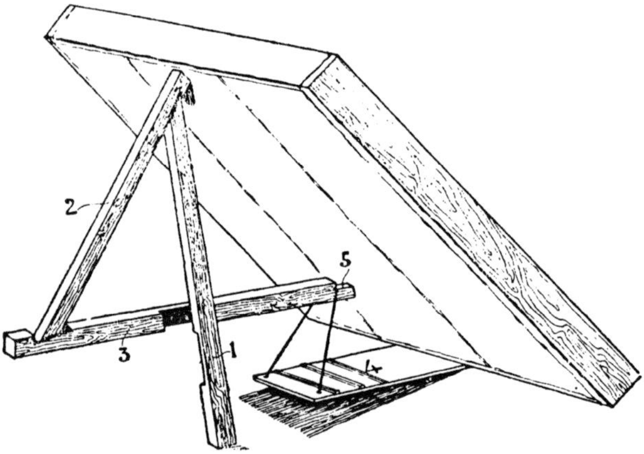

FIG. 9.—Figure **4** trap with treadle. 1, Upright; 2, slanting piece; 3, horizontal piece; 4, treadle; 5, notch for loop which supports the treadle when the trap is set.

When the crushing surface is narrow, the upright piece, No. 1, may be placed between its centre and the wall, so that the rats are at a longer distance under the crushing surface when it falls.

For rats, the flat surface is best if from 3 to 5 ft. in length, and about 3 ft. in width.

For a detailed description for making a Figure **4** trap see Part II.

SIGNALS.

When traps are concealed in runs or covers, and kept set all the year round, it cannot be expected that the person in charge of them will go regularly each morning and raise the lid of the run or cover to see whether or not a capture has been made during the night. He will be less than ever inclined to do so if rats are known to be seldom or never on the premises, and if the traps are merely being kept set to secure the first intruder coming that way. Nevertheless it is most important that a trap should be cleared and re-set as soon as possible after it has caught; while in the case of a trap that merely imprisons, it is obviously very cruel to leave the captured animal to starve.

Some simple device, therefore, is required to call attention to a sprung trap, so that, unless the sign is given, there is no necessity for an inspection.

A signal that will be found to fulfil this purpose effectually is made by nailing a piece of galvanized iron sheeting or tin to a wine-lath, and pivoting the lath so that the disc, when released, either rises or falls, as is required by the position in which the signal is placed.

The size of the disc should be regulated by the distance at which the trap is set from the place whence the signal will be viewed. A disc 6 in. square, if painted white, can be seen easily for several hundred yards against a dark background.

If the arm to which the disc is fixed must be long in

order to raise the signal well above intervening obstacles, the opposite end of the lath may be weighted with wood or metal, so that its length may be considerably reduced. Even then, and in all cases, the arm must be balanced by the position of the pivot-hole in such a manner that only a light hold is required to keep the signal in position while the trap remains set.

Wire is better than string for connecting the signal with the trap, as the former not only lasts much longer but also varies its tension less with weather changes. For a steel trap, this connection may be made with two pieces of wire, the lower being galvanized, about 14 standard wire gauge, and bent into a ring at the top and at the bottom to a hook about half an inch long. This must be set to rather less than a right angle, so that it may catch under the jaw and be retained there. If the angle is acute, it may be caught by the jaw as it turns when the trap is sprung, and thus interfere with the trap closing. The total vertical length of this piece of wire, when the loop has been formed and the arm bent, must depend on the relative position of trap and signal, and be arranged so that the hook cannot catch against anything after the trap has been sprung, and so prevent the signal from going to its proper position. The upper part may be a piece of stout binding wire, copper or galvanized, about 18 gauge, connecting the ring on the lower wire with a nail or screw on the arm of the signal. The length must suffice to fix the arm horizontally when the hook is caught under the jaw of the trap, which, for preference, should be the fixed one.

Obviously, the lower wire must be hooked under the jaw from the outside, otherwise it would be liable to be caught between the jaw and the animal captured, and thus prevent the signal from falling or rising.

The simplest arrangement for the signal is to place it immediately over the trap. If near the place from which it can be viewed, it may be left uncovered, as its position shows whether or not the trap has been sprung. If, on

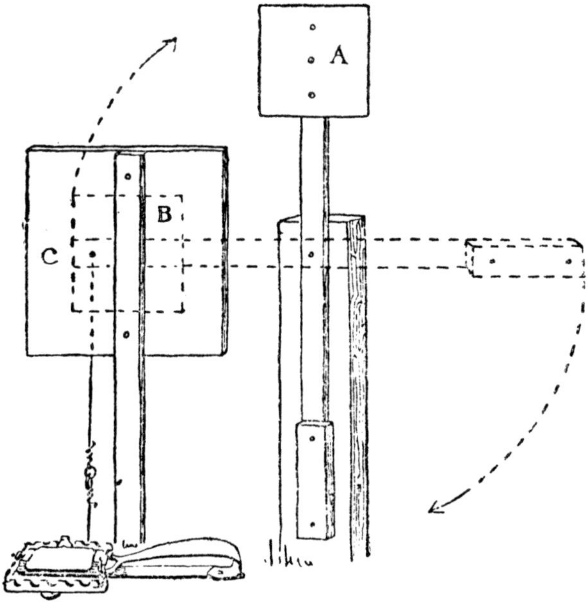

FIG. 10.—Diagram showing the arrangement of a signal set at a distance. A, position of signal when trap has been sprung; B, position of signal while trap is set; C, screen. The trap is shown exposed to make the diagram more clear.

the other hand, it is at a distance, a piece of wood, which for preference should be painted black and be sufficiently large to conceal the signal, should be nailed to a stake and placed in front of it. The signal will then only be visible when the trap has been sprung and the hook which held the signal out of sight is disengaged.

When a trap is set close to the place from which it is visible, a disc of metal is unnecessary, as the signal can be easily seen if it is made of a broad lath and painted white or red according to the colour of the building against which it is placed.

The apparatus required in any conceivable case to connect a signal with a trap is such an extremely simple matter that an intelligent lad can make and connect one. When in position it will last for many years, there being nothing to get out of order. In the majority of cases a signal can be arranged so that it is connected directly with the trap; but when otherwise, it is merely a question of pivoting a lath and fastening a screw or nail at its ends for attaching the wires.

It is well to put the lath in a vice or screw-jack before boring the pivot-hole. This prevents the possibility of the lath being split, and it is also advisable to pass a piece of hot rod iron through the hole when it has been made, so as to char its edges. If this is not done, the hole may become swollen and cling to the pivot in wet weather.

Signals have been in use for many years on the premises referred to in the Preface, and have been found most useful in saving time and labour that would have been otherwise required to examine the signal runs holding steel traps, and the covers concealing the run traps, which merely imprison. They have proved especially useful in connection with traps by hedgerows several hundred yards distant.

For signals wine-laths should always be used because they are flat and of uniform shape, whereas the laths used for plastering are often uneven and twisted.

Oak wine-laths are unnecessary, as those made of deal answer the purpose quite well.

See Part II for detailed description of arrangement for signals to show in the following positions :—

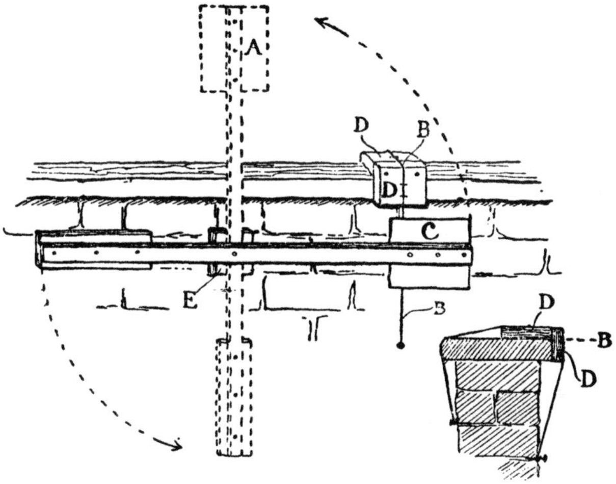

FIG. 11.—A signal to appear over a wall.

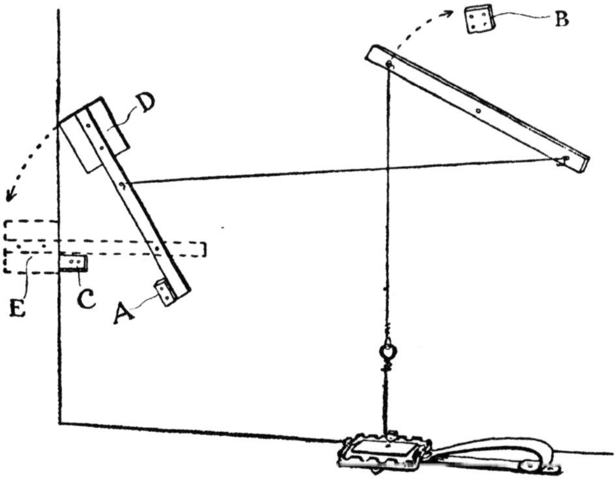

FIG. 12.—A signal for a trap set behind a building.

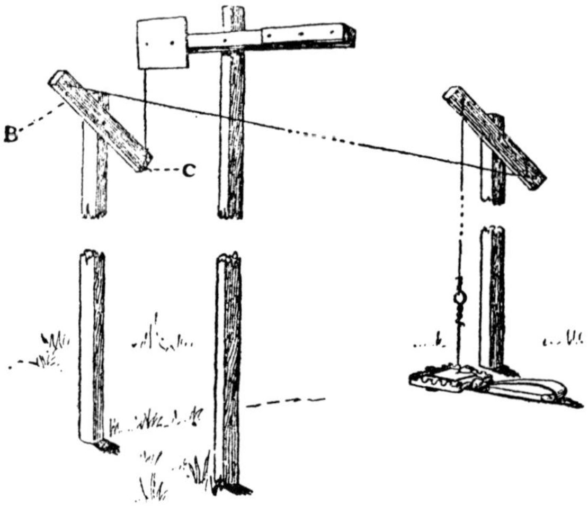

FIG. 13.—A signal to appear on a plane anterior to that on which the trap is set.

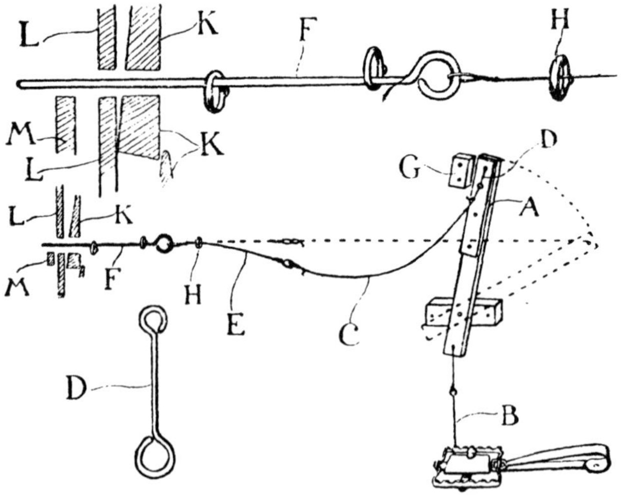

FIG. 14.—Arrangement for connecting a signal outside a building with a trap inside a building.

TRAPPING.

When premises are to be cleared of rats, the task must be undertaken in a systematic manner and continued uninterruptedly. The methods to be employed depend upon the number of rats and the part of the premises they occupy.

No real good will be done by catching a few, for rats are so very prolific (as shown in the Section, "The Habits of Rats; some Facts of General Interest"), that the young ones born will soon outnumber those killed. Unless the number is small, it is a mistake to begin by trapping, for if this is done after several have been caught, the rest will become wary and more difficult to catch.

It is best, therefore, to begin by destroying the colony as far as possible by flooding, ferreting, blocking, poisoning, or a combination of these methods, and, when the number has been materially reduced, to trap the remainder.

After the old inhabitants have been caught, there is no further trouble, as the steel traps need not again be entirely concealed. A rat coming to a steel trap, set uncovered in a position it has not previously visited, will run over the treadle as fearlessly as over a piece of old iron or any other substance.

It may be foretold with certainty that where once rats have been, others will go sooner or later. Therefore, traps should always be kept set, so that the first notification of the arrival of a rat may be the altered position of a signal to show that the trap to which it belongs holds a prisoner.

Unless traps are thus kept set all the year round, rats are certain to take up their abode on the premises from time to time.

However, it is the almost universal custom not to set a trap until rats are known to be on the premises, or have notified their presence by the destruction of poultry, or some other damage. Even then, the traps are put away again after a few rats have been caught.

The reasons why traps are not usually kept set all the year round are not difficult to discover. To begin with, the appliances necessary to enable this to be done, namely covers,[1] are not in general use; their importance is not understood, and hitherto they have not been procurable ready-made for use. Traps, opening at both ends, are not generally stocked by ironmongers.

Steel traps set in the open are liable to catch domestic animals and poultry, and therefore are not left in position after the rats for which they were set have been caught. The ordinary cage wire-work trap either gets sprung by someone kicking it, or by mice while taking its bait. Moreover, burying steel traps and baiting cage traps takes time, so that the trouble incurred is got rid of as soon as possible, by leaving the traps unset or by putting them away until more rats are found to be doing damage.

In addition to this, the necessity for having traps always set if premises are to be kept free from rats is not thoroughly realized, nor is the importance of stopping all

[1] Covers may be obtained from Messrs. Charles Orfeur and Co., Colne Bank Works, Colchester.

holes into buildings. Consequently, as a rule traps are set to catch rats that have obtained entrance to and are working in a stable or out-building, and therefore in a place where it is inconvenient for them to remain.

The aspect of the situation, however, becomes entirely changed when rats can no longer enter the buildings, when the steel traps are placed in the Signal Runs already described, and need not be buried, and the run-traps are protected by a cover so that they can be placed out of doors. They cause no inconvenience there, they cannot be sprung by domestic animals or poultry, and need not be baited.

After premises have been entirely cleared of rats, it is usually unnecessary to bait the run-traps that are in covers and have been set to catch any newcomer. If they are placed against a wall, a rat will attempt to pass through them rather than go outside, on account of the concealment afforded by the cover. If, however, for any reason it is thought well to keep bait in the trap, it is best to use grain as it keeps good longer than other foods. A drop of oil of aniseed or other essential oil, except peppermint, may also be placed in or on the traps from time to time, but this is not generally required.

To save time and prevent unnecessary trouble, it is most important to use signals to declare from a distance whether the trap is set or sprung, so that a special visit and inspection have not to be made.

In order to trap rats successfully, it must always be remembered that they have a very keen sense of smell, and that mankind is one of their natural enemies.

It is because these two facts are not fully realized, that rats are regarded as difficult to trap; whereas they are easily caught if their habits are known, the knowledge utilized and common sense employed.

The chief cause of the belief that rats are difficult to trap, is that the would-be trapper does not understand that the smell of his hand is left on the trap no matter how lightly he may touch it. Some individuals appear unable to realize that, although they themselves do not notice any odour, it is neverthess detected by an animal possessed with a keen sense of smell. Unless this fact is remembered and acted upon, much difficulty will be experienced in trapping rats.

Before setting a trap and especially one that is to be buried, the hands ought to be well rubbed with moist earth, taking special care with the front of the fingers and the palms, to both of which parts it is desirable to leave some earth adhering. This process should be repeated frequently during the setting operation away from the place where the trap is to be set, otherwise some of the earth used might be left near it and be smelt by the rats. When earth is not procurable, moist sawdust or moist sand may be used. The object is to remove all perspiration from the hands and leave a coating of material on them. If a few drops of oil of aniseed are sprinkled on the sawdust, a little of the scented sawdust should be sprinkled on both sides of the trap, but, although the scent may entirely obliterate the smell of the hands, the odour is apt to be associated with danger, and the trap in consequence may be avoided. Gloves cannot be recommended; they are more or less handled whilst being put on and taken off. They are put into pockets and other places impregnated with the human odour, and many hands, especially those unaccustomed to gloves, perspire more while they are being worn.

The first step to be taken, when a steel or wirework trap has been purchased and is required for immediate use, is to remove the smell of the shopkeeper's hands and of those who have also touched it. This is best done by boiling the trap for two or three minutes in sufficient water to submerge it completely. In the case of a steel trap, the boiling water will not damage the tempering of the spring, and the heat imparted to the metal will drive off the moisture quickly, so that very soon the trap will be dry again. If there is not a convenient hook for lifting the trap out of the boiling water, a piece of string may be tied to the trap before it is submerged, and cut off when no longer required.

When a trap has to be handled, several thicknesses of paper should intervene between the hand and the trap. If out of doors, a leaf may be used instead of paper, and when a trap has to be moved from one place to another, the same precautionary measure should be observed, and care taken that the paper or leaf which has been used is not left near the trap.

A rat never voluntarily leaves his hole in haste, but always stops a little time at the entrance, both looking and sniffing with the object of detecting any enemy that may be near. On emerging, he runs close to the wall and only ventures out into the open with extreme caution. Bearing these facts in mind, it is obvious that it is best not to set a trap at the entrance to a hole, and that a run trap should always be set against a wall.

A trap placed at the entrance to a hole may catch a few rats, but many more would be caught during the same period if the trap were set a distance from it. No trap should be set within 6 ft. of a rat's hole, and, when possible, a greater distance should be maintained.

On account of his many enemies, a rat keeps under cover as much as possible, and prefers to pass behind a box, barrel, or any other article that may be standing near a wall, or a piece of wood which is leaning against it, rather than go into the open. For like reasons, he will pass for preference through a passage of suitable size that may be lying in his course, rather than go outside it.

A run for trapping purposes should not be less than 8 in. in height. If the sides are opaque, as when made with wood, it is best to admit light from the top, although light enters from both ends.

In the Signal Run previously described advantage has been taken of this habit, and its deadly effect is the result of a rat's preference for going through the Signal Run on account of the concealment it affords.

As before mentioned, the greatest difficulty is experienced in trapping rats in a place they have frequented for some time. They view with suspicion each fresh article placed there, and smell it very carefully before venturing into it or upon it. For this reason there should not be haste in the attempt to catch rats, but time should be allowed for them to get accustomed to the trap, if it is a kind that cannot be concealed. The trap should not be set until they feed in it regularly.

With this object in view, when a run trap is to be used, the doors should be fastened up to the height which they occupy when the trap is set. This is easily done by setting the trap and then putting a piece of wood or a cork beneath the treadle so that a rat running over cannot depress it and thus spring the trap. Care must be taken, while doing this, not to touch either the piece of wood or the trap with the bare unprepared hand. When the treadle has been propped, the trap should be placed in position against a wall, and some grain, or other bait which rats like and which will not get sour if left for a few days, put into it and also outside both ends of the trap.

When baiting a run-trap, the bait should be laid along its whole length, and not placed only in the middle. The object is to allow the rat to get some of the bait which is actually inside without entering the trap.

It is important also that bait should be laid outside both ends of the trap, and if this is taken, and none from the inside of the trap, the bait outside should be relaid each time it is taken, in order to accustom the rats to approach the trap. Any bait that has been removed from inside the trap should be replaced, for the same reason. In these circumstances, if the trap has not been handled, the rats will soon go into and pass through it fearlessly.

When placing bait outside a trap, it is a good plan to lay a light trail from the hole to the trap, each grain or piece of bait being about 6 or 8 in. or more apart. Rats carry off bait piece by piece to their hole to eat at their leisure, and do not usually eat it on the spot, so that, if much is laid down, they may not come out so frequently in search of food.

An excellent bait to lay in a trail is made by cutting slices of stale bread or toast into squares of about a ¼ in., and putting them into a basin with hot beef dripping, and then spreading them out on a plate until cold. If just enough dripping is used to moisten the pieces, they will not stick together or adhere to the plate.

Wheat or maize is the best grain to use for a trail, and the former is the better because of its smaller size.

Rats are very fond of sun-flower seeds and they are therefore a good bait.

The following is also a good bait :—

Flour	1 lb.
Treacle	3 oz.
Grated or finely divided cheese	3 oz.
Bread crumb	1 lb.

Mix.

Thoroughly mix the flour with the cheese in a basin by stirring them well together until a uniform mass has been made, add the treacle, and then cut the crumb of bread into small pieces, or pass it through a mincing machine, and stir it up with the mixture.

It is advisable to make the floor of the trap harmonize as much as possible with the floor on which it is placed, so that, if there is sawdust on the floor, as in a shop, some should be placed on the floor of the trap. If it is set in a hayloft or stable, some chaff should be scattered over it and around the trap.

It is a good plan, in some instances, when setting a trap not provided with a cover, to conceal the trap and darken the place where it is standing by placing boxes near it or resting boards against the wall over it. In all instances a passage-way must be left along the wall beyond each end of the trap for the rats to traverse.

When a wire-work cage is set in a stable, barn or other building where there is straw, in addition to covering the floor of the trap with chaff, it is well to place some broken straw against the sides and closed end of the trap and also on the top, so as to conceal it. Paper may be used in a similar manner in a packing-house or other place where paper is lying about. In either case, care must be taken that the straw or paper does not in any way interfere with the working of the trap.

In the case of a trap that has not been used for some time, it is a good plan, before placing it in position, to turn a rat into it from another trap, and leave it there for a few hours so that the trap may become soiled. A rat will go fearlessly where by the smell it is evident that another rat has already been.

It has frequently been noticed that, after a few rats have been caught in a trap that secured them alive, no more enter it until it has been boiled or thoroughly scrubbed and washed. This has been taken to mean that those which are not caught smell their former friends and avoid the trap in consequence. When this occurs it is far more probable that the trap has been handled while the rats which were caught were being taken to be killed and during the re-setting, and that it is the smell of the trapper, not that of their former friends, that keeps the rats away from the trap.

When a rat has been caught uninjured in a run-trap or a cage trap, the rat before being taken to be killed should be driven into a cage kept for the purpose, especially if a dog is to be the executioner, as otherwise the trap is almost sure to be handled, and the dog is liable to rub against it. An ordinary cage trap, with the small sloping door at one end, does very well for this purpose. The small door may be propped open with a piece of stick, or held by a piece of string while the rat is driven into the cage. The door is afterwards fastened by slipping a piece of wood of suitable size across it, and wedging it between the wires forming the walls of the trap and those on the other side of the doorway.

It is always desirable, when trapping, to remove the animal that has been caught as soon as possible. On this account, when catching rats in a place they have frequented for some time, it is well not to leave the trap set during the night, unless it is known that the number to be caught is small. On visiting the traps, therefore, for the last time about midnight, it is best to fasten up the run-traps in the manner already described and remove the steel traps, taking care to carefully smooth over the material in which they were concealed.

Rats, as well as many other animals, avoid an article or place which has blood of their own species on it, and therefore blood should always be carefully removed from a trap. It is best, after this has been done, to boil the trap. If the trap has not to be buried, a drop of oil of aniseed or other essential oil may be put on the place which the blood covered.

Bearing in mind the suspicion with which each new article is viewed, if a steel trap is to be used, it is best to bury it, and for setting inside a building the way to proceed is as follows:—

Make an enclosure the size of the trap, against the wall with bricks or pieces of wood, at a little distance from the rat's hole. Stand a thin brick or piece of wood on end against the wall at the hole end of the enclosure, to form a buttress (see the "Terrier Signal Run") to ensure the rats passing over the treadle of the trap. Then fill the enclosure with fine saw-dust to the height of the trap when set, throw saw-dust against the outside of the bricks, and sprinkle it over the top of the bricks and along the wall from both ends of the enclosure. Afterwards lay a trail of bait from the hole across the enclosure and beyond it.

The object of the trail of bait is to accustom the rats to pass fearlessly over the saw-dust, and if only part of the trail is taken it should be made good without disturbing the remaining pieces.

When the bait is freely taken across the saw-dust and beyond it, a perfectly clean 5 in. rabbit-trap should be buried in the following manner in the saw-dust, with its jaws towards the hole. Sufficient saw-dust having been removed, with a spoon that has been boiled or a thin flat piece of wood, to enable the trap to lie on the bottom of the enclosure, a piece of wood or other hard substance, which has not been handled, should be laid beneath one end of the cross-piece of the frame of the trap to prevent it from rocking. A piece of shaving-paper should be laid over the treadle, the loop of the spring and jaws, and the sawdust then carefully filled in around the sides and over the paper, covering it to the depth of about ¼ in. The saw-dust should be well pressed down outside the jaws, and on each side of the spring, and the layer of saw-dust made much thicker over it, to lessen the risk of its becoming exposed.

The saw-dust should be dry, otherwise it is apt to clog and prevent the jaws working properly. Fine dried earth or sand may be used instead of saw-dust for concealing the trap, but it is not so good as fine saw-dust on account of its weight, which makes it more liable to spring the trap if it is set lightly. Coarse saw-dust or bran should not be used, for they are liable to clog the loop of the spring, and also get between the jaws and prevent them coming together.

The advantage of an enclosure over a mere heap of saw-dust is that it prevents the saw-dust sliding when trodden on, and thus causing the trap to become exposed.

The object of the paper is to prevent the saw-dust clogging the loop of the spring or the jaws near their pivots, and to keep it from getting beneath the treadle in sufficient quantity to stop the latter from being depressed easily by the weight of the rat. A sheet of shaving-paper is best because it lies flat, its colour harmonizes with the saw-dust, and it is just large enough to cover the trap properly; moreover, being thin, it is easily crumpled or torn if caught between the jaws.

Another method is to procure a narrow box, sufficiently large to hold a 5-in. rabbit-trap when set, and about 8 to 10 in. deep. Then cut out of each end, opposite to each other, an opening 4 in. wide, extending to within about 2 in. from the bottom, one edge of the opening being 1¼ in. from the inner surface of the side of the box which will be placed against the wall. The object of the opening is to ensure the rat passing over the treadle of the trap. The box should then be filled with fine saw-dust, almost to the level of the bottom of the opening, and a trail of bait laid across it from the rat's hole to a foot or more beyond the box as before mentioned. When possible, it is advisable to place a trap on each side of a hole.

A box about 2 in. deep, and long and wide enough to hold a trap, is usually sufficient.

When trapping to clear premises, the traps should be set early in the day, so that all smell connected with the trapper may have passed away before the rats emerge from their place of concealment for their evening meal. If it is thought that some rats are avoiding traps which have been buried, on account of the loose earth which surrounds them, it is a good plan to dig up the ground as if a trap were buried and scatter a little earth along the other parts of the run, but not to set traps until the foot-marks show that the freshly-dug-up ground is traversed freely.

When burying a trap, it is a good plan to slip a piece of thin stick over the loose jaw and under the free end of the treadle, to support it while the earth is being placed over and around it. This prevents the trap from being sprung.

For out-of-door trapping, a little moss, or some long grass twisted up, may be used to stop sand or fine earth from getting beneath the treadle in sufficient quantity to prevent it from being depressed easily, but with ordinary earth nothing is required.

When burying a trap in earth, care must be taken that there is no stone that can get into the loop of the spring or between the jaws and prevent them from closing. The earth should be thrown outwards, away from the centre of the treadle, for, when this is done, less falls under it than when sprinkled in the opposite direction. The earth must be firmly pressed outside the end of the trap and along the outside of the jaws and spring, as soft earth may cause suspicion or lead to the trap being discovered.

A trowel or painter's stripping-knife when burying a trap in the ground, or an iron spoon when burying it in saw-dust, saves time and is useful, but for the final touches when spreading sawdust, earth, sand or other material over a trap to conceal it, nothing is better than a strong feather, such as a large wing-feather of a turkey or goose, though any strong feather will do.

A fine sieve is handy when burying a trap in the ground, and sieves are sold for this purpose, but, when not procurable, a useful one may be made by removing the bottom of a small strong box, and fastening a piece of perforated zinc in its place.

If a buried trap is found partially exposed, perhaps only the top of one of the teeth showing, or a surface less than an eighth of an inch square, it is nevertheless useless to leave the trap in position, for it is dirty and has been smelt and discovered.

It must be taken away, the surface of the saw-dust or earth smoothed, and a trail of bait laid across it as before. The trap should be boiled for two or three minutes, and then not again touched with a bare unprepared hand. When the bait is again taken freely, the trap should be re-set and buried as before.

A steel trap should always be set longitudinally with the run in which it is placed, and with its jaws facing the direction from which the animal is expected to approach, so that he may be on the treadle as quickly as possible. It is a mistake to set the trap at a right angle to a run. When this is done, the animal is thrown upwards by the jaw which has been crossed, or by the catch, if the trap has been approached from this side, and it is uncertain what part of the animal will be seized between the jaws, even if it is not thrown clear of them. When a 5-in. trap has been thus set, a rat is often merely held and not killed. This cross position is universally adopted by many gamekeepers, but such a practice is obviously wrong for trapping vermin.

The statement is sometimes made that a 4-in. trap ought not to be set longitudinally with the run, lest the spring should throw the rat clear of the trap. However true this may be, it does not apply to 5-in. traps, for it must be remembered that when the trap is sprung, the head, shoulders, and forefeet are already between the jaws, and the effect of the spring can only be to throw the hindquarters up and to cause the rat to be caught across the body, instead of along the body as is often the case. (See also "Setting a Steel Trap.")

When steel traps are set to catch rats frequenting a building, stack, or other place, it is best, after several have been caught, to remove the traps for the next two or three nights, and feed the rats and lay a trail over the places in which the traps will next be set.

Although a steel trap kept set all the year round, to catch any rat that may come that way, need not be buried or entirely concealed, yet it is sometimes advisable to cover it lightly with withered grass, dead leaves, chaff, or broken straw, so as to make it harmonize better with surrounding objects. It is advisable also to set the trap so that the treadle is on the ground level, or to lay a stick, tile, or other substance sufficiently thick to be level with the treadle, across the end of the trap.

The cross-piece of the frame of steel traps is usually riveted to the top of the longitudinal piece of the frame, the result being that, as it is on a higher level, the trap can be rocked from side to side on the longitudinal piece. When setting a trap, therefore, in order to keep it steady, some hard substance must be placed beneath one end of the cross-piece.

When a steel trap—sometimes called a gin—is set in a house for a stray rat, an old thin piece of rag which has been boiled makes a simple and suitable cover for it.

Before concealing the trap, it is well to place a piece of wood, the thickness of the height of the trap when set, with one end against a wall and the end of the trap against it on the side away from the rats' hole, then cover the wood and trap with the rag, and make a trail of bait across it. Sometimes it is advisable to allow the rats to feed on the rag for a night or two before the trap is placed beneath it.

For occasional trapping an excellent plan has been recommended by Mr. R. Sharpe.[1] It consists of making a platform to fit into a tub, sink, or other receptacle, capable of holding water sufficiently deep to submerge completely a rat held in a steel trap. An aperture is cut in it sufficiently large to easily contain a set trap, which is supported by a nail or other projection placed respectively under the spring end of the frame, the under edge of the fixed jaw near its front end, and the cross-piece of the frame beneath the loose jaw. The supports are so arranged that the water only just covers the treadle and other parts of the trap. The aperture in the platform must be sufficiently wide to ensure the jaws not striking either edge when the trap is sprung, and the long aperture for the spring and end of the frame must give room for the spring to work freely.

The jaws are placed against the edge of the receptacle and an obstruction created to prevent a rat passing on to the platform, except across the trap. Mr. Sharpe advises a cover to the receptacle, with a hole cut in the side of the lid opposite each trap, the spring end of all

[1] "Rats; How to Exterminate Them, and the Taking of Wild Rabbits." (Reprinted from the *Journal of the Board of Agriculture*, vol. xxiv, No. 12, March, 1918, and vol. xxv, Nos. 1, 3 and 4, April, June and July, 1918.)

the traps which are set resting on a common central support. An aperture in the lid fitted with a cover enables the bait to be hung in the centre of the receptacle above the water, or placed on a special platform made to receive it. A rat on entering springs the trap, which falls into the water with its victim because the trap is no longer supported by the jaw that was fixed, and thus no trace remains of the captured rat to alarm other rats that have yet to come. The platform may be made to support three or more traps, according to the size of the tub. The traps may be fixed in the set position until the bait is taken freely from the central platform, by wedging a piece of wood between the treadle and the cross-piece of the frames.

Breakback traps without a treadle are best concealed in a heap of sawdust or sand, a trail being laid and renewed until it is freely taken across the place where the trap will be buried. The trap should be placed facing the direction from which rats come, as shown by their footmarks, and completely covered, the bait attached to the tripper being arranged so that apparently it is lying on the top of the sawdust. Breakback traps fitted with a treadle are best set across a run with the end of the trap against a wall, and, when bait is used, it should be placed as a trail across the treadle. If the rat is removed as soon as killed and the trap at once reset, several rats may be caught in quick succession. By removing the trap the last thing at night and relaying the trail, suspicion is disarmed, and, if the bait is taken, probably more rats will be caught the following day.

The risk of a finger getting caught in the trap while it is being set is prevented by raising and adjusting the treadle with a piece of stick about 9 in. long, flattened on both sides at one end and tapered to an edge.

For trapping by the side of or in water see Section "Rats by the River, Stream, or Ornamental Water."

Dead rats ought always to be burnt or buried sufficiently deep to prevent them from being dug up by pigs or other animals, and should never be left to decompose near a trap or on the surface of the ground. Many rats are infested with fleas.

For the successful trapping of rats, the three following rules should never be forgotten :—

(1) Never touch a trap, even lightly, with a bare hand, unless all the perspiration and smell have been thoroughly removed by rubbing the hands with earth or other suitable substance.

(2) Always set a trap by the side of a wall.

(3) Never set a trap within 6 ft. of a rat's hole when able to place it at that or an even greater distance from it.

SNARING.

THIS method of catching rats is useful when steel traps are not at hand, or in places from which traps may be stolen.

For snaring rats, a run must be selected lying through grass or other vegetation sufficiently thick to have caused the route made to be well defined; the noose must be placed across the run and concealed by the vegetation.

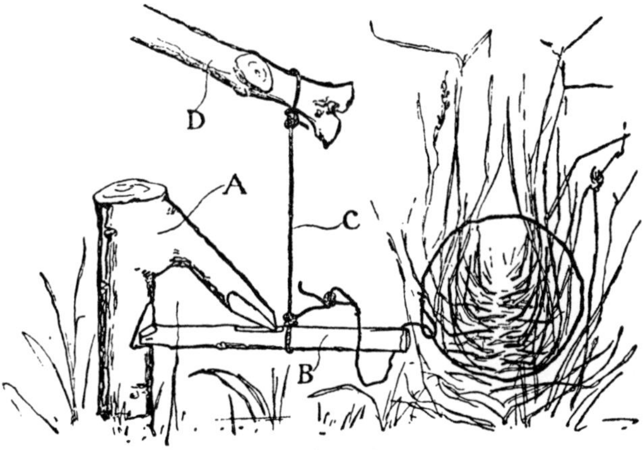

FIG. 15.—Snare for rats.

A snare may be made in the following way. A piece of string is fastened to a thin wire which ends in a noose, the other end of the string being fastened to a stick called the bender, which, when bent, forms the spring. A thin piece of wood, called the teeler, is fastened near the lower end of the string, and, when the snare is set, the bender is held down by placing the teeler beneath a hook and slipping its end into a notch on the stem of the hook, called the peg. The free end of the teeler is split vertically to hold the noose in position. The split is called the grip.

If rats become shy of a snare, it is best to remove the noose for a few days until they again use the run freely, and then re-set, taking great care that the hands have been previously thoroughly deodorized with earth.

Full directions for making a snare will be found in Part II.

FERRETS.

MR. H. C. BARKLEY'S'[1] remarks and advice with regard to ferrets and ferreting for rats are so good that they ought to be much more widely known, and are therefore given here in his own words.

"There are two distinct colours in ferrets; one is a rich dark brown and tan, and the other white with pink eyes; and in my opinion one is just as good as the other for work, though by preference I always keep the white ferret, as it is sooner seen if it comes out of a hole and works away down a fence or ditch-bottom. I have never known a dark-coloured ferret coming among a litter of white ones or a white among the dark; but there is a cross between the two which produces a grizzly beast, generally bigger than its mother, which I have for many years avoided, though it is much thought of in some parts of the Midlands. I fancy (though I may be wrong) that the cross is a dull slow ferret, wanting in dash and courage, and not so friendly and affectionate as the others, and therefore apt to stick with just its nose out of a hole so that you can't pick it up, or else it will 'lay up' and give a lot of trouble digging it out.

"For rat-catching the female ferret should always be used, as it is not half the size of the male, and can therefore follow a rat faster and better in narrow holes; in fact an ordinary female ferret should be able to follow a

[1] "Studies in the Art of Ratcatching," by H. C. Barkley. Published by John Murray, Albemarle Street, London.

full-grown rat anywhere. The male ferret should be kept entirely for rabbiting, as he has not to follow down small holes, and being stronger than the female can stand the rough knocking about he often gets from a rabbit better than his wife can.

"In buying a ferret for work, get one from nine to fifteen months old, as young ferrets I find usually have more courage and dash than an old one. They have not been so often punished, and therefore do not think discretion the better part of valour. However, this will not be found to be an invariable rule. I have known old ferrets that would have faced a lion, and seemed to care nothing about being badly bitten; whereas I have known a young ferret turn out good-for-nothing from having one sharp nip from a rat. Such beasts had better be parted with, for a bad, slow, or cowardy ferret is vexation of spirit and not profitable.

"If I am buying brown ferrets I always pick the darkest, as I fancy they have most dash. This may be only fancy, or it may be the original ferret was white, and that the brown is the cross between it and the polecat, and that therefore the darker the ferret, the more it is like in temper as well as colour its big, strong, wild ancestor. Anyhow I buy the dark ones.

"If I am buying female ferrets, I like big *long* ones, as a small ferret has not weight enough to tackle a big rat and therefore often gets desperately punished. I like to see the ferrets in a tub, end up, looking well nourished and strong; and directly I touch the tub I like to see them dash out of their hidden beds in the straw and rush to spring up the sides like a lot of furies. When I put my hand in to take one, I prefer not to be bitten; but yet I have often known a ferret turn out very well that has begun by making its teeth meet through my finger. When I have the ferret in hand, I first look at its tail, and then at its feet, and if these are clean it will do. If, on the other hand, I find a thin appearance about the hairs of its tail and a black-looking dust at the roots, the ferret goes back into the tub; or if the underside of the feet are black and the claws encrusted with dirt, I will have nothing to say to it, as it has the mange and will be troublesome to cure. All this done, I put the ferret on the ground and keep picking it up and letting it go; if when I do this it sets up the hairs of its tail, arches its back and hisses at me, I may buy it; but I know, if I do, I shall have to handle it much to get it tame. If, on the other hand, when I play with it the ferret begins to dance sideways and play, I pay down my money and take it at once, for I have never known a playful ferret to prove a bad one.

"If when you get the ferret it is wild and savage, it should be constantly handled till it is quite tamed before it is used. Little brothers and sisters will be found useful at this. Give them the ferret to play with in an empty, or nearly empty, barn or shed where it cannot escape. Put into the shed with them some long drain pipes, and tell them to ferret rats out of them. The chances are they will put the ferret through them and pick it up so often that it will learn there is nothing to fear when it comes out of a real rat's hole, and will ever after 'come to hand' readily. You had better not be in the way when the children return to their mother or nurse. I have had disagreeable moments on such occasions.

"I have always given my ferrets bread and milk once

or twice a week, which was placed in flat tins in the middle compartment of the hutch; but care should be taken to clean out the tins each time, as any old sour milk in them will turn the fresh milk and make the ferrets ill. The natural food of ferrets is flesh—the flesh of small animals—and therefore it should be the chief food given. Small birds, rats and mice, are to them dainty morsels, but the ferrets will be sure to drag these into their beds to eat and will leave the skins untouched; these should be removed each day. When my ferrets are not in regular work they are fed just before sunset—if they are fed in the morning they are no good for work all day, and one can never tell (except on Sundays) that one of the dogs may not find a rat that *wants* killing. The day before real work I give the ferrets bread and milk in the morning and nothing on the day they go out until their work is over. This makes them keen. Remember ferrets work hard in a big day's ratting, and therefore should be well nourished and strong; a ferret that is not will not have the courage to face a rat.

"I have listened to all sorts of theories from old hands about feeding ferrets, but have followed the advice of few. For instance, I have been told that if you give flesh, such as rats and birds, to a ferret that has young ones, it will drag it into the straw among the little ones, who will get the blood on them, and then the mother will eat them by mistake. All I can say is, I have reared hundreds of young ferrets and have always given the mothers flesh. It is true that ferrets will eat their young, and the way to bring this about is to disturb the babies in the nest. If you leave them quite alone till they begin to creep about, I believe there is no danger.

"Then many old rat-catchers never give a ferret a rat with its tail on, as they believe there is poison in it. I remember one old fellow saying to me as he cut off the tail before putting the rat into the ferret's box: 'Bar the tail—I allus bars the tail—there's wenom in the tail.' There may be 'wenom' in it, but if there is, it won't hurt the ferrets, for they never eat it or the skin.

"If ferrets are properly cared for they are rarely ill, and the only trouble I have ever had is with mange, which, as I have said before, attacks the tail and feet, and for which I have always used sulphur and lard, and after rubbing it well in a few times I have always found it worked a cure.

"Before going further I should point out to all students of this ennobling profession that the very first thing they have to learn is to pick up a ferret. Don't grab it by its tail, or hold it by its head as you would a mad bull-dog, but take hold of it lightly round the shoulders, with its front legs falling gracefully out below from between your fingers. Then when you go to the box for your ferrets, and they come clambering up the side like a pack of hungry wolves, put your hand straight in among them without a glove, and pick up which one you require. Don't hesitate a moment. Don't dangle your hand over their heads till you can make a dash and catch one. The ferrets will only think your hand is their supper coming, and will grab it, with no ill intent; but if you put it down steadily and slowly, they will soon learn you only do so to take them out, and your hand will become as welcome as flowers in spring.

"True, at first, with strange ferrets you may be bitten; but it is not a very serious thing if you are, as ferrets' bites are never venomous, as the bites of rats often are. I have in my time been bitten by ferrets many dozens of times and have never suffered any ill effects."

Mr. Barkley goes on to describe what often occurs when a ferret, taken from the hutch for a rat hunt, is carried in a box instead of in a bag. He says: "Different professors have different opinions as to what is next to be done with it. Many (and they are good men, too), think you should put it into a box about 18 in. long, 10 in. high, and 10 in. wide—the box to be divided into two compartments, with a lid to each, and with leather loops to these lids through which to thrust a pointed spade so as to carry it on your shoulder. I have tried this plan, but I have never quite liked it. I have found that after a heavy day's work the box was apt to get heavy and feel as if it were a grandfather's clock hanging on your back. Then the ratting spade was engaged instead of being free to mump a rat on the head in a hurry, or point out a likely hole to the dogs. When a ferret was wanted, all the others would dash out and have to be hunted about to be re-caught. Now and then the lids came open and let all out; and now and then I let the box slip off the spade and fall to the ground, and then I felt sorry for the ferrets inside it! No, I have always carried my ferrets in a good strong canvas bag, with a little clean straw at the bottom and a leather strap and buckle stitched on to it with which to close it. Don't tie the bag with a piece of string—it is sure to get lost—and don't have a stiff buckle on your strap that takes ten minutes to undo. Remember the life of a rat may depend upen your getting your ferret out quickly. Never throw a bag of ferrets down; lay them down gently. Don't leave the bag on the ground in a broiling sun with some of the ferrets in it while you are using the others, or in a cold draughty place on a cold day; find a snug corner for them if you can, and cover them up with a little straw or grass to keep them warm.

"If when carrying your ferrets they chatter in the bag, let them; it is only singing not fighting. I have never known a ferret hurt another in a bag. Always bag your ferret as soon as you have done with it; don't drag it about in your hand for half an hour and don't put it in your pocket, as it will make your coat smell.

"When I have done work and turned towards home, I have made it a rule always to put a dead rat into the bag, as I think it amuses the ferrets and breaks the monotony of a long journey; just as when I run down home I like taking a snack at Swindon Station just to divert my mind from the racketing of the train and the thought of the hard seat. When you get home give the ferrets a rat for every two of them if you can afford it, for then they need only eat the best joints. If you have not too many dead rats and want to save some for the morrow, one rat for three ferrets is enough for twenty-four hours, but do not forget to give them water or milk.

"I remember one or two things that I think the student should be told. The first is never put a line on a ferret when *ratting*. It hampers a ferret in a narrow, twisting, turning rat's hole, and cutting into the soft earth at the turns soon brings the ferret to a dead stop. Then rats' holes are chiefly in hedge-banks which are full of roots, and the line is pretty sure to get twisted round some of these, and then it will be a long dig to free it. Remember too, a ferret has to go down the hole and face a beast nearly as big as itself with teeth like lancets and with courage to use them and so should be as free as possible; and lining a ferret is about equal to setting a student with the gloves on to fight against another without them. Then some way back I mentioned ferrets' bells. They are little hollow brass balls with an iron shot in them that make a pretty tinkling sound and are supposed to be tied round the ferret's neck. In my opinion if you put a bell on it you may as well put the ferret in the bag and keep it there. The theory about bells is that a ferret running down a hole jingling its bell will fill a rat with fear and make it bolt, but this is all nonsense; rats are not so easily frightened. Again, it is said that if a ferret comes out of a hole in a thick hedge unseen, the bell will let you know where it is; but I must say I never lost a ferret in a hedge or felt the want of a belled one. I consider a bell a useless dead weight on a ferret, and the cord that goes round its neck to fasten it is apt to get hitched on to a root and hold the ferret a prisoner. A bell is only good for a sharp shopman to sell to a flat.

"I need hardly say never muzzle a ferret when rat-catching. It would be brutal not to let the ferret have the use of its teeth to protect itself with. Muzzling ferrets appertains solely to rabbiting, but it is useful to know how to do it. Take a piece of twine a foot long, double it, and tie a loop at the double. Tie the string round the ferret's neck with the loop on the top; bring the two ends down under the chin and tie them together there; pass them over the nose and tie them there shutting the mouth tight; pass *one* string along the nose between the eyes through the loop on the top of the neck and bending it back tie it to the other loose string from the knot on the top of the nose. Cut the ends off and provided you have not made a lot of 'granny' knots, your muzzle will keep on all day. There are other ways of doing the trick, such as passing the string behind the ferret's dog-teeth, bring it under the jaw, then over the nose on the top of the neck; tie it there and again under the neck. I hate this plan and have seen a ferret's mouth badly cut by the string. I have heard of another plan which is too brutal to mention. Cut the muzzle off directly you have done with it, for I don't suppose a ferret likes having its mouth tied up any more than you or I should."

All who are experienced in keeping ferrets and in ferreting for rats will agree with the views expressed by Mr. Barkley in the preceding pages.

Ferrets for ratting are best kept exclusively for the purpose, for often those used for rabbiting are not of much use; they are unaccustomed to fighting, and often they will not face a rat for fear of getting punished.

No two ferrets are alike, not even white ones, but if it is wished to give them a distinguishing mark it may be done by snipping some hair from the top of the head of one and from the right cheek of another and from the left cheek of a third and so on.

With regard to hutches they are best kept in an open shed or airy outhouse and should be raised about 12 in. from the ground. When the legs are fixed, those beneath the larger compartment may be set back 6 or 8 in. from the end of the hutch, to prevent them from being soiled.

When a hutch is kept in an outhouse, it may have a flat top made with a lid over each compartment. The lids, with the exception of that over the nest compartment, should be a frame covered with wire-netting. This makes the hutch more airy, but when the hutch is kept out of doors it must of course have a slanting boarded roof.

The floor of the middle and large compartment is best made of wire-netting, but it will be advantageous to the

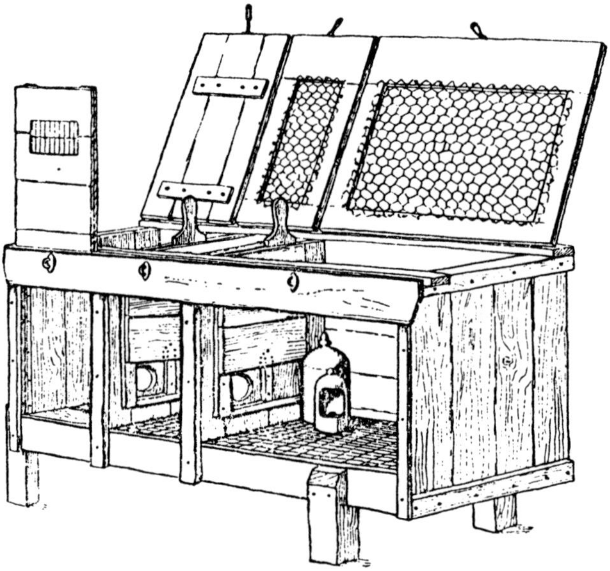

FIG. 16.—Ferret hutch showing drinking fountain in a corner of the large compartment. The front of the middle and large compartment has been removed to show the interior of the hutch more clearly.

ferrets' feet and noses if new wire-work before being used is submerged in water for at least twenty-four hours, or what is better, washed with a strong solution of soda and water. There is always a considerable amount of acid (spirits of salts) adhering to all new galvanized material, as a result of the galvanizing process.

Although in the author's experience wire-work is the cleanest and therefore the best flooring for ferret hutches, it is nevertheless advisable to cover the wire-work with loose boards, which, when soiled, can be lifted out and cleaned. The last 6 in. of the floor at the opposite end to the nest compartment, however, should be left uncovered, so that all foul matter may fall through. Ferrets are cleanly animals and generally use this end of the hutch.

If thought necessary, the boards may be kept from shifting by having nails or screws, with their heads cut off, projecting downwards through the wire-work for about ½ in.

The end of the large compartment, and the portion of the back corresponding to the exposed wire-work and 3 or 4 in. beyond it, may with advantage be covered with galvanized iron or zinc to the height of about 6 or 8 in. The metal must extend downwards to the bottom of the hutch, to prevent filth from soaking into the wood, and to enable the surface to be washed and kept clean.

The back of the middle compartment should also be covered in the same manner, the metal being brought forward 6 or 8 in., for sometimes ferrets make use of the back corners of this compartment.

When the floor of the hutch is made of fixed boards it should slope with a fall of 1 in. or more to a foot, the opposite end to the nest compartment being deficient in the last 6 in. The opening thus created may be covered with wire-work of about ⅝ to ¾ of an inch mesh.

A layer of finely-sifted earth, or cinder-ash, about 3 or 4 in. in depth, should be kept under the end of the hutch, and the soiled portion removed every morning and replaced with clean material. Keep a heap of this under cover, so that there is always plenty for use, even in wet weather.

One or more spare hutches should be kept, so that a wounded or sick ferret can be separated at once from the rest.

The nest compartment should have clean wheat straw once a week, but, before the fresh straw is put in, the floor should be thoroughly swept out, cleaned and then sprinkled with some non-poisonous germicidal disinfecting powder, such as izal, care being taken to shake some all along the edges. If this is done, not only will vermin be kept away, but the larva of any that may be hatched will be deprived of food and killed by the powder.

It must be remembered that hay or barley straw will give ferrets mange.

For mange, it is best to wash the ferrets' feet and other affected parts twice daily with a solution of izal or Jeyes' fluid in the proportion given for washing ferrets. Some other non-poisonous germicidal solution may be used if preferred, and then sulphur ointment should be applied to all the affected parts. The sulphur ointment should be made as follows:—

Sulpur	1 part.
Compound lanolin ointment	4 parts.

Mix.

The open portion of the wire-netting floor of a hutch, and the galvanized iron covering the end, should be washed daily with a solution of izal, Jeyes' fluid or some other non-poisonous disinfectant, as well as any portion of the loose boards that has been soiled, a sink brush being most suitable for this purpose. It is best to keep two sets of loose boards, so that the soiled boards can be at once replaced.

When ferrets are kept in a hutch with a wire-work floor, their feet often become very sore from treading on it, and as there is nothing for their nails to rub against when not at work, they become too long.

Unless these are cut, the ferrets may be crippled. In any case the growth of the nails ought to be watched, and they should be cut when they exceed their natural length.

As the nails are very hard, a pair of nail-cutters are better than scissors for the purpose, for the V-shaped opening of the latter tends to push the nail from between the blades, whereas the edges of the nail-cutter being more nearly parallel, cut the nail without difficulty.

Ferrets are as cleanly as most other animals, but are often kept in a very dirty condition, and when purchased may be found to be swarming with fleas, which may be seen readily on the belly and the inner side of the thighs. The best way to get rid of them is to wash the ferret with soap in a warm bath, to which a little izal or Jeyes' fluid may be added with advantage (see "Dogs"). Then dry thoroughly with a cloth before putting the ferret back into the hutch, which should have plenty of clean broken wheat-straw, so that she may soon get thoroughly warm. The fleas are often very small, so that only the finest tooth comb will be effective in removing them.

Most ferrets are quiet while being washed and appear to like the process, but if restive, one person must hold the ferret and another wash her. Not only should ferrets be washed when dirty or infested with vermin, but the hutch also should be carefully scrubbed from time to time with soap and hot water. It is even advisable to add a strong insect-destroying disinfectant such as izal, Jeyes' fluid, Pearson's antiseptic, or some other non-poisonous insect-destroyer.

Ferrets should be fed regularly every day, and, although the flesh of rats, mice and small birds is undoubtedly their natural food, any kind of meat is suitable. Salt in any form is bad for ferrets, and therefore they should never be fed on salted meats.

When flesh cannot be procured, they may be fed on bread and milk, or on biscuit-meal and milk. Stale bread or biscuit-meal, however, should be scalded with water and allowed to get cold before the milk is added, for food of this kind, if given hot, is apt to scour. A little greaves may be given regularly with the bread and milk or the biscuit-meal and milk, or instead of plain biscuit-meal, the prepared meal mixed with dried meat, similar in composition to meat dog-biscuit, may be substituted. Rats, mice and small birds, however, should be given when they can be procured, and fresh animal food in some form, if the ferrets get scoured, or their excrement becomes slimy. Well-boiled rice with milk may be substituted with advantage for the bread and biscuit, when they are in this condition, if raw flesh cannot be obtained.

When bread and milk is given, care should be taken to crumble the bread thoroughly; if this is not done, the ferrets will carry the lumps into the nest compartment. This will make it damp and give it a sour smell.

With regard to the vexed question as to when ferrets should be fed before being used for work, it must be remembered that rats are their natural enemies, and therefore a ferret will by instinct try to destroy a rat, unless she is either feeling lazy as a result of a heavy meal recently taken or faint for want of food. Mr. Barkley's plan of feeding ferrets in the evening is the best, and his recommendation that they should be fed on the morning of the day before the one on which they are required, and not again until after their day's work is done, is the general practice. It must be remembered, however, that unless ferrets are fed regularly and sufficiently, they have neither the strength to work properly nor the courage to face a rat standing at bay.

Feeding-dishes made of either galvanized or enamelled iron are better than those made of tin, as the latter rust and cannot be kept as clean as the other kinds.

Clean water should always be kept in the hutch, for no animal will take more than is sufficient, provided he has not been deprived of drink.

The best way to ensure a constant supply of water is to keep in the hutch a drinking-fountain such as is used for poultry and pigeons, and a stoneware fountain is preferable, as it can be kept cleaner than one that is made of zinc or galvanized iron.

Should it become foul or covered with vegetation, it may be cleaned by boiling it for a few minutes in a vessel large enough to allow it to be submerged while the opening into the reservoir is on its upper side. If the fountain is put into cold or only slightly warmed water, it will not crack when boiled, provided it is allowed to cool gradually. Wrapped in a cloth, no harm can come to it if thrown against the side of the copper while being boiled.

A fountain that will supply water for several days can be improvised by filling a bottle quite full of water, then stopping the top with a finger, turning it upside down and placing the neck of the bottle in a pan of water, which will prevent any water escaping until enough water has been removed from the pan to allow air to enter the bottle. When this occurs, some more water will escape and again seal the neck until the entrance of more air allows more water to escape. This alternate flow and sealing will continue until the bottle is empty.

The bottle can be kept in the necessary sloping position by placing it in a corner and passing its upper end behind a wire fastened to each side of the corner on a level with the upper part of the bottle, the neck being steadied by a wire fixed across it above the pan. Unless the bottle is sloped, the water cannot escape as the pan empties.

To enable the bottle to be placed easily in position, it is best to hinge the lower wire and shape it to fasten with a hook. This is easily done by placing a screw-eye or staple on each side of the corner, bending one end of the wire into a ring and closing the ring when it has been put through one of the screw-eyes so as to form a hinge. The other end of the wire, having been bent into a hook, can be dropped into the other screw-eye. The pan can be kept from shifting by fixing a thick piece of wood placed against it to the floor of the hutch.

If properly looked after, ferrets will live for five or six years or even longer, but all cannot with advantage be kept in work all this time. Some old ferrets are more reliable than younger ones, but most are at their best during the second and at the end of the first year. Few are of much use after the third year, as they become less quick and tire sooner than formerly.

It is sometimes stated that female ferrets, called bitches or gills, will not remain healthy and may even die if not allowed to breed, so that a male ferret, called a dog or hob, should therefore always be kept with them or be obtainable. On the other hand, there are female ferrets that are kept quite apart from a male ferret and work well for several seasons.

If, as is unlikely, young stock is not required, the mother may be left with the other ferrets, who may eat all the young ones soon after they are born, though a litter sometimes grows up when left in the compartment with the old ones.

Ferrets breed twice and sometimes three times in a year, the period of gestation is six weeks, and there are usually from four to eight young ones in a litter, but sometimes more. Their eyes begin to open after the third week from birth.

If the young ones are touched, and sometimes if only the bedding is disturbed so that the young ones can be looked at, their mother is very likely to eat them. It is therefore prudent to padlock the nest compartment until the young ones are old enough to come out freely and shift for themselves. If it is thought that additional straw is required, it may be put into the middle compartment and the mother will then carry what she requires into the nursery.

Ferrets cannot be handled too much. The more they are handled the more docile they become, and it is well to make a practice of handling them daily if only to take them from the hutch, put them on the ground, and lift them back again immediately.

When young ferrets are too fond of biting when

being handled, they may be cured by dipping a hand in paraffin before picking them up. A savage ferret may also be handled with advantage with a thick glove well soaked in paraffin, which he has been allowed to bite.

It is a good plan also, when feeding or attending to them, to whistle or have a call, as they soon get to know it, and associate it with feeding-time or with being taken out of the hutch. "Come along, come along," repeated several times is easy to say, but any call or whistle will do, provided the same is always used.

When holding a ferret, place the first and second fingers round its neck and let the forelegs rest between the second and third fingers. Thus held, a ferret cannot bend its neck to bite or wriggle out of the grasp.

Ferrets with distemper or "the sweats" should be given twice daily 10 drops of collosol argentum (Crookes') or another of the somewhat similar colloidal silver preparations. Young ferrets just out of the nest may be given 2 drops twice daily. It is best poured into the mouth from a drop-measure or spoon.

THE MONGOOSE OR ICHNEUMON.

THE following was contributed by Mr. George Jennison, of the Zoological Gardens, Manchester, and published as an appendix to the Report of the Medical Officer of Health of the Corporation of the City of London on Rat Repression in the City. 1920.

"The mongoose has a very large range over the warmer parts of India, Egypt, and Africa generally, and varies in size from the Egyptian, which weighs almost as much as a cat, to the Indian which is usually about the size of a large rat, and can therefore follow the rodents into their holes. They are all of a brownish colour, sharp-nosed, exceedingly quick in their movements, yet withal susceptible of being tamed. The Egyptian variety was and, I believe, still is domesticated to serve the purpose of a cat. The Indian—"Herpestes griseus"—with which alone we need concern ourselves, is the Rikki-Tikki of Kipling—the soldiers' pet of most Indian battalions.

"It is very abundant, and for a regular trade should be obtainable in London at £1 a head. Exceedingly courageous and bloodthirsty, it will catch and kill all kinds of small mammals and birds, and even poultry, so that it cannot be used against rats in country districts. Its value as a rat destroyer was first discovered in the West Indies, where nine were introduced in 1872 to help in the struggle against the rodents in the sugar plantations—they multiplied exceedingly, and were so efficacious that in ten years they were saving £200,000 a year to the planters. Their success was their discomfiture; the rats, driven by persecution, became arboreal—the mongoose, unable to follow them, turned upon the poultry, and in their turn have become a pest. The West Indian experiment introduced them to England. About 1894 a prize of £20 was offered by a Manchester newspaper for the best method of clearing warehouses of rats—one competitor suggested the mongoose, and on a favourable report from the Zoological Gardens, Belle Vue, Manchester, he received the prize, and Mr. Cross, Naturalist, Liverpool, was inundated with inquiries for the beast, which was at once extensively employed and is still in demand for the purpose. To newspaper inquiries, Would the mongoose do what was required, and could it be easily kept? we replied that we had used the mongoose with marked effect as an ordinary ferret, to which it is vastly superior, but its extraordinary quickness made it dangerous to handle. It is best left to do its own hunting, which should be arranged as follows:—

"Obtain a box about 2 ft. by 1 ft. by 1 ft., cover the front with 1 in. mesh netting, the door being of the same material. Place a little hay or other litter in one corner of the box and *keep the place clean.* Put the box in a damp- and draught-free corner of the infected warehouse if possible where the sunshine may reach it—feed the animal on small quantities of perfectly fresh meat, also a little ripe fruit—oranges are special favourites—give water to drink and leave the animal there for a week to get used to its quarters. At the end of that time open the door late in the evening and let the mongoose find its way out.

In the morning it will be gone and may not be seen for weeks, but a little fresh meat and fruit, also water, should be placed daily in the box as a temptation to return. It will return from time to time, but will finally disappear, lost or strayed, from two to six months after release, having appreciably earned far more than its cost. If necessary purchase another. Being entirely fearless, active and bloodthirsty, the mongoose kills many rats, but in my mind it is chiefly effective in scaring them from the neighbourhood."

The author very strongly deprecates turning a mongoose or ferret loose in a town, or elsewhere, with the object of destroying rats, or driving away any which may be on the premises. As admitted, a mongoose will destroy poultry, and those let loose in the West Indies did so to a considerable extent.

It must be remembered that those who deliberately loose a mongoose render themselves liable to prosecution, and for the damage caused to the poultry, &c., which the mongoose has destroyed.

As an alternative to liberating a mongoose, the author recommends the use of the "Terrier" Blocking trap, or blocking and flooding, to be repeated until the number of the rats has been very materially reduced, and for the remainder then to be trapped. When all have been secured, traps should be kept set to catch on arrival any other rats which may invade the premises.

FERRETING.

WHEN there is any wind, the direction of ferreting work ought always to be against it.

Ferreting cannot be conducted too quietly, for rats in their holes hear what is going on outside, and, as before mentioned, their sense of smell is very keen. It follows that there must be no smoking, talking, or shouting to dogs. These last, if properly trained, will stand at the hole shown to them, and remain there if a hand be held up. It is, however, often best to let an experienced dog choose the hole at which he stands, as he seems to know from which one the rat is most likely to bolt.

As soon as the ferret is in the hole, everyone should stand back as far as possible out of sight, otherwise a rat may come to an entrance, and seeing someone, disappear down the hole again, rather than run out into the open.

There should always be two persons working together when hedgerows are being ferreted, and they should keep on opposite sides of the hedge, or a rat bolting on the other side of the fence to that in which the ferret was put would escape unseen.

Each person should have a ratting-spade to fill in holes as soon as they have been ferreted, and also such holes as the dogs declare untenanted.

When a ferret lashes her tail on entering a hole, it is a sure sign that a rat is close by, and if she backs partially out of the hole, and then re-enters, and backs out again, there is probably a rat showing fight and disputing her progress.

When ferreting, care should be taken in handling the ferrets, for if bitten by a rat a ferret is apt to take revenge by biting the first thing she meets with, and it may be her master's hand. This remark applies especially to young ferrets which are not thoroughly accustomed to the work, but even an old ferret usually docile, after having been severely punished, may sometimes bite when about to be handled.

If the ferret kills a rat and will not loosen her hold, the rat should not be wrenched away, but the ferret should be held round the neck, and sufficient pressure made to produce a feeling of suffocation. The windpipe must not be squeezed too hard, or permanent injury might ensue. This procedure usually causes the ferret to let go quickly, but should she not do so, one of her paws should be squeezed between a finger and the thumb, and the toes pressed sideways by the thumb being passed over them at the same time, as if a piece of paper were being rolled. This should not be done too hard, or injury to the ferret's foot might result, and it is well to hold the ferret by the neck whilst the foot is being squeezed, to prevent her suddenly letting go the rat and seizing the offending thumb.

It is very important when ferreting, that all holes be stopped thoroughly as soon as the rats are out of them, not only to prevent rats running back into them from other holes, but also that it may be known in future whether or not there are any rats about.

REQUISITES FOR A DAY'S RATTING.

A bag or box for the ferrets.

Ratting-spades.

Two or three nets and the sticks for them.

A line fitted with coloured threads or tapes, and a collar.

A stick about 15 in. long, and the thickness of a little finger.

A sack for carrying the dead rats.

A bottle of water, and a tin pan, for the ferrets and dogs to drink from.

In addition to the above:—

Kneeling-pads are often useful.

For ferreting buildings, a hammer, gimlet, and some 1½ in. iron staples to which the nets can be fastened, may be wanted.

A gun should be carried if the banks of a pond or stream are to be ferreted.

For ferreting stacks, some boards are required to stop the runs around the stack.

Two or three trap boxes for catching up ferrets may be useful on occasion.

If a box is used for carrying the ferrets, the ventilating holes should be on one side only, but such boxes are often made with holes on both sides. Imagine how uncomfortable the ferrets must be with holes on both sides of the box, and a biting north-east wind whistling through.

Manufacturers, as a class, have only a vague idea as to how a ratting-spade should be made, and many of them appear to think that a ratting-spade and a trapping-spade are identical.

A ratting-spade[1] must be light, but yet strong, the handle therefore should be made of a good piece of ash, and the other parts of well-tempered steel, and the bottom edge of the blade must be sharp enough to cut quickly through roots. The ideal spade is about 4 ft. in length, the handle immediately above the blade being not more than 1¼ in. in diameter, and the blade, which should be as light as possible, consistent with the necessary strength, about 8 in. long, 5 to 5½ in. wide across the

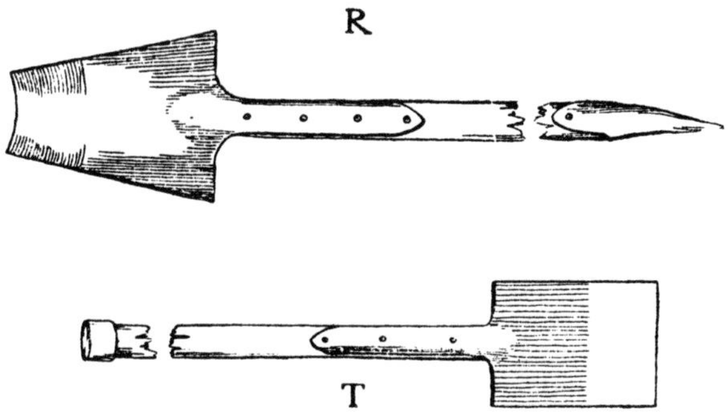

FIG. 17.—R, ratting-spade ; T, trapping-spade.

top, and 3 to 3½ in. wide across the bottom. The blade, although shorter, is in shape somewhat similar to a Norfolk rabbiting-spade, which is smaller, and slightly hollowed at the bottom, and tapers to the square-shouldered top. The handle, instead of having a hook at the upper end, as in the case of a rabbiting-spade, is attenuated for several inches to a sharp point, and cased in iron just as a dibble is cased. The sharp end is required to feel for a

[1] Ratting and trapping-spades are manufactured by Messrs. Skelton and Co., Sheafbank Works, Sheffield; Messrs. Shear and Jackson, Ætna Works, Sheffield.

lost hole; a long dig and much time will frequently be saved by finding it.

A trapping-spade is usually about 3 ft. in length, and its blade, which should be the same width at the top and bottom, about 6 in. long, and $4\frac{1}{4}$ in. wide. But instead of being furnished with a spike at the other end, the handle should be cut off at a right angle, so as to make the end flat, and this should be shod with a band of iron to prevent its edges getting broken when it is used to drive into the ground the pegs to which the traps are fastened.

A ratting-blade will do for a trapping-spade, but a trapping-blade is not suitable for a ratting-spade. If retail dealers do not wish to stock both patterns, it would be better for them to stock ratting-spades, and to affix a spike or iron band to the top of the handle as required.

Two or three nets, with a mesh of not more than an inch, about 10 to 20 yds. in length, and 4 to 6 ft. in width, should always be carried. They prevent many rats from escaping, or at any rate save a great deal of time which would otherwise be spent in hunting them down, and dislodging them from places in which they have taken refuge. Nets are usually sold per yard when stretched, and it is well to remember that when set the length is somewhat less.

Nets are specially useful when rats are lying in a bank separated by a dry ditch from the hedge on the opposite bank. In this case, unless a net is laid against the hedge, a rat is very apt to bolt from an unnoticed hole while the dogs are already occupied, and to cross the ditch and run into the hedge before there is time to stop him. With a net in position as described, the progress of the rat is sufficiently delayed to allow someone to get to him, even if one of the dogs does not do so.

Nets are useful also when ferreting in a lane or narrow roadway, and are best set on the opposite side to that which is being worked. A net should always be placed through a gateway which is in the hedge that is being ferreted, and placed on the farther side of the open space which the gateway creates.

Two or three short nets are much more handy to work with than one equal to their united length, indeed a net of 10 to 15 yds. is often amply sufficient by itself.

A strong line should be passed through the top and bottom of the net along its whole length, and tied at each end to prevent it from slipping out, a free length of cord about 1 ft. or more in length being left at each end beyond, for fastening to a stick, or other support.

The sticks supporting the net should be placed on its outer side, that is, the farther side from where the ferreting is taking place.

The net may be fixed to the sticks by hitching the top cord round them at a level allowing about 4 to 6 in. of the net to lie on the ground. Not only will this enable the net to cover any depressions in the ground, but it will prevent a rat from getting underneath it, because when the rat is in contact with the vertical portion of the net, he will be standing on the part that rests on the ground.

Both ends of the net should be brought forward for about a yard at a right angle to its central portion, so that a rat, after reaching the net, and running along by the side of it, must come back towards the place where the ferreting is going on, before he can escape round the end of the net.

It is well to use nets also when ferreting a building, if there is a roadway or pathway separating the building from one adjacent. If the net cannot be hung on the opposite building so as to cover the holes into it, and the ground is paved or too hard to allow the sticks supporting the net to be forced into it, they may be kept upright by placing them in earth put into sacking bags, rush baskets, pots or tins. The two former are the better, because they are more easily carried from one place to another. When the sticks are thus kept upright, an additional bag or basket filled with earth may be placed about 2 ft. behind each stick, and another stick stuck into the earth and its other end tied to the top of the upright stick so as to form a strong support to it. This precaution is needed, for sometimes the dogs run against the net while catching a rat and are apt so push it down unless it is firmly supported. When the sticks supporting the net are not forced into the ground, it is best, where possible, to attach both ends of the net to a building or other suitable fixture. For this purpose, it is well to carry a hammer and a few 1½-in. iron staples; they can be left in the posts for use on a future occasion.

When ferreting a hedgerow, the drain pipe under a gateway should be blocked at the further end, and unstopped when the gateway is reached, so that a ferret may be run through it. In any case it is well to run a ferret through a dry drain under a gateway; rats sometimes lie there.

When holes in a bank, or side of a ditch, &c., have been covered by vegetation, it is best to ferret them immediately after this has been removed, for when exposed, rats are liable to leave the holes that were made originally in a concealed position. The ferreting therefore, when possible, should be done on the day on which the bank is cleared.

Although a ferret should never be used on a line for ratting, yet a line and collar should always be carried because a lined ferret provides the quickest means of ascertaining the whereabouts of a ferret that is lying up. It is a good plan to let a young ferret wear a collar for a week or more at a time so as to become accustomed to it. If the collar becomes stiff or hard it can be made supple by soaking it in neat's-foot oil.

Accurately to gauge the distance to which the ferret has gone into a hole, coloured threads or narrow tape may be fastened to the line at every yard, while further to discover the distance, and to obviate the possibility of a mistake, different coloured threads may be used in regular order. Red, white, and black threads can be readily obtained, and these colours do very well. To affix the threads, the line should be untwisted sufficiently to allow the bodkin carrying the small bunch of threads to be passed between its strands, the ends of the threads being left about 1½ in. in length. A line should never be knotted; the knot is liable to catch in roots.

When a ferret, or rat, has to be dug out, a stick about 15 in. long is often useful to ascertain the direction of the hole.

Rats are often infested with fleas, which leave them when they are killed and their bodies begin to get cold, so that the sack in which dead rats are carried, after a day's ratting usually contains a number of fleas.

When ferreting an area suspected of containing plague-infected rats, each rat as soon as killed ought to be submerged in a strong solution of cyllin, izal, Jeyes' fluid, Pearson's antiseptic, or some other germicidal solution. If the sack is placed in the same solution, or in boiling water, at the end of the day's work, all the fleas it contains will be destroyed. All rats from an area of possible infection ought, however, to be burnt in a furnace, and it is best to burn the sack with them. Some insect powder may be sprinkled also in the bag that holds the rats before the ferreting is begun.

Although it is not customary to carry water, and a pan out of which the ferrets can drink, yet if this is done it will be found that not only will they gladly avail themselves of the opportunity of a drink after work, but often beforehand as well. The lid of a small tin box does very well for the pan for the ferrets, and if one side is bent out to form a lip, the water not used can be poured back into the bottle, when ferreting in a place where water is not at hand. A larger receptacle with a blunt edge is better for the dogs.

Kneeling-pads will be found useful when listening to ascertain where a ferret is attacking a rat at bay. They are often of use when reaching a ferret, as they are a protection not only against wet, but also against thorns.

When ferreting the banks of a stream, or a pond that has overhanging bushes, it is well to be provided with a gun. Rats, when bolted, often dive into the water, and where it is too wide to allow them to run across the bottom, they come to the surface a few yards from the bank, and swim towards the opposite bank, or any portion of the bank that is overhung with bushes. Unless they can be killed before they reach the opposite bank or shelter, they may not be seen again.

It should be remembered that ferrets dislike getting their feet and legs wet, and that when a ferret returns to the mouth of the hole by which she entered, she may have turned back, because part of the hole traversed has water in it. In this case either another ferret should be tried in the hole, or a "smoke ferret" used to compel the rats to leave it.

As the ferreting of banks of ponds, ditches, &c., sometimes necessitates standing in water or slush, it is advisable beforehand to give boots, when dry, a good dressing with dubbing. This is best done with a stiff paint brush when the boots are not only thoroughly dry, but also warm, the dubbing having been previously melted. If the boots are kept in a warm place after the application has been made, the absorption of the dubbing is facilitated, and more may be applied daily until the leather is thoroughly saturated with it. The application should be made to the soles as well as to the upper leather, and the joint between the sole and the upper leather should not be forgotten.

The following is an excellent recipe for dubbing:—

Boiled neat's-foot oil	1 pint.
Mutton suet	½ lb.
Bees-wax	6 oz.
Finely powdered resin	4 oz.

Melt and thoroughly mix the ingredients together over a slow fire.

When rats have entered a stack, it is to the farmer's interest to thresh the stack at once, irrespective of market prices, to prevent the corn being eaten by vermin (see Section "The Habits of Rats—Some Facts of General Interest"). If, for any adequate reason, this cannot be done for some weeks, the stack may be ferreted, but this method is often incomplete, and ferrets are apt to lie up and get lost.

Before ferreting a stack, unless it stands well out in the open, a net should be placed around it several yards away, so as to give plenty of room for the dogs, and those engaged, to work.

Before putting the ferrets in, it is advisable to go round the stack with a ladder and to fix pieces of thin board about 1 ft. in length, and 6 to 8 in. in width, across the runs which the rats have made on the outside of the stack, to prevent the rats running along them when pursued by a ferret. If the end of the board is tapered to a point for 3 or 4 in. it can be pushed into the stack more easily.

It is advisable also when ferreting a stack, for someone to stand on a ladder on each side to knock the rats off the thatch, for otherwise when followed by a ferret they are apt to bolt on to the thatch, and to re-enter the stack by another hole.

If possible, all the stacks and farm buildings should be ferreted on the same day, so as to prevent rats from passing during the night into the stacks and buildings that have been ferreted, from those that have not been visited.

It is sometimes convenient to carry several trap-boxes for catching ferrets which have lain up and cannot be found, although, whenever possible, it is better to dig a ferret out at once.

When a trap-box is used, it should be baited with a rat that has had the skin of its belly ripped, so that the entrails are exposed. The box is then placed against the hole by which the ferret entered. All the others should be closed.

If a ferret has been bitten badly she should be put into a hutch by herself, and not be used again until quite well. The wound should be carefully washed with warm water, and collosol iodine ointment, iodex, or tincture of iodine applied.

If the wound festers, it should be carefully cleaned twice or more daily by sponging it with warm water before the application of the ointment or tincture.

As the sponge is certain to become contaminated by the discharge from the wound, it should be well washed after use, and then placed in a covered jar containing some germicidal solution, and left there until again wanted. Izal, one teaspoonful, or Jeyes' fluid, two teaspoonsful, to the quart of water will do.

Sick ferrets, too ill to take their usual food, may be given raw meat, milk, or an uncooked new-laid egg.

DOGS.

In his pursuit of the rat, man must rely to some extent on the help of his dog, and no apology is needed for setting out principles of training, and methods of rearing, that may enable an intelligent animal to make the best return to his master. Most old sportsmen are well convinced that while many men keep dogs, only a small proportion know how to do so properly. For the great campaign against the rat, man must equip himself with the best possible means to the end he has in view, and, as a good dog may help very considerably in keeping rats at a distance, a discussion of the best means of looking after the dog cannot be considered out of place. To begin with, there is a book[1] containing useful hints and amusingly written by the late Mr. H. C. Barkley, from which, by the permission of Mr. John Murray the publisher, a couple of pages or so may be quoted.

"I will first begin on their masters, for to make a good dog, a good master is also absolutely necessary. Anybody that has thought about it knows that as is the master, so is the dog. A quiet man has a quiet dog, a quarrelsome man a quarrelsome dog, a bright, quick man, a bright, quick dog, and a loafing idle ruffian a slinking slothful cur.

"First of all, then, the dog's master must understand dog talk, for they do talk, and eloquently too, with their

[1] "Studies in the Art of Rat-catching."

tongues, their ears, their eyes, their tail, and even with the hairs on their back. Having learnt dog language, use it to your own dog in a reasonable way; talk to him as a friend, tell him the news of the day, of your hopes and fears, your likes and dislikes, but above all use talk always in the place of the whip. For instance, when breaking in a young dog not to kill a ferret, take hold of the dog with a short line, put the ferret on the ground in front of him, and when he makes a dash at it say, 'What *are* you up to? War ferret! Why I gave four-and-sixpence for that, you fool, and now you want to kill it! Look here, (picking the ferret up and fondling it) this is one of my friends, smell it (putting it near his nose), different from a rat, eh? Rather sweet, ain't it? War ferret, war ferret!' Repeat this a few times for two or three days, and when you first begin working the dog, and he is excitedly watching for a rat to bolt, first say 'war ferret' to him, and he will be sure to understand. Should he, however, in his excitement make a dash at the ferret, shout at him to stop, and then, picking up the ferret, rub it over his face, all the time scolding him well for what he has done; but don't hit him, and probably he will never look at a ferret again.

"In my opinion there is nothing like a thrashing to spoil a dog; reason with it and talk to it, and if it is worth keeping it will understand and obey. Mind, a dog must always obey, and obey at the first order. Always give an order in a decided voice, as if you meant it, and never overlook the slightest disobedience. One short whistle should always be enough. If the dog does not obey, call him up and, repeating the whistle, scold him *with a scold in your voice.* Don't shout or bawl at him for all the country to hear, and the rats too, but just make your *words sting.* If he repeats his offence put a line and collar on him and lead him for half an hour, telling him all the time why you do so, and he will be so ashamed of himself that the chances are he will obey you ever after.

"There is another thing a master should always do for his dog himself and do it with reason. See to his comfort; see that he has good food and water and is comfortably lodged. Don't let him be tied up often without water, and with food thrown into a dish that is already half full of sour and dirty remains of yesterday's dinner. This is not reasonable and is cruel. Keep all clean, kennel, food, dishes, water and bed."

Dogs are often kept in an enclosure with an out-building attached, an arrangement that follows the plan of the kennel for hounds; the out-building fitted with a bench for dogs to lie on. The writer is of the opinion, however, that a properly constructed kennel provides a far better bed for a dog on a cold night. Even if the owner has the space and can afford to build an enclosure to keep the dog within bounds, without the use of a chain, a well-made kennel inside that enclosure is distinctly better than a building fitted with a bench. If kennels, on the plan of those used for hounds, exist already, the dog may be made comfortable by placing a tub or deep box on its side, on the bench or floor with plenty of straw, and partially boarding up the former top that is now the front of box or tub, to keep the straw from falling out. If this is done, it will be found that a dog will desert the bench and lie in the tub so that there will be no doubt about his choice. Should a tub be used instead of a box, some boards may be put in to make a flat surface. With this addition the dog lies more comfortably, and the tub can be cleaned more thoroughly if this floor is not fixed. There is nothing better than an ordinary kennel, provided the roof projects sufficiently to shelter the dog's bed from rain, and provided the kennel itself is draught-proof. Obviously the floor should always be inside the front, back, and sides, but often it may be seen nailed to the bottom of these parts, and as a result the floor becomes wet from rain running through the joint.

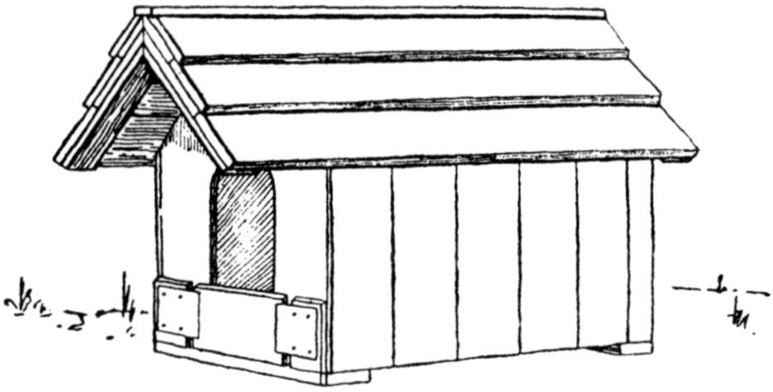

FIG. 18.—Dog-kennel with eaves and movable front at entrance.

While the entrance is best made in the centre of one end, the roof should project over the entrance from 12 to 15, or even 18 in., and from 3 to 6 in. at the back and sides.

The reason for placing the entrance in the centre is that it is thoroughly protected by the roof, and the dog, lying in the kennel, can see what is going on outside. It is quite easy to add a projecting roof to a kennel that lacks one. To keep the straw from falling out, a piece of wood, from 4 to 8 in. in height, according to the size of the kennel, and 2 in. wider than the entrance, may be placed across the lower part of the outside of the entrance as shown in fig. 18. This movable front can be kept in position if it is overlapped on each side by a piece of wood of corresponding height, with the grain placed transversely. A still neater method may be found by so placing a plate of iron, 8 to 10 standard wire gauge, that its inner edge is on a line with the side of the entrance, and screwing it to a block thicker than the movable piece of wood across the entrance, so that the latter can be moved easily up and down. A piece of wood, flush with the floor of the kennel or placed slightly below it, may be nailed across between the blocks to keep the movable piece from dropping too far. By the aid of this simple arrangement the straw is kept in the kennel, and by removing the piece of wood the floor is easily swept up.

There is a passing fashion of making kennels with a door at the back or even at the side for inserting the straw, but these are obviously more draughty than the ordinary ones. The chains sold for dogs are usually too short, and it is well to join two or more of them together to give the animal a better time. The joining is best effected by the use of an S hook which may be obtained from any ironmonger, the open ends to be hammered up when they have been passed through the chains. Another way of giving more freedom to a dog is to pass a strong wire through a ring, fasten each end of the wire securely, and then attach the dog's chain to the ring. If the wire is attached to posts, the dog is liable to wind the chain round one of them and thus get held to it. To prevent this a staple should be put across the wire, and driven into a strong peg, sunk in the ground, at the chain's length from the post, thus providing a stop for the ring. Another method is to fasten to poles projecting beyond the post a piece of wire netting, too high for the dog to jump over, one of the poles being placed against the farther side of the post to prevent the dog passing round it.

When a dog is kept in a meadow, a stout, slack wire can be laid round it, and kept in position by a post in each corner, this post being sloped a little outwards. If the ends of the wire are neatly joined, a large thick ring, placed on the wire, will slip over the join without catching against it. The dog's chain may be fastened to the ring by means of a stout S hook, or spring hook, that will allow the ring to slip round, so that the same place on it is not always being rubbed against the wire. The dog while chained to the wire should be taken round the meadow several times, then called from the opposite side and given some dainty when he has run along the course of the wire. In a few days he will learn to range the meadow. The kennel may be placed outside the wire, so that the dog can see all over the meadow, and turn to the right or left as he leaves it. Every corner post must have a hurdle or piece of wire netting placed against it, and projecting inwards to keep the dog from passing on its inner side.

There is a right way and there is a wrong way of fastening up a dog. Most people choose the latter method, and are astonished if the dog gets loose. The staple to which a chain is attached must be placed horizontally, and the chain passed through it from *below*, and the cross-bar laid across the staple, as shown in fig. 19. This done, a dog can never get away because its chain has become unfastened. If, on the other hand, the cross-bar is carried on and put through the ring on the chain, it is liable to slip out of place, to be tipped against the post into which the staple is driven, and so be drawn through the staple. This will never happen if the cross bar is laid across the top of the staple, for then the weight of the chain will keep it from being displaced.

FIG. 19.—A chain properly connected with the staple.

If the chain be put through the staple from above, as shown in fig. 20, the dog is sure, sooner or later, to get loose. The cross-bar will work below the staple, and be tipped more or less vertically against the post, and may then be pulled through. Drive the staple into a stout post in the ground, or else into a wall previously plugged with wood. If the latter method is followed, the mortar between the courses of brick selected should be removed to the depth to which the staple will reach, and to a width sufficient to receive a piece of wood about 2 in. wider than the width of the staple. When the piece of wood, slightly tapered at the end, has been driven in and firmly wedged between the bricks and the mortar at its sides, the staple should be hammered into it parallel with the grain, and if this is done properly it can never be

FIG. 20.—A chain wrongly connected.

pulled out. The plug should be made of soft wood, and the holes for the prongs of the staple should be bored with a gimlet as in the case of the post. Without this boring it may be difficult to drive the staple in sufficiently far. Never remove a brick, or part of a brick, to make room for the plug of wood that is to receive the staple.

If this is done, wood and staple will sooner or later be pulled out of the wall together. Take care that the chain cannot be fixed round any post, or projection, and so keep the dog from entering his kennel. A front corner of the kennel should be as close as possible to the post to which the dog is chained. Sometimes a chained dog rushes at strangers, and is pulled up with a jerk on reaching the end of his chain. By fastening a spring to two links of the chain, on the kennel end, the chain is shortened to the full extent to which the spring can be extended, and the jerk is thus avoided. When a dog is taken off the chain, put the spring hook inside the kennel, instead of allowing it to remain on the ground ; it will thus be kept clean and dry. Always keep a large bowl or trough of water within the dog's reach, for choice in a corner between the post and the kennel, or if in a yard, in the angle formed by the back of the kennel and the wall. In this way the bowl will not be turned over by the dog's chain. Writing of water serves as a reminder of the popular belief that a stick of brimstone put into the dog's water will impart medicinal properties to it. In point of fact sulphur, or brimstone as it is sometimes called, is not soluble in water and so far from imparting medicinal properties, it is of no more value than a pebble or piece of brick would be. Sublimed sulphur, that is sulphur in the form of a very fine powder, acts as a laxative when taken internally. One or two teaspoonsful, or even more according to the size of the dog, may be mixed with its food and will be eaten readily.

When a male dog is chained in the open, a post should be put into the ground at one side of the kennel, at the extreme end of his chain, so that he cannot get caught round it. A shallow depression should then be made round the post, about 2 ft. in diameter.

Use wheat straw for a dog's bed, never barley straw or hay. When putting fresh litter into a kennel, take the dog off the chain for a few minutes and allow him to make his bed. He likes to shape it to suit his own fancy and scrape the straw about until the arrangement is complete. If he is not free, the chain is likely to get entwined with the straw which will be dragged out of the kennel as he leaves it. In hot weather no straw is needed, but the kennel should be brushed out several times a week and scraped with a scraper such as is used for rabbit-hutches, fowl nests or pigeon cotes. A savage dog may be safely held by the loose skin of the neck immediately behind the jaw, provided the hand is placed so that the thumb points forward. If in any other position, the dog can turn its head so as to bite wrist or hand. The dog that is wild and will not keep to heel may be restrained and punished by placing one of his fore feet through his collar, thus compelling him to run on three legs. If he is kept like this for a few minutes, and scolded, he will soon learn to obey orders.

Advantage may be taken of the great dislike most dogs have to the smell of camphor, to keep them away from door-posts and other places that they defile. The best way to use it is to dissolve 1 oz. of camphor in half a pint of methylated spirit, and squirt the solution from a syringe over and around the places which it is wished to protect. The application should be made daily, until the dogs have discontinued their visits.

Where ordinary soap is used for washing dogs, it is well to add either izal, Jeyes', or some other germicidal fluid to the water.

For izal, one tablespoonful to the gallon suffices; for Jeyes', twice as much. If the disinfectant floats on the surface of the water, the mixture is too strong. Soft water is better than hard. Dogs should be combed while in a lather so that any fleas may loose their hold, and become entangled in the soapsuds. Before washing a dog, remove its collar, and be careful to wash its neck as well as its body, for fleas often congregate there.

Many dogs kept in a house are treated with unintentional cruelty by their owners who do not realize how strong the draughts are along the floor, and that a dog on a mat or in an unlined basket has no protection from them. It is to avoid these draughts, as well as to obtain a softer bed, that dogs will prefer a chair or sofa to the floor. The warmest and most comfortable place in a house for a dog is a box made of match-board, large enough for him to lie down in when surrounded by bedding, and about 4 to 6 in. higher than he is when he stands up. The box should have a top nailed to it, and space left for an entrance by reducing the height at one side.

Although a dog may be taught at a very early age that a ferret is a friend, and not a foe, he should not be used for ratting before he is seven to ten months old. Before taking a young dog out with ferrets, it is advisable to let him kill one or two rats released from a cage trap. Such rats to be turned out into an open space, and the dog held until they begin to run away. In no circumstances should the dog be allowed to attack a rat that is held in a steel trap. Not only is the dog liable to hurt its teeth against the trap, but he is much more likely to be severely bitten than when the rat is free. At the same time it is a very unsportsmanlike proceeding to allow a dog to attack even a rat that cannot defend itself.

To make a dog understand that he is not to touch ferrets requires only a little patience. It is best to begin by putting a ferret into a wire-work rat-trap or a wire-work cage so that the dog can see and smell it, the dog being held by a short cord. When he appears to know that he may not touch the ferret he may be loosed, and watched, to see how he behaves when he thinks he is alone with the ferret. The next step in his education is to place a line on the ferret, and a slip on the dog, and allow the ferret to go near the dog. Later the ferret may be allowed to run about loose, the dog still being kept on the slip; the final training is the actual work. Let the dog see the ferret put into the hole, and let him kill the rats that bolt. Hold him on the slip, and whenever the ferret appears say: "Ferret, ferret," in a reproving tone, and the dog will soon understand that the animal is helping him at his sport.

If any apology is needed for this rather long dissertation on dogs, it is to be found in the fact that a well-trained dog is a great advantage to ratting, and an ill-trained dog is of little or no use. It is, moreover, a master's duty to attend to his dog's health and comfort.

TRAILING.

ATTRACTING rats from one place to another by means of a trail is a very ancient custom, but it is not used to-day as frequently as it might be. Almost any substance possessing a strong scent will serve, and red herrings have been employed frequently for the purpose. Essential oils are, however, more suitable, oil of aniseed, oil of caraway and oil of rhodium being the most useful. They may be used alone, or mixed together in equal parts. Oil of peppermint is believed to repel both rats and mice.

A trail may be used to lure rats to the shelters where food has been placed, and where it is proposed to lay poison or set traps subsequently. This method is especially useful for drawing rats to one or more places, when it is known that a certain number are about, as in coverts, plantations, thick hedgerows, &c., and also in parks and open spaces frequented by rabbits. In this way the rats living in some of the rabbit-burrows may be brought for destruction from a considerable distance.

With regard to oil of rhodium, or oil of duty as it is also called, it is so frequently quoted as a lure for rats, that it may be mentioned that it is distilled from the roots of a convolvulaceous plant called rhodorrhiza, but it is seldom sold, a factitious product being usually supplied in its stead.

The three most usual formulæ for producing the spurious oil of rhodium are as follows :—

(1)	Oil of copaiba	1 oz.
	Oil of almonds	1 oz.
	Otto of rose	10 drops
	Oil of rose-geranium	10 drops
	Mix.	
(2)	Oil of sandalwood	½ oz.
	Oil of rose-geranium... ...	15 drops
	Oil of almonds	1½ oz.
	Mix.	
(3)	Copaiba balsam	1 oz.
	Oil of almonds	1 oz.
	Otto of rose	20 drops
	Mix.	

A trailer may be made by taking several strips of flannel, linen or other material, about 16 in. long and 2 in. wide, and doubling them in half lengthways, and then tying them round about 2 in. from the double end, so as to make a loop. A piece of strong string or tape about 9 in. long should then be passed through the loop and fastened to it, and the trailer then boiled for a few minutes. When taken out of the water, it should be wrung in a cloth and dried. Never let it be touched with the hand.

For use, the trailer may be moistened with an essential oil or one of the mixtures set out above, and the string tied to a stick of sufficient length to make a suitable handle. A ring or small staple on the end of the stick enables the string to be easily fastened and removed.

The trailer should be drawn close to a fence, wall, hedge, or other place along which a rat is likely to travel, and care taken not to walk on the ground over which it will be drawn. After it has been used, it may be untied from the stick, and put into a tin box or covered jar with a tight-fitting lid, so as to prevent the smell of the trail pervading the house.

POISONING.

THE opinion has been expressed recently, and on more than one occasion, that it is practically useless to destroy rats because the larger the number killed, the better the food supply and housing accommodation for those which remain, and that with these improved conditions their number increases more quickly than before. Therefore, the best way to remedy the evil is merely to shut off the food supply by making stores rat-proof, and burning edible refuse or keeping it in rat-proof receptacles until it can be got rid of.

The author very strongly dissents from this line of argument which mentions only one of the many methods which should be employed simultaneously to lessen the number of rats, and he attaches no value to the statistics so often quoted to show that the rat population cannot be reduced beyond certain proportions. Reducing continually to a number which can be estimated, and not beyond it, merely points to the want of organization and of knowledge in trapping, and the other methods called for when the number of rats is small. This task is in reality much easier than that which is presented when the opposite condition exists.

Rats will never be exterminated, but their number may be reduced to a minimum and kept at a minimum, if there is a continual and universal war carried on against them. It is merely a matter of organization and the general employment of proper repressive measures, one of the most important of which is keeping traps set throughout the year in all premises on which rats have been found. This measure is attended with but little trouble, but it secures a large death-roll. (See Section "Conclusion and Recapitulation.") Where rats have been, there other rats will go sooner or later, especially when pigs or poultry are kept, or food-stuffs are manufactured or stored, and traps should be kept always set to secure them on arrival. They should not be set, as is now generally done, when they have made their presence known, and have had time to do damage and perhaps increase their number. This is unnecessarily late.

Indifference to the presence of rats throughout the country has become so ingrained that an organized and systematic destruction of them can only be secured by fining and continuing to fine, even heavily, those who do not take sufficient measures to free their premises and keep them free from these destructive vermin.

Government control will never be effective for this purpose because it will never be conducted on business lines, and the work controlled by Government officials will burden further the already overtaxed ratepayer.

A permanent diminution in the number of rats throughout the country will begin when the County Councils assume control. They must do their duty to those who are doing their utmost to keep the rat population down, by issuing a summons and having a fine imposed on those who neglect their duty. Properly organized, the Rat Campaign should be more than self-supporting.

It must not be supposed that there is any wish to do away with the Rat Department of the Ministry of Agriculture. On the contrary, it is hoped that it may long continue the most useful work with which it is now engaged. Moreover, it is necessary that there should be a Government department for the reception and distribution of precise information, and for the development of agricultural propaganda.

For the continuous war against rats, poison is essential, but it is important to understand that a colony of rats cannot be destroyed by poisoning alone. Although, when rats are very numerous, poison affords a good means of lessening their number, yet according to the situation, blocking, flooding, ferreting or fumigation, as well as trapping and snaring, must be resorted to in order to destroy those that have escaped. Trapping and snaring should be begun four or five days after the poison has been laid. The mistaken idea that poisoning alone is sufficient to exterminate rats is one of the causes why so many rats continue to be found on a given farm or property after poison has been laid. The large number found on the place a few months later are those that have not been killed by the poison, together with their offspring and descendants and those which have migrated from the surrounding district, as well as their offspring and descendants.

The popular way of administering poison to rats and mice is to spread some of the poison on squares of bread, and place it in their holes, or even lay it about in the open at night. This practice is often attended with serious consequences. Not only is the poison liable to be eaten by dogs, cats, poultry, pigeons, &c., but even children have been known to pick up the poisoned pieces of bread.

Another objection to spreading poison on pieces of bread or other solid substances is that the rats or mice, if they dislike the poison, will push or carry the bread with the poison out of their holes. Thus they expose the poison which had been carefully concealed, and, as it was thought, placed out of reach of domestic animals.

The safest way to administer arsenic and carbonate of barium is to mix it with meal, as in this form it cannot be carried. Strychnine also may be used in this manner, but in the case of phosphorus it must be mixed with grease, and is therefore liable to be treated as previously described.

Since the passage of the Rats and Mice (Destruction) Bill, 1919, poison has been used very largely both in towns and in the country. With the object of obtaining information as to the most efficient poison to use and the ingredients best suited to mix with it, and also for convenience in placing different kinds of food bases, poisoned and unpoisoned, side by side, and enabling the number of baits laid to be easily counted, it has become the custom to use paste sufficiently thick to be cut into pieces about the size of a hazel nut. This method allows the introduction of tallow, for which rats appear to have a special liking, and other kinds of grease and material not found in a dry powder or mealy form. Bread cut into slices, covered with a poisonous paste and then cut into cubes the above-mentioned size, has also been used.

It is useless to place poison on a large scale in hedgerows, coverts and plantations, more than twice, or at the most three times a year. The rats that took a little of the poison on the last occasion on which it was laid, but in quantity not sufficient to kill them, appear to remember it, or they can recall the smell of the essential oil used to entice them, or in the case of strychnine, to conceal its odour and taste, and they carefully avoid eating anything of a similar nature. For this reason it is most important that the whole area to be poisoned should be treated simultaneously and in one day.

In the case of docks, wharves, farms, and food factories near a town to which rats are continually being carried, or are travelling, poison may be laid more or less throughout the year. In these cases, rats are continually arriving from ships, or from the neighbouring country or town as the case may be ; consequently they have had no previous experience of poisoned food on the premises.

For the purpose of systematic poisoning, boxes should be constructed about 2 ft. in length, 8 to 12 in. in height, and 1 ft. in width, water-tight at the top and raised from the ground about an inch by two or more strips of wood nailed transversely to the bottom ; the boxes being kept against a wall by means of stout pegs driven into the ground. The pieces of wood forming the front and ends should be separated about an eighth to a quarter of an inch to admit light.

At each end an aperture should be left 2 to 3 in. high across the whole width of the box, which should be fastened with a padlock, and contain a glazed earthenware pan or enamelled iron dish which should be thoroughly cleaned from time to time. The pan may be kept in position by wooden blocks.

It will be found almost useless to have boxes constructed for holding the poison, unless they are placed in charge of someone who will be held responsible for the food being in a clean condition. If this is not done, poison that is not eaten when first laid down may become musty or covered with excrement so that the rats will not touch it. It must be the duty of the person in charge to go to each box daily and remove any rats that may have died in it, replace the poisoned food consumed, and if necessary, to burn any spoiled food remaining. The dish, if in a foul condition, must be properly washed before placing fresh poisoned food in it. Care should be taken when washing the dish that it is handled as little as possible.

It must be remembered that where there is plenty of food about, the poisoned food will not be touched unless it is made attractive.

There are very few subordinates who do not require supervision, and therefore someone in authority should inspect the boxes from time to time and see that the man in charge is attending to them properly.

As regards the destruction of rats, great good would be done at docks, if the boundary between them and the neighbouring town had along it a line of boxes for poison, and trapped "Terrier" Signal-runs such as have been described in the Section "Traps," and a trail drawn from time to time along the line.

In this case two or three kinds of food might be used, or each box scented with a different essential oil and the same box always used for the same kind of food or scent. Special care should be taken to place a poison box, and one or more trapped Signal-runs against any shed near the boundary fence, as rats entering the docks will probably keep under cover of the fence until they reach a building. If this were done, it would check to a considerable degree the passage of rats between the docks and the town, now taking place to a greater extent than is realized.

Shelters are very useful when poisoning coverts or hedgerows infested with rats. They may with advantage be used in addition to placing poison in the holes, for by their means rats from a hole that has been overlooked may take the poison with the rest.

It is well, before beginning to construct a shelter wanted for immediate use, and while making it, to rub the hands frequently with earth, as mentioned in the Section "Trapping."

A large box turned upside down, with the centre of its edge against the wall resting on a brick, makes a very good shelter for the inside of a building. Another way of making a shelter in or near a building is to place an inverted box without a lid in the centre of a larger box without a lid, the size of the larger one being sufficient to allow a space of 2 or 3 in. all round the smaller box.

Before placing the boxes in position, a notch about 3 in. wide and 2 in. deep should be cut in the centre of each edge of the smaller box, and a hole of similar dimensions made in each side and end of the larger box immediately above the bottom. These holes must be placed so that there is a clear view through both boxes from side to side and from end to end when they are placed in position. Blocks nailed to the bottom of the larger box ensure the smaller box being kept in position.

The food, and subsequently the poison, when placed under the centre of the smaller box cannot be reached by fowls or domestic animals.

Out-of-doors when the weather is fine, a hole about 3 ft.

long, 2 ft. wide and 1 ft. deep, may be dug and boards laid over it, an opening being left at each end sufficiently large for the rats to enter. Alternatively, the enclosure may be formed by earth thrown up in ridges in the form of a square, a large gap for entrance being left on each side and at each end, facing one another.

It is important that the entrances be opposite to one another, so that a rat entering can see the other opening, for rats prefer to enter a shelter with several openings rather than a cavity with one only.

A covering to the shelter may be made by laying sticks across it, and placing turf, bracken, &c., on them. A hurdle covered with straw, and another hurdle laid on the top to keep the straw in position, makes an excellent cover for a shelter, and if the hurdles are tied together, the cover can be lifted as a whole without the straw shifting.

It has been customary for very many years to add essential oils to bait for rats whether poisoned or unpoisoned, with the object of making them more attractive. Recent experiments seem to show that baits which have not been flavoured are taken more readily than those which have been thus treated. Without doubt rats are attracted by essential oils, and in proof of this may be cited the large number which follow a trail. (See Section "Trailing.") However, it does not follow that because rats are attracted by an odour, that they like food flavoured with it. Laying a trail to where the poison is placed, or toasting cheese in a ladle in the building in which poison has been laid, would draw the rats to the place as efficaciously as mixing an essential oil with the food. If it is wished to add an essential oil, the usual proportion is about one or two drops to each pound of bait.

Sugar, or treacle, has been added to bait and poisoned food for rats for centuries under the belief that it makes it more attractive, but again recent experiments demonstrate that unsweetened food is often preferred. When used, sugar has generally been added in the proportion of one part to twelve to fourteen parts of the meal or mixture.

Before laying poison in outbuildings frequented by rats and in shelters constructed to deal with rats inhabiting the premises, it is best to feed the rats for a few nights so as to accustom them to go for food to the places selected. To ensure their doing so as far as possible, a trail (see Section "Trailing") may be drawn to the different shelters where food has been laid, or in the building selected cheese may be toasted in a ladle.

The following is a good bait:—

Flour	4 oz.
Tallow	1 lb.
Bread-crumb	1 lb.

Mix.

and is made as follows:—

Melt the tallow and mix it with the flour until a uniform mass has been made, then cut the crumb of bread into small pieces or pass it through a mincing-machine and stir it up with the mixture.

Of greasy substances, tallow is preferred to dripping or lard.

The fondness of rats for fish is well known, and there is no better bait for them when they have taken up their quarters in a stack, granary, mill or other place where only grain can be obtained, for they will probably welcome a change of diet.

In any case it is best to cook the fish thoroughly; it

can be then readily broken up for mixing with the poison.

Any fish will do very well for the purpose, even that which has become slightly tainted. In the latter case, it may be put with plenty of grease into a hot oven and thoroughly cooked.

The fish, unless very small, should then have the head and tail removed, and be boned, and the flesh thoroughly broken up and mixed with sufficient flour, oatmeal or bread-crumbs to make the required amount. Pounding the ingredients in a mortar or passing them several times through a mincing-machine imparts a fishy flavour to the whole.

When wanted to convey poison, the mass should be spread on a flat surface, and either arsenic or carbonate of barium sprinkled over it from a fine dredger kept for the purpose, arsenic being in the proportion of one ounce to each pound of fish mixture, and carbonate of barium about one part to four parts by weight. If strychnine is used, it should be in the proportion of eighty grains, very finely powdered with twice the quantity of sugar of milk, to each pound of fish mixture. When mixed thoroughly with the poison, it should be placed in the shelters.

Of the three poisons, arsenic and carbonate of barium will be found to be taken the more readily, because both of these substances are tasteless and odourless.

Before putting poison in hedgerows it is advisable to place in each hole, meal or a mixture similar to that to which the poison is to be added, but a night should intervene between the food being thus laid in the holes and poison being placed there. Some rat-catchers place food twice in each hole before poisoning, but one supply of food is sufficient.

It is an advantage to place the food in concealment, not only because rats feed more freely when this is done, but because when the poison is thus laid, there is less fear of its being eaten by domestic animals or poultry.

All holes should be baited with poison in addition to the shelters. This is to ensure the poison reaching all the rats, and even those which, though too young to leave their holes, may be old enough to do so very shortly.

An interval of a week should be allowed to elapse between laying poison and closing the hole in which it has been placed. This gives time for any rats that frequent the locality, and whose hole has been overlooked, to find the poison.

Plenty of poison should always be laid, so that every rat may have as much as he will eat.

It is a simple matter to mix poison with a food-stuff and to introduce it into a rat's hole, but it by no means follows when this has been done that the rats will eat it. For poisoning, therefore, to be successful, care must be taken that the mixture is of such a nature that the rats do not detect the poison, and that it is a food which they like sufficiently to induce them to eat it.

Rats undoubtedly like a change of diet, and for successful poisoning it is sometimes necessary to pander to this taste and to change the flavouring, although bread or oatmeal is the best base to use for bringing the mixture to the required bulk. Tallow, cheese, oatmeal browned in an oven, biscuit meal, fish, cooked liver, blood and meat are all usually taken readily, and when premises greatly infested with rats have to be cleared, poison mixed with different flavourings may be laid simultaneously, so that all tastes are satisfied.

Salt in small quantity appears to be relished by rats and some other rodents.

To render the accidental taking of poisons less likely, it has been made illegal to mix arsenic with food-stuffs without colouring the mixture, and for this purpose Prussian blue, lamp black or chrome green answers very well, as only a small amount of either of them is required to colour a large quantity of poisoned food. Rat-catchers and game-keepers, possibly through ignorance of the law, do not usually add colouring matter to the arsenic they use, but as rats take poisoned food coloured with Prussian blue, lamp black or chrome green almost, if not quite, as readily as they take the same mixture uncoloured, the use of colouring should be enforced, not only for arsenic, but also for carbonate of barium, strychnine, phosphorus, squill and any other poison that may be used.

Although there are poisons as dangerous, and even more dangerous than arsenic, it is somewhat strange that arsenic is the only poison of which the sale to anyone who is not of "mature age" is prohibited by law. It must be coloured before being sold.

As the law at present stands, a child who is known to the chemist, or who is introduced by someone known to the chemist, can be supplied with strychnine provided both sign the chemist's poison sale book, but there is no stipulation that the strychnine must be coloured. Carbonate of barium, although odourless and tasteless, is not deemed a poison under the Poison Section of the Pharmacy Act, and therefore may be purchased and sold by anyone. Nevertheless, on account of it being tasteless and odourless, it is at least as liable as arsenic to be mixed accidentally with food.

In the event of a death occurring through strychnine, or other poison, sold to a child, although it is probable that the coroner would censure the chemist for having sold it, yet, as the law stands, the chemist would have committed no legal offence.

When placing poison in holes in hedgerows, walls, or by ditches or streams, two persons should work together, one going on each side to prevent any holes being overlooked. Each person should be provided with a spoon on a long handle for introducing the food or poison into the holes.

A suitable spoon for introducing the poison into holes can be made by any blacksmith out of a piece of round rod iron about five-sixteenths of an inch in diameter. It should be about the size of a small tablespoon, but less pointed, the width of the bowl not exceeding one and three-quarter inches, and the iron stem being about a foot long. The last 5 or 6 inches must be beaten into a socket to receive a wooden handle, for preference made of ash, about 4 feet 6 inches in length, and seven-eighths of an inch to one inch in diameter, but not any thicker, or it will be heavy to carry and awkward to use. To demonstrate this size it may be mentioned that the diameter of a sovereign is seven-eighths of an inch, and the diameter of a shilling, fifteen-sixteenths of an inch. The socket may be fastened to the wooden handle by a screw, in the same manner in which a rake or Dutch hoe is usually fastened to its handle. Another method of fastening the spoon to the wooden handle is to cut a thread in the end of the iron stem and screw it into the bottom of a strong ferrule attached to the wooden handle. In this case the bottom of the ferrule has a hole with a worm cut in it and is made sufficiently thick to hold the stem of the spoon firmly when screwed into it. In the latter case the iron stem of the spoon need not be more than 7 or 8 in. long.

For all practical purposes a large galvanized iron spoon, such as may be purchased at almost all iron-mongers for about threepence, answers very well. There is usually a hole near the end of the handle of the spoon, through which it may be screwed to a wooden handle, but should the hole be too large, a thick piece of strap leather makes a good washer. To make the fastening of the spoon to the wooden handle more secure, it may be bound with wire or string.

For general use about buildings, a spoon attached to a short handle (spoon and handle together being about 2 ft. in length) is more useful than the long handle used by rat-catchers and game-keepers. They like this kind because it enables them to place the meal in a hole which is on the opposite side of a ditch.

It is a dangerous practice to lay poisoned food in stacks while they are being built, with the idea that it will be eaten by any rats or mice that may get into the rick. If it were certain that all the poison laid would be eaten by vermin this procedure might be permitted, but as a matter of fact the greater part of the poison so laid may remain uneaten. Then when the stack is threshed there is not only the danger that some of it will become mixed with the grain, but that it will be eaten either by horses or cattle with the straw, or picked up by poultry or domestic animals during the threshing, if it gets separated from the straw.

All rats killed by poison ought to be buried deep or burnt, and not be put on a manure heap, or left on the surface of the ground where they can be reached and eaten by pigs or other animals.

Many substances have been used from time to time for the destruction of rats. Most of them are more or less poisonous, but as there are some which are much more efficacious than the rest, it is recommended that these only be employed. Mention will be limited therefore to arsenic, carbonate of barium, squill, strychnine and phosphorus.

Although all these poisons are efficacious, they vary very much in the way by which death is produced. Strychnine and squill are the most humane, and both act quickly. The other three are much slower in their action and cause more suffering. The symptoms produced by each will be mentioned when dealing with it under its separate heading.

It is unfortunate that the cheapest, and in many ways the best poison to use, is not the most humane, but this cannot be helped. There must be no sentiment introduced, the rats must be killed by the method least dangerous to mankind, domestic animals and poultry. The more thoroughly the present race of rats is destroyed the fewer descendants there will be to suffer.

It may be mentioned here that there are no grounds for the statements often made by the vendors of rat poisons that after eating their mixture the rats dry up, and cause no smell if they die under a boarded floor, &c. The quantity taken is not sufficient to produce this result, although, in the case of arsenic, putrefaction may be delayed.

Arsenic.

Arsenic has the very great advantage of being both odourless and tasteless, and cannot therefore be detected when mixed with food. This being the case, many evil-disposed persons have used it for the purpose of murder, but by a merciful dispensation of Providence, a poison which lends itself so readily to the designs of the wrong-doer has another well-marked property besides that of a poison, and that is its power of preserving animal tissues. For this reason, arsenic is largely used by taxidermists for the preservation of skins, and when it is carried into the tissues of the body by the circulation it preserves them for a very long period. So it happens that many murderers have been hanged on the testimony obtained from the exhumed bodies of their victims even after a long period of burial, the arsenic found in the tissues clearly proving that death was due to the administration of this drug.

On account of arsenic being tasteless and odourless, it is largely used for the destruction of rats and mice, and is the principal ingredient in many of the advertised poisons. It is generally used in the proportion of rather more than 5 per cent.

Its administration is accompanied with thirst, purging, and often with nervous symptoms, such as paralysis and convulsions. It is probable that severe abdominal pain is produced, as in the case of human beings.

Many game-keepers and others buy rock arsenic and grind it themselves, under the belief that they are obtaining the drug in its purest form, but such is not the case. Rock arsenic being the crude drug as it forms in the chimney of the retort in which it is volatilized, contains many impurities, whereas the pure drug may be obtained from a chemist in the form of a powder. Not only therefore is the latter more potent, but it has the advantage of being already finely powdered, and ready for use.

The following mixture will be found suitable for poisoning rats:—

Arsenic	1 oz.
Prussian blue	5 gr.
Fine oatmeal, to make...	1 lb.
Mix.	

To this may be added a little grated cheese or half a small tea-spoonful of salt, or in larger quantity:—

Arsenic	1 lb.
Prussian blue	80 gr.
Fine oatmeal, to make...	1 peck (about 14 lb.)
Mix.	

Cheese or salt may be added as before mentioned in suitable quantity.

When a pound of poison is to be made it is best to put about a table-spoonful of oatmeal and the Prussian blue into a large mortar kept specially for mixing poisons. Rub the two substances together until the Prussian blue is thoroughly broken up, no more dark spots seen in the mixture, and no blue streaks made when the ingredients are rubbed. When thus thoroughly mixed, the arsenic and some more meal should be stirred in gradually and the whole rubbed together until it is a uniform colour. The contents of the mortar may then be placed in a basin with more meal, and when thoroughly mixed, still more meal added and so on, until the ingredients have become evenly distributed.

When mixing for a large quantity, it is best to rub the

Prussian blue and a little meal together, then mix them in a large basin with the arsenic added by degrees. Some meal should then be spread out on a large surface such as a tray or large sheet of paper, and some of the arsenic mixture sprinkled carefully over it from a dredger. This should then be mixed together and again spread out, and more meal placed on it and more arsenic mixture sprinkled on the top of it, then the whole mixed together again, and so on, until all is thoroughly incorporated. It may then with advantage be passed several times through a sieve, so as to mix it still more thoroughly. A wire sieve such as is used for cooking will be found suitable, and thirteen holes to the inch a good sized mesh. Care should be taken when mixing not to allow any of the ingredients to come into contact with the hands.

The following formula is useful:—

Arsenic	1 oz.
Wheat flour, or bread finely divided	6 oz.
Tallow, finely divided suet, or dripping	2 to 4 oz.
Prussian blue or lamp black	5 gr.
Fine oatmeal, to make ...	1 lb.
Mix.	

If wished, sugar or an essential oil may be added to the above recipe in the proportions previously mentioned.

As arsenic is tasteless and odourless, it may be added in the proportion previously given to any base desired.

The thirst produced by the poison often causes rats to leave the buildings in search of water, but they do not always die away from them.

Rats poisoned with arsenic decompose slowly, but they

begin to smell musty in about a week or ten days' time. An interval of at least a month should be allowed to intervene between the poisoning and ferreting, to give time for the dead rats to begin to decompose, and thus lessen the tendency for the ferrets to eat them.

CARBONATE OF BARIUM, CALLED ALSO CARBONATE OF BARYTA.

This mineral has been used for very many years for the destruction of rats and mice, but although its action may be slow, it has the advantage of being inexpensive and comparatively harmless to domestic animals and poultry; as it is tasteless and odourless it is readily taken with any food with which it may be mixed. It has been estimated that 1½ to 2 gr. is sufficient to kill a rat, but more than 10 to 15 gr. are required to kill a cat or fowl, and more than 100 gr. to kill a medium-sized dog. A 60-gr. dose, however, has been fatal to a man.

This poison causes intense thirst, and is therefore used when it is wished to induce the rats to leave a house or building to obtain water before they die, which the slow action of the poison enables them to do. All the rats however, do not always avail themselves of this opportunity to lessen their sufferings, and they die and decompose under flooring or behind a wainscot. This poison produces purging and convulsive movements and hæmorrhages in the stomach, intestines and kidneys. It probably causes severe abdominal pain. Death may occur, according to the amount of poison taken, within a few hours or from two to three days.

There are three kinds of carbonate of barium: (1) The commercial; (2) Precipitated by soda; (3) Chemically pure. Of these, the precipitated by soda is better than the commercial for poisoning rats because it is not gritty, but the commercial is generally used. The latter is inexpensive, and the precipitated by soda costs about half as much again, whereas the chemically pure is four times the price of the commercial quality and for this purpose possesses no advantage over the precipitated by soda preparation. Only the carbonate should be used; other barium compounds are generally refused by rodents.

For use, carbonate of barium should be mixed with oatmeal, bread-crumb, flour, biscuit-meal, or any other substance of which rats are fond, in the proportion of about one part of carbonate of barium to four parts, by weight, of meal or any other substance which is to be used, but as it is tasteless and odourless it may be mixed in larger proportions. It may also be mixed with pollard (middlings) and sufficient grease to make it tasty. Grated or finely divided cheese may be added with advantage.

Oatmeal may be made more palatable by being spread out in a thin layer on a tin or plate, put into an oven and removed as soon as it becomes slightly brown.

The meal with which the carbonate of barium is to be mixed should be coloured as in the case of arsenic, and the same method adopted for mixing the ingredients as has already been mentioned in detail when dealing with arsenic.

The following mixture will be found useful :—

Carbonate of barium ...	$3\frac{1}{2}$ oz.
Prussian blue	5 gr.
Salt	a small half tea-spoonful.
Grated or finely divided cheese	$\frac{1}{2}$ oz.
Fine oatmeal, to make ...	1 lb.

Mix.

or in larger quantity:—

Carbonate of barium ...	3 lb.
Prussian blue	80 gr.
Salt	1 oz.
Grated or finely divided cheese	4 to 6 oz.
Fine oatmeal, to make ...	1 peck (about 14 lb.).

Mix.

For the following recipes which have been used with great success on premises belonging to what was formerly the London and North Western Railway, the author is indebted to the late Mr. W. T. Evans, the Rats Officer of the Company.

Formula 1.

	lb.	oz.
Oatmeal	56	0
Carbonate of barium	21	0
Tallow	22	8
Salt	1	12
Oil of aniseed		5

Making up about 100 lb.

To be laid in small pieces about the size of a hazel nut.

Formula 2.

	lb.	oz.
Carbonate of barium	56	0
Tallow	56	0
Salt	1	12
Oil of aniseed	0	5

To be spread on bread ½ in. thick and cut into cubes ½ in. square.

Instructions as to Mixing.

Formula 1.—The tallow is first melted in a boiler. The barium carbonate is then brushed through a fine wire sieve to break up the small lumps, and is well stirred with a wooden stick into the fat. Next the oatmeal and salt are gradually added, and finally the oil of aniseed, the whole being continually stirred to get it thoroughly mixed, for there is a tendency for the barium carbonate to settle to the bottom.

Formula 2 is made up in the same way, of course without the oatmeal. The mixtures are allowed to cool slightly before being placed in the tins. In the case of Formula 2 it is necessary to keep the mixture well stirred during the time it is being put into tins.

A steam jacketed boiler is used for mixing large quantities of the ingredients, but small quantities can be made in a large saucepan or bucket.

Squill.[1]

For many centuries the red squill or sea leek (*Scilla maritima*), a liliaceous plant growing along the shores of the Mediterranean Sea, has been used as a poison for rats, and recently it has become a popular "official" poison in Great Britain. It possesses the advantage of not being poisonous to human beings or domestic animals or poultry when taken in small quantity.

Rats eat it readily, and it produces death in a few hours apparently by poisoning the nervous system. The first symptom noticed is laboured breathing, and this is

[1] The author is indebted to officers of the Rat Department of the Ministry of Agriculture for information with regard to their most recent observations and experiments in connection with squill.

followed by paralysis of the hind quarters, the rat crawling and dragging its hind legs. Death appears to result, soon after this occurs, from heart failure. Sometimes blood issues from the nostrils. Squill evidently acts as an irritant poison, for the stomach is usually inflamed and the brain is also often found in a congested state.

Squill is used as a poison by merely chopping the bulb and mixing it with food, or by drying the bulb and then grinding it to powder. One part of powder represents about five parts of bulb. Cooked bulb may retain its toxicity for two or three weeks, but the powder remains effective for a much longer period. Another method is by using an extract made by macerating the sliced bulb, and finally pressing out all the liquid which can be obtained from the sodden slices, and mixing it with the solution in which the bulbs have been soaked.

1 to 2 gr. of the powder, and 5 to 10 gr. of the bulb, appears to be a fatal dose for a medium-sized rat.

The old way of poisoning with squill, which is still used with success, is to make a pancake with plenty of grease—egg is not necessary—and place one part of finely chopped bulb to every four parts, by weight, of pancake between two layers of the batter, and then fry the mixture. When cold the pancake is cut into pieces about ½ in. square, and laid in the rats' holes or runs.

The Ministry of Agriculture recommends mixing the liquid extract with an equal quantity of fresh milk which has been scalded, and allowed to cool. Oatmeal may be added to the milk, while it is being heated, in quantity to make a thin porridge when the squill extract has been added. Bread, finely divided, may be used instead of oatmeal, thus making a thin bread and milk mixture.

When this method is employed it is well to feed the rats for a few nights in the saucers or pans in which the porridge will be placed. When saucers are not available, the porridge may be placed on a slate, tile, or board.

The following preparations are recommended by the Ministry of Agiculture :—

(1)	Chopped squill	4 parts
	Cheese, grated...	5 "
	Fat	5 "
	Meal (oatmeal or flour) ...	6 "
	Mix.	

Make a thick paste, cut into pieces (biscuits) of about 50 gr. weight (about the size of a small walnut), and bake lightly in an oven. This keeps fairly well if properly prepared.

(2)	Chopped squill	6 parts
	Bread-crumbs...	15 "
	Uncooked minced kippered herring	4 "
	Fat	5 "
	Mix.	

Make a paste, lay pieces about 50 gr. in weight (about the size of a small walnut). This preparation must be made as required and used at once, as it only retains its toxic value for three or four days.

(3)	Chopped squill	1 part
	Flour	4 "
	Mix.	

Make into a dough with water and milk, roll out, and cut into small biscuits. Bake in a cool oven.

Note.—Any of the above can be made with powdered

red squill if available, using, however, smaller pieces for bait (20 gr., i.e., about the size of a filbert). Two grains of a fully toxic squill powder is the medium lethal dose in any biscuit.

The toxicity of squill varies according to the season of the year at which it is gathered, and the locality in which it is grown.

Messrs. L. Rozon and Co., 36-37, Mincing Lane, London, E.C.3, are importers of red squill bulbs.

The following firms supply squill preparations :—

The British Drug Houses, Limited, 22-30, Graham Street, City Road, London, N.1.

Messrs. Haller and Co., 325, Borough High Street, London, S.E.1.

The Rational Co., 30, Mark Lane, London, E.C.3.

Messrs. Boots Pure Drug Company, Nottingham.

Some of these firms supply the poison in powder form. Messrs. Haller's preparation should not be diluted with more than half its volume of milk during preparation.

Unless thick gloves are worn the hands will become very sore after contact with squill bulbs.

Strychnine.

This powerful poison is often used for the destruction of rats and mice, but on account of its deadly properties it should be used only under special conditions, and as a change, rather than for general use. On account of its extremely bitter taste, and the faint odour which it possesses, it is taken less freely than either arsenic or carbonate of barium, although a much smaller quantity of the poison, when taken, acts as a fatal dose. For this reason some rat-catchers add a little strychnine to the arsenic and meal of which their poison mainly consists.

Sulphate of strychnine is the best preparation to use, as it dissolves more quickly than the alkaloid, although more slowly than the hydrochlorate, and the bitter taste of the latter probably becomes apparent sooner than in the case of the sulphate. Half per cent. is a good proportion to use for rats.

As a bitter, or a sweet, when in the crystalline form imparts its flavour much more quickly than when minutely divided, it is best to rub the strychnine into a very fine powder before mixing it with the food. The addition of sugar of milk enables this to be done more readily than if the strychnine is powdered by itself. About double its weight of sugar of milk should be added to sulphate of strychnine for this purpose.

Oatmeal, spread on a tin or plate and put into an oven until it becomes slightly brown, is a good substance to mix with strychnine, and biscuit-meal also goes well with it, a little Prussian blue being added as already mentioned.

Sweet almonds make a good flavouring and scenting ingredient for the food to which strychnine is to be added. For this purpose the almonds should be pounded with a little meal, so that any oily substance which escapes may be taken up by the meal. When thoroughly broken up, the almonds should be mixed with more meal and pounded, and the mixture then added little by little to all the meal to be used, until the two substances are thoroughly incorporated. The ground almonds sold for cooking do very well for this purpose.

Bicarbonate of soda in equal quantity is said to reduce the bitter taste of strychnine.

Saccharin, which is estimated to be four hundred to five hundred times sweeter than cane sugar, has been used to mask the bitter taste of strychnine, an ounce of saccharin being equivalent to several pounds of sugar.

Another good substance to mix with strychnine is liver, cut into slices, and fried in the ordinary way, and then passed through a mincing-machine. About 80 gr. of sulphate of strychnine should be added to each pound of meal, biscuit-meal, liver or fish. Liver or fish may be mixed with an equal quantity of meal, and sufficient tallow or dripping to make it form a mass.

For mixing meal, fish, liver, &c., with the poison, it should be spread on a piece of thick paper, and then powdered with the mixture of strychnine and sugar of milk (from a pepper-pot kept for the purpose), and thoroughly mixed.

If the holes are too large, a piece of wire gauze, coarse muslin or perforated cardboard may be fixed inside the lid. When the poisoned food has been prepared the paper should be burnt.

The poisoned food should be placed in the shelters in which the rats have been fed, so as to prevent the possibility of any being eaten by domestic animals or poultry.

The following mixture will be found useful :—

Sulphate of strychnine	rubbed together to a very fine powder	80 gr.
Sugar of milk... ...		160 gr.
Prussian blue		5 gr.
Sweet almonds, pounded or ground		2 to 4 oz.
Fine oatmeal or biscuit-meal, &c., to make ...		1 lb.

Mix.

Grated or finely divided cheese in the same, or a greater proportion, may be substituted for the sweet almonds. Although the odour of toasted cheese attracts rats and mice, it must be remembered *that the degree of heat necessary to toast cheese will decompose strychnine,* and therefore a mixture containing cheese and strychnine must not be treated in this manner.

However, to cause the odour of cheese to pervade premises, it is best to toast cheese in a ladle by holding the latter over a lamp.

The two following recipes for coating grain are taken from an article by Mr. William F. Schlupp, entitled "Dealing with the Rodent Pest" which appeared in the December, 1920, number of the *South African Journal of Industries*—published in Pretoria :—

Coated Grain—Formula 1.

Powdered strychnine alkaloid ...	1 oz.
Baking soda...	1 oz.
Saccharin	1 tea-spoonful.
Laundry starch	½ cupful.
Wheat	10 quarts.

Add the starch, saccharin, baking soda, and strychnine, to 1 quart of water, heat gently until a clear paste is formed, stirring continually. Pour the paste over the grain, mix thoroughly so that every kernel of wheat is well coated, then spread the latter out and dry it.

Coated Grain—Formula 2.

Powdered strychnine alkaloid ...	1 oz.
Baking soda	1 oz.
Saccharin	1 tea-spoonful.
Flour	3 table-spoonsful.
Wheat	10 quarts.

Mix together, dry the strychnine, baking soda, saccharin, and flour, then add a little cold water, and stir to a smooth creamy paste. Pour this over the grain, mix thoroughly, and spread the wheat out to dry.

PHOSPHORUS.

For many years phosphorus has been used as a poison for rats, mice and other vermin. Although from its peculiar smell and taste it might be thought that animals would not eat it, yet experience has shown that rats and mice will do so. It is taken, however, much less readily than arsenic or carbonate of barium, both of which on account of their being both tasteless and odourless are eaten without their presence being known. Strychnine, in spite of its bitter taste, seems to be preferred to phosphorus. Squill is usually eaten readily.

Phosphorus, however, has done good work, and is useful as an alternative poison; it has the advantage of being disliked both by dogs and cats, although poultry, pheasants and partridges will eat it. Another advantage it possesses is that after a short time it becomes non-poisonous in the body of the animal that has eaten it, on account of the oxidizing change which it undergoes. Dogs, cats, and pigs are far less likely to be poisoned by eating rats destroyed by phosphorus, than rats killed by either arsenic or strychnine. It might be thought that the luminous nature of the phosphorus would frighten rats, but this does not appear to be the case, nor are they frightened by uncooked fish, as many a housekeeper has found to her cost. When fresh, fish are often phosphorescent to a considerable degree.

About 4 per cent. is considered the best proportion of phosphorus to use.

The following methods for preparing phosphorus paste may be employed.

Phosphorus Paste.

Recipe 1.—Ingredients for making 1 lb. of poison.

Flour	3 oz.
Prussian blue	5 gr.
Boracic acid	40 gr.
Tallow, lard or beef dripping	6 oz.
Glycerine	3 tablespoonsful
Phosphorus	½ oz.
Dissolved in redistilled bisulphide of carbon	½ fl. oz.

The paste should be prepared as follows:—

Put a little of the flour into a large mortar, add to it the Prussian blue and boracic acid, then rub the three together until they are thoroughly mixed and no dark spots can be seen in the mixture, or blue streaks when the ingredients are rubbed. Then add the remainder of the flour, little by little, well rubbing and mixing the ingredients together, and continuing to rub and stir until a uniform mixture has been formed.

To three table-spoonsful of glycerine add sufficient water to make a pint, and having stirred them together, pour a little on to the mixture of flour and Prussian blue and boracic acid and mix them until a paste has been formed. Then add the remainder of the water, little by little, stirring well in the interval, so as to keep the ingredients in the form of a paste. When they are mixed intimately, turn the paste into an enamel-lined saucepan, and boil sufficiently for a thick paste to be formed, stirring all the time. Then turn the contents of saucepan into a basin, and set aside until it is quite cold.

To half a fluid ounce of redistilled bisulphide of carbon add half an ounce of phosphorus, and set it aside until it is thoroughly dissolved. Pour the bisulphide of carbon, with the phosphorus dissolved in it, on to about a quarter of the tallow, lard or beef dripping placed in a mortar, and rub them gently together, taking care not to press hard on the mortar so as to cause too much friction. When the ingredients are thoroughly mixed, add the remainder of the tallow, lard or dripping, little by little, until a uniform mass has been obtained. To this mixture of bisulphide of carbon, phosphorus and grease add a little of the cold paste, and rub them well together, then add the remainder of the paste until a mass weighing one pound has been formed.

For making one pound of paste, a saucepan which will hold a pint and a half will be found a convenient size, and it is best to boil the paste over a gas or oil stove, as the heat from a fire scorches the hand and thus interferes with continuous stirring. Another advantage of a gas or oil stove is that there is no risk of the paste becoming smoked. The stirring should be done continuously to prevent the paste becoming burnt against the side of the saucepan, and it should always be stirred in the same direction, as otherwise it is liable to become lumpy.

It will be found that the proportions of flour and water given here will make more paste than is required for one pound of poison, but this has been done intentionally. It has been found by experience that different individuals are liable to make the paste of a different consistence, although all are following the same directions, and there is always a certain loss, because some of the paste adheres to the side of the saucepan, and at times a little paste gets hard from the heat and is best set aside.

Tallow or lard are more easily worked than beef dripping. When dripping is used, it is best scraped into flakes, as in this form it mixes much more readily with the ingredients.

Too much care cannot be taken when dealing with phosphorus, as friction or even exposure to the air will cause it to take fire. For the latter reason it must always be kept, and cut, under water, and after being cut it must be quickly transferred into the bisulphide of carbon. This is not only to prevent the phosphorus catching fire by exposure to the air, but also to prevent the evaporation of the bisulphide of carbon which takes place very quickly.

The required amount of phosphorus should be put into a soup-plate filled with water, and cut into flakes. When under water, the phosphorus while being cut can be steadied with a fork, although a finger may be used safely for the purpose. When it has been thoroughly subdivided, it should be placed in the bisulphide of carbon, and left there until it is dissolved, when it will be ready to be added to the tallow, lard, or dripping.

When the phosphorus dissolved in the bisulphide of carbon has been poured into the paste, it will be found that in consequence of the volatile nature of the bisulphide of carbon the disagreeable smell will have practically disappeared.

It must be remembered that the phosphorus will catch fire if mixed with the paste while the latter is hot.

As the cost of phosphorus and bisulphide of carbon is

trivial, it is best to entrust the preparation of the required amount of phosphorus in solution to a chemist. The risk of burnt fingers, or possibly more serious damage, as the result of the phosphorus becoming ignited is thus avoided.

As soon as the phosphorus in solution has been poured into the paste, the bottle that contained it, together with the cork, should be burnt, to prevent any phosphorus that may adhere to them becoming ignited by exposure to the air after the bisulphide of carbon has evaporated.

The knife and fork also, if these have been used, should be passed through a flame, so that any particles of phosphorus remaining may be burnt.

Care must be taken that the basin, pestle and mortar, and spoon are washed in cold water. If the paste adhering to them is brought into contact with hot water, the phosphorus will catch fire.

In order to weigh the paste, a pudding-basin should be placed on a pair of scales and counter-balanced either with weights or a bag containing sand, shot, or any other substance which may be convenient for the purpose. The paste placed in it can then be weighed accurately.

Recipe 2.—Put the required amount of tallow into a wide-mouthed bottle, and introduce into it for every pound of tallow, half an ounce of phosphorus cut into flakes, taking care that the phosphorus is well covered by the tallow. Then place the bottle in a saucepan of cold water and allow it to become heated to about 150° F. and keep the tallow at the above-mentioned temperature for about five minutes, so as to allow the phosphorus to become thoroughly melted. Then take the saucepan off the fire and add a pint of proof spirit (not methylated

11

spirit) for each pound of tallow. Cork the bottle firmly, and having taken it out of the water, shake it well until the phosphorus becomes uniformly diffused, forming a milky-looking fluid. The mixture when cooled, will afford a white compound of phosphorus and tallow from which the spirit spontaneously separates, and may be poured off to be used again ; for none of it enters into the combination, but merely serves to comminute the phosphorus, and diffuse it in very fine particles through the tallow.

This compound, on being warmed very gently, may be poured out into its own weight of fine oatmeal, wheat-flour, or powdered biscuit, to which Prussian blue has been previously added as already described. This dough, when made into pellets without being touched by the hand, may be laid in the shelters, or the rat-holes, but not near wood or other inflammable material.

The following scale of proportion may be of use to those who wish to make the mixture :—

First Scale.—Two ounces of tallow, lard, or dripping, half a drachm of phosphorus, half a gill of proof-spirit. (A gill is equal to a quarter of a pint, or ten table-spoonsful as marked on a medicine glass.)

Second Scale.—Quarter of a pound of tallow, lard, or dripping, one drachm of phosphorus, one gill of proof-spirit.

Third Scale.—Half a pound of tallow, lard, or dripping, quarter of an ounce of phosphorus, half a pint of proof-spirit.

Fourth Scale.—Three quarters of a pound of tallow, lard, or dripping, three drachms of phosphorus, three gills of proof-spirit.]

Fifth Scale.—One pound of tallow, lard, or dripping, half an ounce of phosphorus, one pint of proof-spirit.

As previously mentioned, tallow is preferred by rats to either lard or dripping.

The following hints may be of use to those who make this preparation :—

The bottle used, must be at least half as large again as is required for the quantity of the compound to be made when mixed with the spirit which must be added to diffuse the phosphorus through the lard. If this is not done, there will not be sufficient room to allow the contents of the bottle to be thoroughly shaken together.

The phosphorus must be kept under water until wanted, the water then poured off, and the phosphorus dropped directly from its bottle into the lard, so as to avoid touching it with the hand.

The cork should be kept out of the bottle containing the lard after the phosphorus has been added, and the bottle placed up to the neck in a saucepan of cold water, then put on the fire and never left.

A finger should be put into the water from time to time to try the heat, but not into the bottle. The instant it is too hot to be borne with comfort, the bottle should be taken out, and the phosphorus will be seen melted at the bottom. After adding the spirit and corking it down, it should be well shaken for about half a minute before putting it aside to get thoroughly cold, so that the spirit may float to the top; after that, the bottle should be uncorked, and the spirit poured off. The compound is then ready for use. The mixture must be kept always closely corked: the more air-tight it is the better it keeps.

With regard to keeping the spirit for another time, this

may be done by rat-catchers, or those who make up phosphorus paste for sale. Private individuals, who make a little perhaps once a year, or not as often as that, may be advised to throw it away and procure more when required, for the spirit retains the odour of phosphorus.

More than the proper proportion of phosphorus should never be introduced, or the vermin will not touch it. A large pickle-bottle does very well both for mixing lard and phosphorus, and for keeping the paste in; being wide at the mouth there is no necessity to melt the mixture for use before the fire, because it can be scooped out with a knife, spoon, or flat stick. Before putting the mixture away, the bottle should not only be tightly corked, but also have bladder tied over it, and be kept in the dark. In this way it will keep good to the last.

The phosphorus must be kept at all times under water and away from fire, for as previously mentioned, it will catch alight instantly if out of water and burn most furiously. It follows, that the safest plan is to buy only the amount required for present use.

The preparation of phosphorus made with flour, according to Recipe 1, is useful for destroying cockroaches, but a quarter the quantity of phosphorus is sufficient. A small quantity should be placed in the centre of a piece of glass about 2 in. square, and the glass laid in the places which the cockroaches frequent. No dead cockroaches will be found lying about, as after eating it they die in their holes. The glass should be washed every morning, so that the fresh paste may be laid on a clean surface. Any paste not eaten should be burnt. The paste should be kept in a jar, tied down with bladder, or oiled paper.

VIRUS.

FOR some years an attempt has been made, with varying success, to destroy rats and mice by giving them baits infected with a preparation known under the general name of Virus. It is a matter of common knowledge that the destructive power of virus is caused by microbes of various kinds which produce fever, and are fatal if taken in sufficient quantities. The first virus to be used was a mouse typhoid fever bacillus, but there are several on the market at the present time which depend for their action on different kinds of microbes. All these microbes have one thing in common, they are closely related to some of the bacteria which cause disease in man and certain domestic animals. Mention may be made of the *Bacillus enteritidis* of Gaertner, which is the cause of numerous outbreaks of food poisoning in man, the paratyphoid bacillus, and the hog cholera bacillus. The discovery of the first microbe used as a virus, viz., the mouse typhoid bacillus, was made accidentally as the result of experiments made while looking for the cause of the fatal outbreak among some mice which were being kept for scientific purposes. The facts having been ascertained, it was thought that good might be done by introducing mice typhoid among the multitude of mice and voles then causing great damage to agriculture in various parts of the country.

Cultures of the mouse typhoid bacilli were made by

inoculating them on artificial culture media, such as broth, and by this means the bacilli were multiplied. By mixing with food specially prepared for mice, the experiment thus conducted proved satisfactory, and it was thought that the same substance might be used for the destruction of rats. But rats ate the culture without taking any harm.

Further research was then undertaken with the object of increasing the virulence of the mouse typhoid bacilli, and on close examination it was found that these bacilli were most numerous in the organ of the body called the spleen. This organ was therefore removed from the bodies of mice that had succumbed to the mouse typhoid fever, and the preparation made from it was injected into other mice, which, in their turn, were taken ill and died. The process was continued on these lines until the virulence of the disease was increased to such an extent that it was found that when the virus was eaten by rats it was fatal to them.

Another method, more commonly employed for the sake of its greater efficacy for enhancing the virulence, is to place collodion sacs filled with the culture into a part of the abdomen call the peritoneal cavity of the animal in question. The product obtained is then treated in the same manner, and a few repetitions of the process bring about the desired degree of virulence.

After a time it was found that rats that had taken only a small quantity of the virus had been rendered immune. It was then found necessary to prepare a stronger virus by taking the spleen from diseased rats, and dealing with it as in the case of mice. The specific virulence of virus of the rat is very easily lost after its cultures have been passed through several stages, and this is why many applications of virus are unsuccessful. It is also worth noting that the quantity of virus taken by the rat does not give a definite indication of the result that will be obtained, because there are marked differences in the susceptibility of different rats to one and the same virus. Since many rats must have become immune already, having been vaccinated so to speak, by small quantities of the poison, a virus capable of destroying such immune rats will have to be far more virulent than any now in use. Although there are certain kinds of virus in present use whose strength may not affect the domestic animal and poultry, it may be asked how long this condition will continue when the virus has been brought to still greater potency ? It may be said that the greater the strength of the virus required to destroy one species of animal, the greater the danger that other species will be affected in a fatal degree if they happen to eat it. In support of this view it may be mentioned that on a farm where the original mouse typhoid bacilli were used carelessly, food kept for calves became contaminated. There was an outbreak of fever among the calves, and many died.

In these circumstances it is not surprising that there are many people who doubt whether it is wise to spread mouse typhoid and other fevers produced by bacilli belonging to the same group of organisms, throughout the length and breadth of the land, thus exposing water, milk, and other food stuffs, to the risk of contamination. In this connection it must be borne in mind that epidemics of the human disease, typhoid fever, are known to have been caused repeatedly by the contamination of milk, water, or food-stuffs, with the excrement of human beings who were, or had been, suffering from this disease.

It must also be borne in mind, that virus which has been laid for rats has been eaten by rabbits with a fatal result. It is probable, that the rabbits which have not eaten sufficient virus to produce death become carriers of the disease; these rabbits may be killed for human food.

Recent observations have confirmed strongly the suspicion that virus, even where it is stated to be harmless to human beings and domestic animals, may, in certain circumstances, be very dangerous to both. Not many years ago twelve young men, working in a large London store, were taken seriously ill. They all ultimately recovered, but for a time there was grave anxiety as to whether or not some of them would survive. All the sufferers in question took their meals in the same dining-room. All partook of the same food, but, after the most careful inquiry as to the quality of the food and the cleanliness of its preparation, and of those who handled it, nothing could be found to account for the epidemic, and its cause remained a mystery for some time. It was evident that there must have been something in connection with the food in this particular dining-room to account for the outbreak, since similar food had been distributed from the same kitchen to four other dining-rooms, and no case of illness had occurred.

Twelve days after the outbreak a bad smell was noticed in close proximity to the dining-room in which the trouble had arisen. The floor being taken up, forty dead and decomposing mice were found lying by the side of the hot-water pipe, whither they had probably gone to obtain warmth when feeling ill. Thereupon investigations were resumed, and it was ascertained that two days before the outbreak, virus had been laid for the destruction of mice in this dining-room, and in one of the pantries, but in these two places only; it had been spread on bread, and the bread left on the floor so that the mice could get at it easily. The food stored in the pantry in question was chiefly bread, butter, and cheese, which was distributed indiscriminately among the five dining-rooms of the establishment, so that it was inferred that the food became infected in the dining-room, and not in the pantry. Whether the food was contaminated by the mice, or in some less direct manner, is not known to this day, but it is thought that they may have carried the virus on their feet to the tablecloths, plates, &c., or may have infected the tablecloths with their evacuations. Alternatively, it is possible that milk, water, or other food, may have been contaminated in one of the above ways, or by flies. That virus was the cause of the epidemic is more than possible, for Dr. Klein, the eminent bacteriologist, found microbes in materials sent to him for examination which had a distant similarity to the microbes forming the active property of the virus used to destroy the mice. The objection to spreading virus, or any other poison for rats or mice on bread, or any other solid substance, is mentioned in a section headed "Poisons," and need not be repeated here.

It is claimed for virus :—

(1) That rats and mice that have eaten it die in the open.

(2) That the disease is infectious, so that the rat having eaten virus communicates the disease to others.

(3) That virus is harmless to domestic animals, poultry, and human beings.

The statement that rats and mice die in the open after eating virus is not borne out by the facts. Experience has shown that many, if not most of them, retire to a place of concealment and there die. This is what happened in the case of the forty mice referred to above. As far as concerns the manner in which disease is spread, those who have conducted experiments do not agree with the statement that virus produces an infectious disease. They consider it probable that if rats that have not eaten the poison die when they are caged with other rats that have eaten it, it is because they have become infected by eating their comrades who have succumbed to the disease. The bacilli are contained in the carcases of the animals that have died, and, as everybody knows, the rat is a cannibal. Another likely mode of infection is by eating food that has been contaminated, either by direct contact with the excreta of rats that have eaten poison, or by the bacilli from such excrement being carried to food on the feet of these or other rats who have run over it. The claim that infection passes from rat to rat by contact has not been borne out. In experiments conducted in the King Institute, Madras, at the request of Colonel W. G. King,[1] it was found indeed that this particular claim could not be established. Dr. Hossock, experimenting in Calcutta, could not secure positive results as to transmission. In Burma, the Government established a special temporary laboratory,

[1] "Plague and the Destruction of Rats," by Colonel W. G. King, C.I.E., I.M.S. (retired), Late Sanitary Commissioner for Madras *Journal of the Royal Institute of Public Health*, December, 1910.

with the object of using virus on a large scale, should the claim of infection by contact be borne out in practice. After more than eighteen months' work the officer-in-charge (Captain Saigol, I.M.S.) greatly increased the potency of the virus, and found it would kill individual rats fed on the culture but, again, no transmission of the disease occurred.

As to the alleged harmlessness of virus to dogs, cats, pigs, and poultry, enough has been said to justify the gravest doubts as to whether this will continue, whatever experiments may have shown in the past. The epidemics referred to already among human beings and calves tend to show that the virus now in use is not free from danger, while the varied experience of those who have used it continues to show that virus cannot be relied upon to do the work for which it is intended. The great uncertainty associated with its action is due, not only to variation in its virulence, but to the susceptibility of individual rats. The statement that virus is innocuous to human beings, domestic animals and poultry is, at least, an unfortunate one, as it leads to more careless handling and treatment than would be practised if the possibility of danger were to be admitted. Attention ought also to be called to some very significant facts. The United States Government recently carried out extensive experiments with the viruses. The experts have published their conclusions, and have summed up with the statement that the "bacterial viruses" have signally failed to accomplish their mission. Though not always harmless to man, they lose their virulence rapidly, and they are comparatively expensive.

Finally, our own Ministry of Agriculture has stated, in

its own guarded but not insignificant fashion, that it declines, in any circumstances, to advocate the use of any virus in the destruction of rats. Why then, it may be asked, is virus still used? The methods of its preparation can hardly commend themselves to the community at large. There are some thoroughly efficacious poisons on the market and virus possesses no advantage over them, whereas its disadvantages are obvious.

BLOCKING.

THERE is a very simple method by which large numbers of rats infesting dwelling-houses, warehouses, or shops, can be destroyed. This method, known as "blocking" is little known and seldom practised, and yet, when poisoning and ferreting cannot be resorted to easily, where "flooding" is impossible and the number of rats is too large to make trapping successful, the "blocking" method offers remarkable advantages.

The first step to be taken is to feed the rats in the room or cellar they are accustomed to frequent. An arrangement, to be described hereafter, is made for closing from a considerable distance the principal hole, or the door, after all other exits have been temporarily stopped, so that the rats have only one entrance and only one exit. Food should be laid daily in the principal hole and in the room as far as possible away from the hole which will be blocked. For choice it should be concealed behind boxes or boards with a trail of bait laid each night, from the hole along the wall of the cellar or room, to where the food is placed in bulk. On the night the rats are to be killed, and indeed for a night or two previously, meal, or some other kind of food which cannot be carried away easily, should be put down on the spot where the rats are fed, so as to ensure their being as far as possible from the main exit. When the rats have become accustomed to go regularly to the spot chosen for their food, the night of destruction can be fixed, and by the time it has arrived, all holes except the principal hole should be blocked with temporary stops. If the door is the means of entrance, a movable prop should be substituted for the fixed prop used hitherto to keep it open. When it is considered that the rats are all in the room the door is closed and the rats are trapped. Dogs may then be sent into the room to complete the work, but should men or boys go in to kill the rats, they are advised to wear gaiters or to tie a piece of string round the bottom of their trousers, as a hunted rat may run up them. After the slaughter the dead rats should be removed at once, fresh food put down, the blocking removed from all holes temporarily stopped, and the door opened as before. When it is found that rats are feeding regularly again the process of "blocking" can be repeated from time to time until all have been killed, or it is apparent from the amount of food taken that only a few remain. Traps should then be set for the remainder,[1] and the trapping persevered with until the last rat has been caught. If any blood is spilt in the destruction of rats, all traces must be carefully removed. The best time for the first blocking is from half to one hour after the premises have been left in quietness. The process may be repeated at intervals until midnight, by which time most rats have had their evening meal.

To "block" successfully, some ingenuity is required to adapt the methods to existing conditions, but if that ingenuity is displayed, it is possible to deal so effectively with the trouble that not one rat can escape.

[1] See Section "Trapping."

All holes out of doors, or in walls, door-ways or ground floor of a detached building, or in the door-ways or outer walls of an inhabited dwelling, should be closed permanently. On the other hand, holes on the inside of the house or a building not detached may be trapped and left open, so that rats coming to them from neighbouring houses or premises may be destroyed. This is why it is often best not to stop permanently the holes in a warehouse, shop or dwelling-house. Rats like to have several ways of escape in case of danger. They are undoubtedly very conscious of the crusade against them, and if one exit is closed entirely they will quickly make another one to take its place. Arrangements for temporary closing should be made several days before the night fixed for "blocking," so that rats may become accustomed to any change in the surroundings of the entrance to the hole. They are very nervous animals and may be frightened away from some of their runs temporarily, so that it is well that they should resume the use of all, and enter the room freely from any one of them until the night comes when all but one are closed. To ensure that the rats will use the entrance that will be left open purposely, bait should be laid around it and even thrown into it daily, so that they become accustomed to go to it for food, even though there are people in the room. There is nothing better for a temporary stopping than a brick or box filled with earth or sand. This may be kept from shifting by a few nails driven into the floor and projecting about half an inch above it, so that, when brick or box is dropped between nails and wall, it cannot be moved sufficiently for the hole to be exposed, as might otherwise occur, for example, if the box were pushed in the scrimmage.

The arrangements for stopping the hole that is left open depends, of course, upon its shape and position. When the floor, as well as the skirting-board, has been gnawed, a block of wood sufficiently wide to cover the opening may be used, or two pieces of wood of sufficient width—about three-quarters of an inch thick—and nailed together at a right angle, will do very well. If the exit is in the corner, and the skirting-board is gnawed through

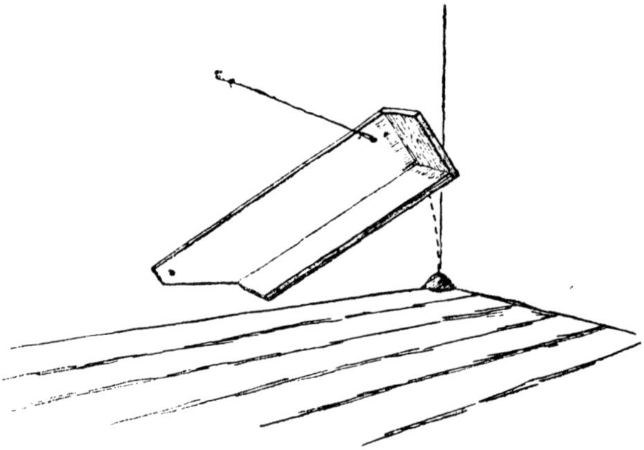

FIG. 21.—Wooden stop suitable for corner.

at both the sides that meet at that corner, a square piece of wood should be nailed into the angle formed by the two pieces of wood already mentioned, thus serving to block the part of the hole that would otherwise be left open. The piece of wood should be 1 ft. or more in length, and the vertical piece about 3 in. longer than the other.

The stop thus formed may be pivoted on the skirting-board by a screw passed through the vertical piece near its unattached end. When not in use the block may be suspended by a short piece of string. When on account of the unevenness of the floor, or wall, or any other cause, a wooden stop cannot be conveniently fitted to the hole in the corner or in the wall, there is a simple substitute in the form of a bag half filled with dry sand. This may be suspended from a nail or hook immediately over the hole. A second piece of string is attached to the lower edge. This passes out

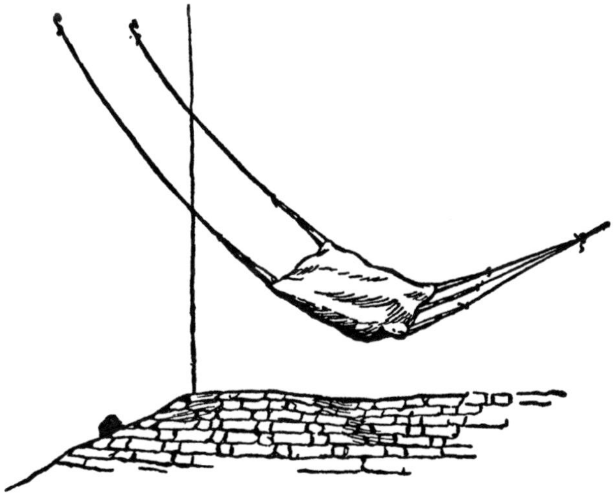

FIG. 22.—Sand-bag for stopping hole.

of the room, and when pulled, draws the bag away from the wall to the required distance, keeping it suspended till the string is released. Then by force of gravity, the bag will fall and block the exit.

The length of the string which suspends the bag must be adjusted carefully. See that while it allows the bag to rest on the ground for an inch or more, it gives sufficient distance to enable it to strike the wall with a force that will jerk the sand to the wall side, and thus keep it up against the hole. To ensure this, the suspending string must be several feet in length ; if it is not, the sand-bag cannot be drawn far enough from the wall to give it the necessary force when released. In some cases the bag will fall more evenly if it is suspended by two strings. There may be three to hold it away from the wall, one in the centre and one at each corner, being joined 18 in. or 2 ft. from the bag. The nearest staple or screw-eye, through which the piece of string passes from the bottom of the bag, must be so placed that the bag swings straight against the centre of the hole. The string suspending the block, or holding the sand-bag from the hole, should be carried, by the most direct route, to a distance from the room sufficient to enable it to be released without the approach of the operator being heard by the rats. As a rule pulleys are not necessary at the corners, a stout staple or screw-eye is generally sufficient to keep the string in position and allow it to run when released. If the staple or screw-eye, through which the string passes, cannot be fixed conveniently into a beam in the ceiling, or some other part of the room, it may be attached to a pole placed horizontally and supported at each end, either against the side walls or by two poles, crossed at the top to form the fork in which the horizontal pole can be lodged. To prevent the strain that is caused by raising the sand-bag from pulling over the support, it can be steadied by a piece of wire or string attached to the fork and fastened to a nail in the wall or floor. The poles forming the support should be kept as far as possible from the hole which the sand-bag is to stop, and the bottom of these poles should be fixed to a proper distance apart, either by a piece of string or by nailing a lath to them.

A partially filled sand-bag may also be used if the aperture which is left open is in an uneven brick or stone floor at a little distance from the wall, and it can be so arranged that it will drop right over it. The bag must be sufficiently large to enable it to spread out for 3 or 4 in. beyond the hole's circumference, and care must be

FIG. 23.—Sand-bag suspended over hole.

taken not to handle the lower part of the poles or any articles connected with the stopping arrangement that the rats are likely to approach. If they can scent a human being all their suspicions are aroused, and a suspicious rat is not easily caught. When a hole is in a lath-and-plaster wall, the use of a sand-bag is not advisable as the weight is liable to damage the wall. In such cases a thin board, 3 or 4 ft. in length and wide enough to cover the hole, or even the lid of a large box may be used. Either should be suspended from its upper corners by short pieces of string fastened to nails driven into the studs in the wall to which laths are nailed. The position of the studs can always be ascertained by tapping lightly with a hammer until the sound shows that percussion is over a solid substance. To make quite sure that the position of the stud has been found correctly, a fine bradawl or steel point or thin nail may be driven through the plaster on to the stud. When the position of the hole, in relation to the studs, makes it difficult for the board or lid to be made to swing straight to the wall when released, on account of the different lengths of string by which it is suspended, a lath may be nailed horizontally to the studs, and the nails, screw-eyes, or staples from which the board or lid is to be suspended fastened to it. The object of having the board 3 or 4 ft. in length, or using the lid of a large box, is to allow either, when raised, to be sufficiently distant from the hole to prevent its position alarming the rats that use the hole.

The lid of a large box or a board is generally best for stopping a hole that is several inches above the ground, or just above the skirting-board. In such cases the board must reach to the ground and, to keep rats from getting behind it and thus gaining their home, it is advisable to have a piece of wood fastened to the wall on either side of the area which will be occupied by the lid, and projecting outwards an inch or more beyond it. When there is a skirting-board, it is well to fasten a strip of wood, the same thickness as the skirting-board, to the back of the sides and across the top of the lid, so that there is no space between the edges of the lid and the wall.

To keep a door from shutting when rats are being fed in a room, a piece of wood may be nailed to the lintel, projecting from it sufficiently to leave a space not less than 4 in. between the door and its post. A cloth may be tied round the end of the piece of wood to act as a buffer when the door shuts against it.

If there should be an aperture below a door in a room or cellar in which rats are to be caught, caused by the threshold having been worn, it may be stopped in the following manner by a partially filled sand-bag. Take two wine-laths, an eighth of an inch less than the width of the doorway, so that they can be lifted in and out easily, make two grooves on each post by nailing narrow pieces of wood on each side, and drop the laths into them. The pieces of wood, which are close to the door and form the door-side of the grooves next to it, must be only the thickness of the lath. The space between the door and lath, corresponding to the thickness of the outer boundaries of the nearer grooves, can be filled by nailing another lath to the first. This must be the same length as before, less the width of the front surface of the outer or door-side boundary of the groove on each side. This outer lath must be further shortened to prevent friction against the door-side boundary of the grooves. The second lath should be placed across the doorway, about 2 or 3 in. from the first, and the half-filled sand-bag laid in the space between these two laths.

The object of these laths is to prevent the sand-bag from bulging and getting out of position, in which case it may prevent the door from shutting closely when the prop has been removed. By making the laths movable it is possible to take them away with the sand-bag during the day. Do not touch lath or sand-bag with bare hands. They should be lifted from the hinge side of the doorway so that the part handled may be away from that which the rats cross to enter the room. The sand-bag and laths could be marked so that the respective ends are

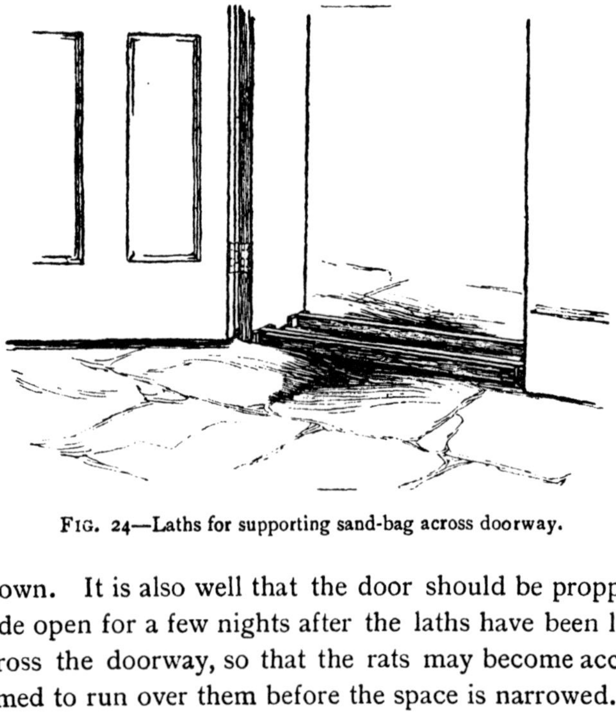

FIG. 24—Laths for supporting sand-bag across doorway.

known. It is also well that the door should be propped wide open for a few nights after the laths have been laid across the doorway, so that the rats may become accustomed to run over them before the space is narrowed.

A simple device for closing the door of the room or cellar that has no hole in it, and in which rats have been fed, is to fix a hook near the top of the door, and a pulley or screw-eye to the post or lintel. Pass a piece of string, with a loop at one end, over the pulley or through the screw-eye and attach it to the hook; then tie to the other end a sand-bag of sufficient weight to close the door quickly. To allow the rats to enter, the door can be propped open by a piece of wood, about 6 to 8 in. long, with a string attached to it. When this is pulled away, the door will be closed immediately by the weight of the sand-bag. The cord attached to the piece of wood may be passed through a screw-eye on the opposite door-post.

If the door is fastened by a latch falling by gravity, a piece of wood should be wedged under the latch so that when the door closes it passes over the catch, otherwise the door will not close properly. If the door is fastened by a spring-bolt, a nail should be driven into the door, and the handle of the bolt fastened back to it, or, alternatively, the spring or bolt may be temporarily removed. The former method, however, is more simple and amply suffices.

It is well to clear the floor of the room or cellar in which killing is to take place, and if rats are numerous, to provide shelters in the corners, or against the walls, into which they can run when disturbed. These shelters can be made by standing a box or piece of wood, the larger the better, on bricks and placing bricks or straw round the exposed sides. This encloses the space beneath box or board, leaving only two entrances, one each side, against the wall. A box with a lid, and a hole cut in the box at each end, next to the wall, is the best form of shelter; such holes should be about 3 in. long and 2 in. high. Where rats are numerous and the process of blocking may have to be resorted to several times before the premises are cleared, a piece of fine wire-netting may be fastened across the top of the box beneath the lid or cover, so that the imprisoned rats can be controlled more easily. On entering the room, such holes may be stopped by placing a brick in front of each of them, and the occupants of each box can then be dealt with separately. The animals can then be run into a cage or driven out at once and killed. If food has been placed in the shelters as well as about the room, before "blocking" takes place, the rats will have grown accustomed to go into them. Provision should be made for plenty of light while the rats are being killed, but if lamps or candles are used, they must be placed where they cannot be knocked over.

On entering the room after the block or sand-bag has been dropped, first turn up the light and then throw a large bag, half-filled with sand, over the block or sand-bag to ensure it not being shifted. The rats will run first to the hole by which they have entered, and there is often a scrimmage at this place so that the string that is suspending the sand-bag is apt to get pulled. This should therefore be cut at once, or be unfastened, and the larger sand-bag should be within easy reach, because it is important to thoroughly secure the exit as soon as possible. Put the dead rats out of the house at once, and when possible, into a tub containing a germicidal solution; they are often infested with fleas which leave them as soon as the bodies grow cold. In a district where plague-infested animals are or have been known to exist, it is very necessary to kill these fleas, and the best way is to put all dead rats into a furnace, boiling water, or into some strong germicidal solution. If neither boiling water nor solution is available, submerge the rats for an hour or more in cold water, but if there is a furnace or such covered fireplace as may be found under a copper, it is best to throw the dead rats into it at once, unless the number of killed is too large.

Sometimes rats may be found to congregate in a yard in which timber or lumber has been collected, and it is very difficult to deal with them by ordinary methods, but such a colony can be caught and killed by the use of the "Terrier" Blocking Trap, fig. 7, if sufficient care and attention are given to its use. For description and method of using, see Section "Traps."

In conclusion, a piece of blocking work on a large scale that was done at a knackery in Berkshire a little while ago may be mentioned. There is an outhouse with a single door into the yard and, as the knackery is near some light, wet ground, it is hardly an exaggeration to say it was alive with rats. As they all had the flesh diet they needed, it was decided to feed them with meal in the outhouse referred to, and the man on duty in some public works in the neighbourhood was requested, at a certain hour on a certain night to pull a string, and by so doing, close the heavy outhouse door. This he did, and early on the following morning the men employed in the knackery, armed with spades and accompanied by dogs went into the outhouse. The "bag" weighed more than 4 cwt.

FLOODING.

An effectual and simple method for driving rats from beneath the floor of a stable or outbuilding, and from holes in a bank or in the ground, in order that they may be killed by dogs or otherwise, is to fill the holes with water, and keep them filled for four to five minutes. It must be remembered that rats remain vigorous after being submerged for two minutes and even longer, but if their shelters are filled with water, not only must all the rats capable of running either leave their shelter or be drowned, but any young ones incapable of escaping will also be destroyed.

Many poultry-farms are infested with rats because traps have been found ineffectual to destroy the colony or even to reduce its number, and poisoning is considered unsafe. To get rid of the rats, therefore, the concrete floors of the houses are not infrequently broken up to get at the rats and afterwards these are relaid. This labour and expense are unnecessary. As a first step, water-carts should be collected from neighbouring farms or towns so as to obtain a large supply of water, as poultry-houses often occupy a considerable area and it is important in such a case to flood all the main burrows under each house simultaneously. Before the flooding is begun, the horses should be removed from the carts lest they become frightened by the scrimmage, and nets should be placed around the area about to be flooded, or when this is not possible, against the contiguous houses; failing nets, all holes near-by must be blocked temporarily with bricks, wood, &c. All holes in the area which has been flooded should be carefully filled in before treating the next house in a similar manner. In future "Terrier" Signal Runs or "Terrier" Death Runs ought to be kept against all the houses if they are to be kept free from rats.

It is well to procure the traps before arranging for the flooding, so that they may be placed in position at the end of the day's work. It is advisable also to have a tub or other receptacle containing a germicidal solution into which to throw the dead rats so that the fleas may be killed, otherwise they are liable to attach themselves to the poultry. Fleas soon leave a dead body in search of a new host.

Before beginning operations in an outbuilding, it is best to clear it, as when this has been done, exits previously concealed are sometimes discovered, and the rats are more easily killed when they bolt.

The neglect of proper arrangements for an adequate supply of water is a frequent mistake when this method of bolting rats is attempted. The large amount of water which is absorbed by the ground is often not realized.

For operations on a small scale, a barrel on wheels, such as is used in a garden, is very handy for flooding, but before starting operations, every available pail and can should be filled and put in readiness for use.

It is best to send the water down the principal hole, and if plenty of water is available, simultaneously down other holes also which are thought to communicate. The holes must be kept filled for four or five minutes to ensure all the rats being drowned which have not left the burrow.

The signal to begin pouring may be given by a whistle or by tapping the wall, or any other convenient means of communication.

If a hole is in a corner, it is well to place on edge across the corner a piece of board about 2 to 3 ft. in length and about 6 in. wide, keeping it in position with a few bricks, and closing the apertures by throwing earth against the bottom of the board, and the cracks between its ends and the wall. By this means a receptacle is formed into which the water can be quickly poured without being wasted by running over the floor of the outhouse.

If a hole is away from a corner, it may be surrounded by three or more bricks, earth being thrown against the outside of the bricks as already suggested. An alternative plan is to place over the rat-hole a small box with an aperture at the bottom about 3 in. in diameter, keeping it in position with bricks and earth.

When the holes have been kept filled with water for about four or five minutes, it may be allowed to soak away, and then they should be filled in immediately. In a few days time when the ground has settled, the flooring should be well rammed and made good.

Before pouring the water in, the area to be flooded should be surrounded with nets, as when ferreting.

A large water-cart with a few yards of canvas hose, for preference rubber-lined, attached to the tap, which must be of large bore (not less than $1\frac{1}{4}$ in. water-way, or about the diameter of a penny), will do a great deal of execution in a few hours. It will drive out the occupants in banks, where the soil is not very light, as well as from hiding-places in the ground, or below the paved or concreted floor of outbuildings. As a makeshift, a deep wooden trough may be used instead of a hose to convey water from the cart to the selected hole. If it is slung from the tap so as to give it a little play, and a brick or log of wood is used to stop the wheel of the cart when it is in the required position, there is no difficulty in placing the cart at the right distance from the hole to enable the flooding to be done quite easily.

When dealing with buildings, unless the hose can be put down the hole into which the water is to be poured, it is well for the hole to be surrounded with bricks and earth, or for some other arrangements to be made as already described.

It is best to have at the free end of the hose about 6 or 8 in. of zinc piping, or what is better (because it is harder and more rigid), a piece of tubing made of sheet galvanized iron. If the tubing has three or four rings of wire, about half an inch apart, soldered to it at one end, the hose can be bound firmly to the tubing which has been passed into it for about two inches. The metal end to the hose enables it to be inserted more readily into the holes. The hose should be introduced into the uppermost hole, and all lower ones stopped directly the water begins to escape from them in large quantity, but not sooner, as rats often bolt from lower exits when the water begins to flow down from the top. The object of the water is to drive the rats out, not to drown them.

Banks and hedgerows can be more thoroughly and more quickly cleared of rats by means of a water-cart with a suitable tap and hose, than by ferreting. All rats capable of running are bound to quit the burrow when it is filled with water, and the rest will be drowned. There is not the delay that occurs when a ferret fights a rat standing at bay, nor is there the delay which occurs in digging out a ferret lying up with a rat or nest of young ones. Moreover, when ferreting, the rats which have escaped to a remote part of the burrow are often left in it. Poisoning never kills all the rats in the area in which it has been laid. Some are always left for re-stocking unless they can be trapped or killed in other ways.

If there is no exit at the top of the bank, and the hole into which the hose is inserted is in the side of the bank, it should be blocked when the water rises to it, so as to make the water rise still higher in the bank in case the hole runs upwards. This ensures complete flooding. The metal tube at the end of the hose enables stopping to be done, but the tube should be held, and if a rat endeavouring to escape is felt against its end, the tube should be removed to allow the rat to leave.

When rats are in the banks or hedgerows which surround a field growing grain, directly it has been cut, their holes should be flooded, for as soon as the crop has been carried the rats will move on, unless the stack is built on the ground in the field, in which case they may at once go into it.

An hour or so may be profitably spent also by taking the water-cart over the field immediately after the crop has been carried, and flooding the rat-holes, and in some cases those of the mice and voles as well. Mice and voles do more harm than is generally supposed, the damage which they have done being attributed to other causes. One or two terriers should accompany the water-cart to kill the rats, mice, and voles as they bolt, and it is well to fix a net along a hedge before flooding the rats' holes close to it.

All holes should be filled in as soon as they have been flooded.

It would be an advantage if manufacturers affixed to all municipal water-carts and to all farm water-carts a tap with $1\frac{1}{4}$ in. water-way, and a thread cut on the outside of the tap to which the hose union could be attached when the rats' domains had to be flooded.

Union and hose might be sold with the cart. The thread of the screw should be protected by a collar when the hose is not in use. Too large a water-way has the disadvantage of emptying the cart more quickly than is necessary.

Time would be saved by having a pump for filling the cart attached to it, so that water could be obtained from the nearest pond, stream, &c. A strong wooden surface strengthened by cross pieces and having a bore in its centre, sufficiently large to allow the end of a suction-pipe to pass through it and with an arrangement to fix it there, would keep the end of the suction-pipe near the surface of the water. This arrangement would prevent leaves and other vegetation from being drawn into the suction-pipe, as would occur if it rested on the bottom of the pond.

In districts in which there are high banks, rats' holes above the tap level of the cart may be flooded by having the filling pump arranged to force water to the required level.

Two water-carts in use save time, for one can be filled while the other is being emptied.

FUMIGATION.

WHEN ferrets are not available, and it is wished to drive rats from a hole in a bank or in the ground, or to suffocate them in their retreats, chemicals may be used. The proper chemicals when ignited or generated, produce fumes in which rats cannot continue to breathe. This method of driving rats from their hiding-places, or killing them there, is also of use when a rat stands at bay in a position from which a ferret cannot or will not drive him.

Sulphur is the chief ingredient in most preparations sold for this purpose, and when exposed to the air will burn readily after it has been thoroughly lighted. When used under conditions where the air is limited in amount, and is filled with the smoke and fumes generated, another ingredient must be added which will burn freely under such conditions and thus assist in the combustion of the sulphur. Nitre fulfils this requirement, and, moreover, whilst burning it creates a flame and a hissing noise. Mixed with sulphur, nitre forms the active composition of most smoke-ferrets, the ingredients being held together in a mass by a small quantity of tallow. Although when air is impregnated with the fumes of burning sulphur, no animal can continue to breathe it, yet the efficacy of a "smoke-ferret" or "vermin choker" as it is sometimes called, is materially increased by taking advantage of the well-known fact that animals which choose to live in a dark hole may be driven from it by the introduction of a light, and this combined with the hissing noise produced by the burning nitre causes the rats to rush from their holes.

Some manufacturers, in order to remove the colour of the sulphur and thus conceal the ingredients of the smoke-ferret, add a small quantity of red oxide of iron to the composition so as to give it a brick red appearance, but the oxide of iron is of no real use.

To make smoke-ferrets in small quantities, the sulphur, nitre, and tallow, must be mixed well together, and the mass then taken out, divided, and made into sticks.

When made in large quantities, the ingredients are put into a mixing-machine, which does the work better than it can be done by hand, a harder mass being produced.

A suitable mixture for smoke-ferrets in small quantities is as follows :—

Sulphur	1 part.
Nitre	2 parts.
Tallow	a sufficiency.

Mix.

Smoke-ferrets of a size suitable for bolting rats are usually sold in sticks, about 4½ in. long and about 4 in. in circumference, their weight being usually about 2½ oz., so that, calculated roughly, a pound weight of the ingredients makes half a dozen, and each will burn in a hole for nearly ten minutes. The price (rat size) used to be about three shillings a dozen.

It is well to remember when mixing sulphur with nitre that neither charcoal, nor any substance which will produce charcoal, must be added, or gunpowder may result.

The formula for gunpowder is :—

Nitre	75 parts.
Charcoal	15 parts.
Sulphur	10 parts.

As many rat-holes extend for some distance, it is a mistake to use too small a smoke-ferret, but on the other hand there is nothing to be gained by using too large a one.

Smoke-ferrets are best lighted with a fusee, as there is often difficulty in getting them alight with a match on account of wind. When fusees are not available, the end of the smoke-ferret may be moistened with a little methylated spirit.

As soon as it is well alight, it should be pushed as far into the hole as possible, by means of a stick with a flat end, the direction of the hole having been previously ascertained by passing the stick along it.

As soon as the smoke-ferret is in position, the hole should be quickly closed with a piece of wood or metal previously placed in readiness, all the other apertures having been closed beforehand.

For using smoke-ferrets, it is best to be provided with several pieces of thin wood or metal about 6 in. square, a piece being laid over the entrance of each hole, which if necessary, should be previously scraped level so that no smoke can escape. This method of closing is better than blocking the entrance with a clod of earth, for although the piece of wood or metal effectually prevents the smoke from escaping, it is easily displaced by a rat wishing to bolt. The piece of wood or metal must be laid over the hole again as soon as possible after it has been pushed aside. When working on a steep bank or over a wet ditch, it is convenient to have each piece of wood or metal attached to a peg by a piece of string.

In plague-suspected areas the authorities would do well to have a smoke-ferret placed in all used rats' holes before they are closed, so as to ensure the destruction of the fleas in the rats' nest.

Another somewhat similar method is to heat sulphur and charcoal in an iron vessel, and drive the fumes from it through an iron pipe with bellows into the rats' quarters, but this apparatus is more inconvenient to carry about than "smoke-ferrets" and it is more difficult to avoid inhaling the fumes than when using "chokers."

A portable form of the Clayton apparatus which has been used for many years to destroy rats on ships, has been employed recently in rat-infested areas.

It cannot be too strongly urged, that if premises are to be kept free from rats, all holes must be filled in as soon as the rats have been driven out of them.

The United States Department of Agriculture and our Ministry of Agriculture recommend the asphyxiation of rats in their burrows by a wad of cotton waste or other absorbent material saturated with bi-sulphide of carbon, and pushed into the rats' hole. The opening is then closed with soil to prevent the escape of gas.

Bi-sulphide of carbon cost before the war about sixpence per pound, it now costs two shillings per pound (about thirteen fluid ounces, which is half a pint and rather more than half a gill). There is a crude product, containing impurities, consisting of other sulphur compounds which might be procured formerly for about threepence or fourpence a pound. The price now is ninepence per pound. About 4 to 5 oz. is the smallest quantity which is effectual in a short hole, and for a large burrow much more must be used, so that with the cotton waste each small plug costs at least threepence.

This method is useless under many paved floors, as holes exist which allow the fumes to escape.

An additional disadvantage attaching to this method beyond its cost, is that, as the fumes are colourless, there is no means of knowing if they have penetrated to the full extent of the burrows, as would otherwise be shown by the fumes appearing at each exit; or except by the smell, if they are escaping, and then the opening cannot be easily located, as is readily done by seeing the smoke, when smoke-ferrets are used.

It ought to be remembered that bi-sulphide of carbon is highly inflammable, and poisonous when inhaled.

During the war, rats were killed in large numbers by the enemy's gas, and it has been suggested that the gas method should be used to destroy rats in this country. It is obvious that such a procedure would be dangerous. The fumes cannot be confined to the rats' burrows nor to any given area, so that not only would the health of human beings be endangered, perhaps to a serious extent, but the lives of domestic animals would be threatened, as well as those of rabbits, poultry, game, both feathered and furred, and possibly of sheep and cattle.

If a highly poisonous gas were the only means of destroying rats in large numbers, there might be areas in which it would be expedient to adopt this measure, after care had been duly taken to protect those engaged in the work, and drive away all living creatures that it was wished should be preserved; but, as before mentioned, the work can be done in many situations as quickly and thoroughly, perhaps even more so, and entirely without danger, by driving the rats from their holes with water, as fully described in the Section "Flooding." A water-cart suitable for doing this is already in every town and on most farms, but this simple and inexpensive method is practically unknown. The dogs required need not be trained as when ferrets are used, for almost any dog will kill a rat.

VARNISH AND RAT-LIME TRAP.

A method of catching rats inside buildings, on plates covered with lithographic varnish or rat-lime, has recently been tried with success. Dr. Howarth, the Medical Officer for the City of London, has reported that catches of sixty and eighty have been made in some cases.

The varnish, after being warmed by placing in boiling water the container holding it, is spread with a knife, or a painters' stripper, about one-sixteenth to one-eighth of an inch in thickness, on straw-board or thick paper measuring about 15 in. by 12 in., leaving a margin of an inch or more free from varnish ; bait, if used, being placed in the centre. The varnish under favourable conditions will remain effective for three or four days, after which it must be scraped off and fresh varnish used. It hardens more quickly in a cold temperature.

Failure will result from the following causes :—

(1) If a Varnish Trap be laid in a current of air, so that the draught causes a hardening of the surface of the varnish. This will prevent the feet of a rat from sinking in sufficiently deep to adhere.

(2) If a rat's feet are wet or moist the varnish will not stick to them.

(3) If the trap is laid in a wet place.

In very hot kitchens, boiler-houses and other places in which the temperature is high, a stronger varnish is required.

One pound of varnish makes six traps 15 in. by 12 in.

Lithographic varnish for catching rats may be obtained from the following firms at the prices quoted.

John Kidd & Co., 11, Wine Office Court, Fleet Street, London, E.C. 4:—

Large tins (about 4 lb.) 10s. net, post free.

Small tins (about 1 lb.) 3s. net „ „

Dane & Co., 91-92, Shoe Lane, E.C. 4:—

2 lb. tins, 4s., postage extra.

B. Winstone & Sons, 100-101, Shoe Lane, London, E.C.4:—

2s. per lb., postage extra.

When ordering, rat-catching varnish should be specified.

For an occasional trap this method may be useful, but sixty or eighty rats can be caught in an evening at much less cost by Blocking (see Section "Blocking"), or with a "Terrier" Blocking Trap (see Section "Traps") which will be as serviceable at the end of twenty years as on the day it was purchased.

Bird-lime has been used in a similar manner to varnish, but for this purpose it is made more sticky, so that it can hold a rat. It is sold under the name of Rat-lime. It may be obtained from:—

Messrs. Kay Bros., Petergate Mills, Stockport, Lancashire.

H. H. White, 9, Canning Place, Liverpool.

THE RODIER SYSTEM.

SOME years ago Mr. Rodier, of Collins Street, Melbourne, devised a system which now bears his name, for the destruction of rabbits in Australia. His method is to catch all the rabbits alive, kill the females, and release the males unharmed ; his idea being that an excessive number of males will so harass the females that they will become unfertile, while if young are produced they will probably find and destroy them. Mr. Rodier claims to have cleared in twenty years an area of 64,000 acres in the centre of a rabbit-infested district.

Mr. George Jennison, of the Zoological Gardens, Manchester, has applied this system to rats, and read a paper at Birmingham in July, 1920, before the Conference of Rat Officers at the Congress of the Royal Sanitary Institute, giving the result of five years' work on the Rodier system, which he stated had reduced the number of rats caught in the Manchester Zoological Gardens to half the previous number. His method is as follows : In the Belle Vue Gardens there is a large room which rats have frequented for more than forty years and in which they have been trapped and killed. This room he converted into a blocking trap (see Section "Blocking"), the entrance being closed about once a fortnight. The captured rats were driven into a sack, their sex ascertained by a rat-catcher, the females killed and the males liberated.

Mr. Jennison, as the result of his five years' experience,

recommends that the Rodier system should be universally applied to rats.

The table published by Mr. Jennison of the results of his trappings in the room at Belle Vue, from October, 1915, to June, 1920, apparently does not bear out his statement on page 203, which is: "summed up, Belle Vue, under five years, has reduced its rats gradually one half," for it shows that from October 11, 1915, to the end of June, 1916, that is roughly in nine months, 263 rats were caught; and from July 1, 1919, to the end of June, 1920, 216 rats were caught; but in any case, from the information supplied in his paper, a statement cannot be accepted that the number of rats at Belle Vue has in any way been materially reduced, for he merely deals with the number of rats trapped in the room.

If, during the five years, Mr. Jennison had kept Belle Vue bristling with Run-traps, and concealed steel traps, and had destroyed every rat which was caught; and at the end of that time found that only half the number of rats were captured, the statement might have been fairly made that only half the number of rats visited the Gardens. It would be fair to assume that if a rat had avoided one trap, he would have been caught in another.

Mr. Jennison admits that rats which have been released under the Rodier System are not easily re-caught, and according to his table, 541 male rats had been released during the five years. If, therefore, at the end of five years, fewer rats frequented the room, may it not be supposed that the released rats had passed the word round amongst their friends that the room should be avoided, and food obtained elsewhere? Rats' intelligence is rather apt to be under-estimated.

However, be this as it may, the vast difference between the habits of rabbits and rats makes the Rodier System not only unadvisable, but practically impossible of success if applied to rats.

The damage done by rabbits affects vegetation alone, whereas rats not only lessen the food supply, but they do an enormous amount of damage to poultry, to buildings, and to the merchandise and articles contained therein, while they also carry disease to a much larger extent than is generally realized. As male rats are as destructive as females, and carry disease at any rate to an equal, but probably to a far greater, extent, on account of their more roving habits, it is extremely undesirable to liberate them.

Mr. Jennison states that after the first year of vigorous extermination by all known methods, rats must only be caught uninjured. It follows, therefore, that there must be no poisoning, no fumigation, no snaring, no ferreting, or driving rats from their holes by other methods to be killed by dogs, no use of steel or break-back traps, no rats killed when stacks are threshed. The capture of rats is reduced, therefore, to blocking, and run cage-traps, which although extremely useful are not suitable for universal application, and, alone, are not sufficient for trapping on even a moderately extensive scale.

Blocking is suitable for premises which rats frequent, and is especially useful where they exist in large numbers. Run traps, even at a pre-war price, are far too expensive to be in general use in numbers sufficient to keep down the rat population. They are unsuitable for hedgerows, the sides of streams, rivers, and other places outside enclosed premises, where it is most important that rat destruction should be carried on throughout the year by methods most applicable to each situation.

By far the largest number of rats trapped annually are caught in steel traps. In many respects these are the best traps, for they can be concealed and they are very much less expensive than Run-traps. If Mr. Jennison's plan were carried out, rat capture and destruction throughout the country would be reduced to a minimum.

It is only professional Rat Catchers who dare to handle live rats in order to determine their sex. The public in general cannot readily determine the sex of a rat until it has been killed, and even then, especially with young rats, mistakes are often made.

It is extremely improbable that a male rat will be liberated merely in order that he may assist in worrying females, when he is suspected of having killed young poultry or caused loss or done damage in other ways. Rats are not generally caught for amusement, but to stop the damage which they are doing.

Although the Rodier System may be beneficial where rabbits are a source of trouble, with regard to rats its alleged advantages are too theoretical, and the details necessary for conducting it are not sufficiently practical. For universal adoption it would be not only useless, but dangerous. Rats are constantly on the move and often travel long distances by night. They will not alter their habits to justify a system.

RATS IN THE HOUSE, SHOP, WARE-HOUSE, &c.

WHEN rats are in a house, the first step to be taken is to ascertain how they obtained an entrance. Usually it will be found that they have come by one of the following ways :—

(*a*) Through a broken grating made originally for ventilating the space beneath a floor, or through the unprotected light and ventilation-opening to a cellar. A small mesh wire-netting protector should have been used.

(*b*) From a defective old brick drain, or through a broken pipe or the aperture formed by a badly laid pipe in a stone-ware pipe drain communicating with a brick drain, or with a sewer, or when the plug is out of the cleaning arm in the intercepting trap. Through the hole in the wall for the drain pipe not having been properly filled in.

(*c*) Under a door when the threshold has been worn into a hollow sufficiently deep to form a suitable opening.

(*d*) Through an open untrapped pipe from a scullery sink.

(*e*) Through the opening made in an outer wall to allow the water to escape when the floor is washed down.

(*f*) By climbing up ivy, fruit-trees, or plants growing against the house ; or climbing up in the angle formed by a water-pipe and the wall, and entering through a window, or a hole under the roof.

(*g*) From adjoining premises by a hole they have made or found in the party-wall; or by passing along the roof, or gutters, and thence effecting an entrance.

In the parts of London, Bristol, Sunderland, Yarmouth and other places in which black rats (*Mus Rattus rattus*) are found, special care should be taken to render the upper parts of buildings rat-proof and to keep traps set there throughout the year. Black rats frequent chiefly the upper parts of houses, warehouses, &c., and may be seen on a bright moonlight night in London and elsewhere crossing the streets on the telephone cables—not the telegraph wires as some highly imaginative folk have been heard to declare.

When there are more than a few rats in the house, it is probable that their holes communicate with a drain; or, if the house is semi-detached, with the adjoining premises. Needless perhaps to add, they may be reaching the house both by way of a defective drain and also from the neighbouring premises, as well as by other openings connected with the outside.

Before other measures are taken, wire-netting with a ½-in. mesh and made of wire not less than 19 standard wire gauge, should be affixed to the frame of all cellar windows which open inwards and to a movable frame if the window opens outwards and to all openings not fitted with a window, and a careful search made round the house in order to be sure that there is not a broken air grating, worn threshold, or other means of ingress hitherto overlooked.

As mice very often obtain an entrance through unprotected cellar windows, it is advisable to affix wire-work with a mesh sufficiently small to exclude them as well as rats.

In connection with old houses, there are often brick drains, the existence of which is unknown because they have long been out of use and are not marked on the plan of the drains. It is most important to find if they do exist in order that they may be removed.

When a rats' hole is in the basement of a house, it is advisable to hold a light to it, or a piece of smouldering brown paper, or other suitable burning substance, and if there is a draught from the hole, it should be followed without delay in the manner to be described, as the draught may come from an opening in the drain of the house.

The only certain way to find out where a hole leads to, is to trace it, and this should be done as follows :—

A piece of material about the size of a duster should be passed down the hole as far as it can be pushed, and the roof of the hole then taken away until the cloth is reached. After all loose earth has been carefully removed, the cloth should again be pushed further down the hole and the earth taken away as far as the cloth, in the same manner as before. This method should be continued until the end of the hole is reached.

Unless care is taken to keep the hole carefully plugged with the cloth, the loose earth will quickly fill it and all trace will be lost.

This method of tracing should be adopted in all cases in which rats come up through a paved floor into a house or closed outbuilding, and no aperture can be found through which they made their way under the floor.

In the author's experience, a hole in a scullery, which was traced in this way for several yards, was found eventually to pass through an aperture in the outer brick wall of the house into a disused brick drain. This had been left intact, although the architect in charge of the new system of drainage, which had been supplied a few years previously, had marked the drain in question on his plan as having been taken away.

When a brick drain is found, it should be carefully followed, and if not in use, entirely removed. If a purpose is served, the brick drain should be replaced by stone-ware pipes.

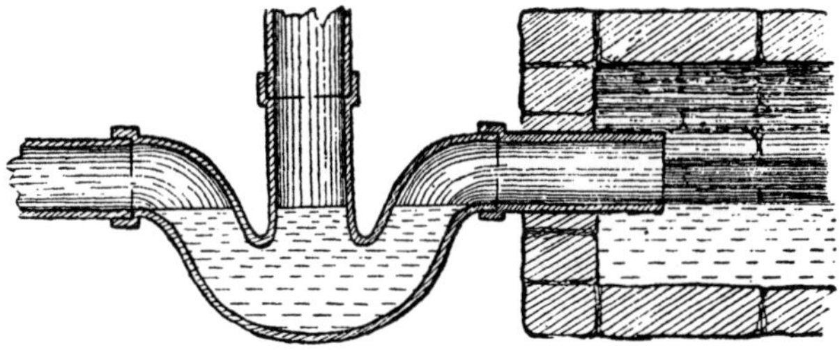

FIG. 25.—Stone-ware trap with inspection inlet fitted to a brick drain.

If the drain cannot be followed in consequence of its passing under a building or trees, its continuation should be uncovered and the undestroyed portion bricked up at both ends, or, if in use, joined to the stone-ware pipes at both ends, by a trap (fig. 25) with an inspection inlet. By continuing the inspection inlet upwards with pipes to the surface of the ground, or nearly so if a grating is not required, the trap can be readily cleaned if it should become blocked. To do this, remove the grating or stone which covers the top of the inlet, and lift out with a ladle attached to a long handle any sediment that may have collected. Before the inspection inlet is covered in, the trap must be filled with water.

The object of a stone-ware trap at both ends of the undisturbed portion of the brick drain is to prevent any rats that may make their way into it, either through an undiscovered hole already existing, or by opening up an old hole, from getting into the new stone-ware pipe drain. When the brick drain cannot be removed, if not in use for sewage, it is advisable to place the traps at a level that will ensure the water in it being always several inches deep, so as to prevent rats from remaining in the drain. It is, however, best to remove the brick drain entirely, when it is possible to do so. In cases where portions of it must be left, all holes leading into it should be carefully sought for and stopped with brick and mortar or cement.

Where ivy, creepers, or fruit-trees grow against a house, rats are liable to enter by climbing up them, and in order to prevent a secure foothold being obtained to the roof, a space of at least 2 ft. should be kept between the top shoots and the gutter.

This, however, is not sufficient to stop them from reaching the roof, but an effectual barrier can easily be made by placing a board about 7 in. wide along all the walls of the house against which ivy or trees are planted. The board should be fixed immediately below the gutter, almost at a right angle to the wall of the house, a sufficient slope only being given to it to enable rain to run off. The brackets or holdfasts, which keep it in position, should be placed on its upper surface; and it should be cut to fit the gutter supports accurately, when they come in the way of its proper adjustment.

If a rain-water pipe has to be passed, not only should the board which is against the wall be cut to fit it closely, but an additional piece should be affixed so as to project around the water-pipe, its supports being on the upper surface, as in the case of the board itself.

If some of the walls of the house are free from creepers, it is necessary to carry the board only a few feet along them from the corner of the wall which is fully protected, as above described.

If the board is given several coats of paint, it will last many years, and if the colour chosen is similar to that of the gutter, its appearance will not be unsightly; in fact it will scarcely be noticed.

When rats come from adjoining premises, it is important to get the neighbours' active co-operation in continuous war against them. Ascertain first how they get into the house and then take the necessary measures to deal with them. Holes should be followed as before described, and if they are found to pass through the party wall, they should be filled in with brick and cement unless in a position in which they can be continuously guarded by a trap.

When all the known inlets have been stopped, and the measures above described have been taken to prevent an entrance being gained in future, "Terrier" Death Run traps or 5 in. rabbit traps in "Terrier" Signal Runs ought to be kept set all the year round against the house at the points of probable approach.

When there is a large number of rats in a house it is difficult to exterminate them, and success will not result from the measures employed, unless the object aimed at is pursued seriously, and with perseverance.

Obviously, poisoning should not be resorted to, and ferreting and flooding are unsuitable in most instances, and in any case can be carried out only to a very limited extent. Trapping also is inexpedient where there are a great many rats, unless a large number of traps are set simultaneously, because when a few have been caught, the remainder become frightened of the traps and avoid them, so that recourse must be had to other means to reduce their number to a considerable extent, before a resort is made to trapping.

The best method for doing this is to feed the rats in a room or cellar, to which they are accustomed to go, and in which an arrangement has been made for closing from a distance the principal hole or the door, all the other holes having been temporarily stopped beforehand as fully described in the Section "Blocking."

When a rat is frequently heard running behind the skirting-board of a room in which there is not a hole, and there is no hole in an adjoining room, near to which traps may be set, the rat may be caught by cutting a hole in the skirting-board and trapping it as described in Part II.

It may be mentioned that no permanent good will be done by laying quicklime or caustic soda in a rats' run or by smearing with tar the sides of a hole or the places they pass.

If a rat or a mouse dies in a house during the summer months, the simplest way to discover the precise spot where the body is lying, is to catch several blue-bottle flies with a butterfly net. Then having closed the windows and door of the room in which there is the odour, liberate the flies and notice where they all settle;

that will be the place below which the dead animal is lying. If there are no blue-bottle flies in the house, they can be procured by putting a piece of meat out of doors and catching those that settle on it.

Rats frequently lie under the wooden flooring of factories, stores, or sheds, built on a meadow or waste ground outside a town, and tenanted only during working hours.

It is often inexpedient to ferret such places as these, because not only is there a large area covered by the buildings, but if a ferret were to lie up in one of the numerous rat-holes in the ground beneath the buildings she could not be reached, and it might be difficult or even impossible to recover her on account of the many openings around.

Then again restaurants, hotels, and butcher's, baker's and grocer's shops, and in fact any premises on which food is sold or stored, are liable to be infested with rats. There has often been considerable difficulty in destroying them, not only on account of the surroundings, but also for want of sufficient time outside business hours to deal with the matter.

Premises can, however, be cleared and kept free in the future by the method known as Blocking and the subsequent use of a "Terrier" Blocking trap. When the rats are caught in this trap they can be driven at once into a Drowning-Box, and the goods near by need not be moved, as must be done when the rats have to be killed after being blocked in a room or storehouse. Subsequently, in the case of buildings, "Terrier" Signal Runs or "Terrier" Death Run traps may in addition be kept set against the outside.

When a street or area in a town is infested with rats, blocking is the best way to reduce the number to a minimum; for probably the runs connect most, if not all, the houses. If the arrangements are carefully made so that the blocking is done simultaneously, the area will soon be cleared.

To carry this out, a cellar or room on the ground floor should be prepared as already described, in every house or every other house according to the size of the infested area, and after feeding the rats there for a week or more the date for the slaughter should be arranged and a time fixed for it to take place. The process may be repeated three or four times on the first night and afterwards two or three times a week, until from the amount of food taken, it is evident that only a few remain; these should then be trapped and "Terrier" Blocking, Death Run, or Signal Run traps be kept set continuously in the future, for other rats are sure to go there sooner or later.

To draw the rats to the cellar or room in which they are being fed it is a good plan to toast cheese there in an iron spoon for the first few nights.

It would well repay the owner of premises infested with rats to make it to the interest of one of his employees to stay once a week for an hour or so after closing-time, or return after an hour's interval to drop the sand-bag or doors of a "Blocking" trap and kill any rats whose retreat has been cut off by either of these means.

It is well to bear in mind that when there is no worn threshold or broken ventilating grating or open cellar window, the rats may possibly be coming from a defective drain. As a preliminary measure, it is well to introduce a smoke-ferret into the drain. In this case the smoke-ferret referred to is the kind used by sanitary inspectors for testing drains, and not the smoke-ferret mentioned in a preceding section for making rats bolt from their holes.

When there is a plaster ceiling to the kitchen, room, or store frequented by rats, it will be well to take up the end boards of the floor above and run a ferret between the joists. Should rats be lying there it would be well in some instances to pull down the ceiling to prevent their using it again as a place of concealment. This is not as serious a measure as it sounds. Canvas may be glued and nailed to the under surface of the floor above to prevent dust falling through between the boards. The canvas and the joists may be afterwards whitewashed should a white ceiling be desired.

If the ceiling is wanted to deaden sound, it may be cut away for about six inches at each end of the joists, and the space between the joists filled in by a piece of board sloping upwards from where the ceiling terminates to the bottom of the floor where it touches the wall, so as to prevent rats again getting between the joists. Care must be taken that the space between each side joist and the wall is rendered rat-proof. If the wall is a lath and plaster partition, the board next to the wall should be removed and the bottom of the space boarded and then filled in with bricks and mortar or concrete up to the floor level. In the case of a wall, if there is a doubt as to its being rat-proof, its surface should be cemented.

Any panelling behind which the rats have a run should be removed and the wall made good.

To keep rats out of a basement there is nothing better than a floor of concrete with a top of cement, which may be carried up the walls for 6 or 8 in. if the brickwork be soft.

A dozen or more "Terrier" Death Run traps, or trapped "Terrier" Signal Runs, according to the size of the premises, will tend, if kept at work all the year round, very largely to reduce the number of rats that have been drawn to the premises and will prevent them from increasing in number. Several might be kept permanently in the kitchen, store, or shop frequented. In this case a movable light frame, covered with wire-netting, may be placed in front of the cover or run with a space between them to prevent the cover or run from being knocked and the trap sprung in consequence. See that the signal remains visible.

As before mentioned, it is better to leave the holes open in a room where food is cooked or stored, for if blocked up, rats will make fresh holes, and their presence can always be ascertained by sprinkling some sand or sawdust around the principal hole.

RATS IN THE OUTBUILDING.

It is very important that rats should be kept out of all buildings for, entrance once obtained, a rat usually takes up quarters there throughout the winter; whereas if unable to find shelter, he will pass on and search for it elsewhere. In doing so he is certain to be caught in one of the run-traps that are kept set, *if they have been properly placed.*

It is a common practice to pile timber, brushwood, bricks, tiles, empty boxes, cans and other articles, or rubbish of various kinds against the walls of an outbuilding, and to allow coarse vegetation, especially nettles, to grow against it. If premises are to be maintained free from rats this practice must be discontinued. The ground against outbuilding walls must be kept clear so that any holes can be easily seen.

When all the outside walls of buildings have been cleared of rubbish of whatever kind, and when all rat-holes have been stopped, there should be a systematic destruction of the rats on the premises. All their holes should be ferreted or flooded in the manner already described in the Section "Flooding," and immediately afterwards, they should be filled in to prevent any rats that may be subsequently dislodged elsewhere from taking refuge in them. It must be understood that the holes in a building or block of buildings already treated, should be filled in before those in the next building or block of buildings are ferreted or flooded.

When the walls of an outhouse are of wood, and boarded on the inside as well as on the outside, no hole leading to the space between the two sets of boards should be permanently stopped immediately after a ferret has been put into the intervening space. It must be remembered that a rat can easily climb up between the partitions and thus escape the ferret. In this case a piece of paper should be pasted or tacked over the hole, which may be permanently closed with wood or galvanized iron when the paper has remained undisturbed for two or three days. If the paper is broken, a trap should be set to catch the rat, and as soon as he is caught, a fresh piece of paper should be fastened over the hole in order to ascertain whether another rat is concealed between the walls.

Before the ferreting or flooding is started, the outbuilding should be emptied as far as possible. Not only are bolting rats killed much more easily when the space is clear, but nests and places where the rats have been lying are often found, although their existence has not been suspected.

When it is necessary to keep the door of the outbuilding open to obtain light while the ferreting or flooding is going on, a net with a mesh of not more than 1 in. should be stretched across the lower 2 ft. of the doorway.

It is best to run a piece of string through the top, bottom and sides of the net, so that the string may be twisted round nails placed for the purpose on each side of the doorway. By this means the string and net with it can be made to fit tightly to the bottom and sides of the doorway, and yet plenty of loose net can be left to entangle a rat which is trying to escape.

The rats actually on the premises are the most difficult to dispose of. In order to catch them, steel traps have usually to be carefully buried, and, if several rats have to be caught, run-traps that catch alive must be tied up for a few nights before they are set, so that the rats will feed freely in them. Those that come in the future will be easily trapped, as no such precautions will be necessary if the directions recommended in these pages are carried out with thoroughness.

For preference, all outbuildings should be concreted or paved, and where this has been properly done, rats cannot get through the floor from the inside nor under it from the outside without being observed; provided always that the ground against the walls is kept free from vegetation, rubbish, &c.

The threshold of all doorways must be made good, and to prevent them from again becoming worn through in the centre, a piece of iron $1\frac{1}{2}$ to 2 in. in width and about $\frac{1}{4}$ in. in thickness may be firmly fixed along the edge of the threshold against which the door shuts. If the joints of the frame are weak or the frame is much gnawed at the bottom, the ends may be carried up each side of the frame for about 6 in., as shown in fig. 26. A thinner and narrower piece of iron is sufficient for a doorway if the normal traffic is light. A stone threshold may be treated in a similar manner, the hollow that has been worn below the level of the iron being filled in with cement, a piece of iron having been placed in the centre of the hollow below the transverse iron, to take the weight of the traffic on it over the former hollow.

This simple expedient not only prevents the inner part of the threshold becoming worn across the centre, but stops the splintering of its inner edge which otherwise occurs when it is struck or trodden upon by a hobnailed boot, or by the shoe of a horse.

The doorways of outbuildings and stables on the premises referred to in the preface, treated in this manner more than forty years ago, are practically as good to-day as when the iron was first affixed. An old wheel tire does very well for the purpose, and any blacksmith can easily bend it to fit the doorway.

FIG. 26.—Iron affixed to protect edge of threshold.

The floors of many outhouses and dairies are concreted, paved, or tiled, and there is an opening through the wall for the escape of water when the floor is washed down. All holes of this description should be covered with a grating on the outside to prevent the entrance of rats, as described fully in the Section "Rats in the Stable."

If the bottom of a door has been gnawed or broken, it

is best to nail a piece of wood across its entire width, so as to cover all the holes, while if the edge of the post has been gnawed, the hollow should be filled either with a piece of wood or putty. In the latter case, a few nails must be driven into the post until their heads are flush with the surface, so as to give a holding for the putty. A piece of galvanized sheet-iron (24 gauge), rather larger than the damaged surface, should then be nailed over it. This will further be held in position by the piece of tire iron across the threshold as previously described.

When only the corner of a door has been gnawed, it may be repaired by inserting a piece of wood or by nailing a piece of galvanized sheet-iron to the inner and outer surfaces of the door and filling the space with putty. It is best to fix one piece of iron first and then apply the putty, pressing it firmly against the door which has previously had a few nails driven into it to keep the putty in position. The other piece of iron should then be nailed on, and the putty smoothed off. A corner mended in this way will last for many years, for the putty becomes very hard in course of time, and is protected from injury by the pieces of iron.

When a door shuts in front of a raised threshold, an aperture large enough for a rat to get through often exists between the two; this opening may be closed by nailing to the door a piece of wood of sufficient thickness to block it by overlapping the threshold, about half an inch or more.

An opening of this kind may escape observation for a long time, because it can be seen only from the inside and when the door is closed. All doorways should be examined from the inside when the door is shut, to ensure that no opening through which a rat can pass is overlooked.

When a rat finds a door ajar, he frequently gnaws the corner of it, and the contiguous portion of the door-frame, so as to make a permanent opening through which he may go in and out; but as prevention is better than cure, it is not amiss to nail a piece of galvanized sheet-iron to the corner of a door and the contiguous portion of the door frame.

When the door opens inwards, one piece of iron should be fastened to the side surface of the door-frame to protect the edge of the surface against which the door shuts, and another piece to the back surface of the door-frame which is flush with the back of the door when it is closed, and a piece also to the corner of the inner and outer surface of the door.

When the door opens outwards, a piece should be fastened to the inner and outer surfaces of its corner, and to the outer or front surface of the door-frame on a level with the pieces fastened to the door, and to the side surface of the door-frame. This is done to protect the edge of the surface against which the door shuts.

When the sill is above the level of the floor or ground, its edge should be protected with a piece of galvanized iron about the same length as the piece on the door. It is well to affix it about a quarter of an inch below the upper surface of the sill to prevent its edge from getting trodden upon and bent.

Plates placed in these positions will effectually prevent corners from being gnawed, but will not interfere with the shutting of the door. A plate about 3 in. high and 2 in. wide will be sufficient in each case.

For stopping small holes in wood-work or in wooden floors, galvanized sheet-iron is very useful. In all cases the piece of iron should overlap the hole on each side by about an inch. A piece 3 by 2, 4½ by 2½, or 6 by 3 in. will cover most holes.

Zinc is often used for the purpose, and although hard enough to prevent mice re-opening a hole, it is too soft to be effectual in the case of rats. The author has before him a piece of stout zinc through which a rat gnawed a hole in order to effect an entrance into attractive premises.

It is convenient to keep a sheet of galvanized iron for stopping holes and protecting surfaces of wood, and a pair of small metal shears for cutting it. A bradawl which has broken off short and has been sharpened is a good tool with which to punch the holes in the iron for the flat-headed nails used to fasten it on.

Sheet-iron is sold in 6-ft. lengths, with a width of 12, 18, 24, 30, and 36 in. respectively, and is galvanized in all these sizes. Twenty-four gauge will be found a suitable thickness for closing all holes made by rats. It has been pointed out that new galvanized material should be submerged in water for at least twenty-four hours; or, better, washed with a strong solution of soda and water to neutralize and remove the acid. If the acid is not removed it will destroy any paint applied.

It may happen that rats get into a loft from time to time and climb down a corner of the walls into the out-house or stable beneath, or they reach the corner by running along the top of a wall of a building and cross the party-wall. When this is the case the hole in the loft or party-wall may be left open, and a trap kept permanently set on a shelf about 12 in. below it arranged as shown in fig. 27. A piece of biscuit or cheese-rind can be kept hung against the outer edge of the shelf, or a drop of oil of aniseed put on the treadle of the trap from time to time to entice rats to the place.

FIG. 27.—Arrangement for setting a steel trap in a corner beneath a hole or run.

It cannot be too fully realized that if premises are to be maintained free from rats, traps must be kept set all the year round. It may happen that it is not convenient to keep a trap set in a run outside a particular building on account of the width of the passage-way or for other reasons. When this is the case, a steel trap may be kept set in a run inside the building, provided its walls are made of wood or other material through which a hole can be cut. (See fig. 28.)

The run which should be arranged on the principle of the "Terrier" Signal Run, must be closed at the inner side, ends, and top, to prevent entrance to the building. As an alternative to the trap being reached from the outside, the top of the run may be made movable.

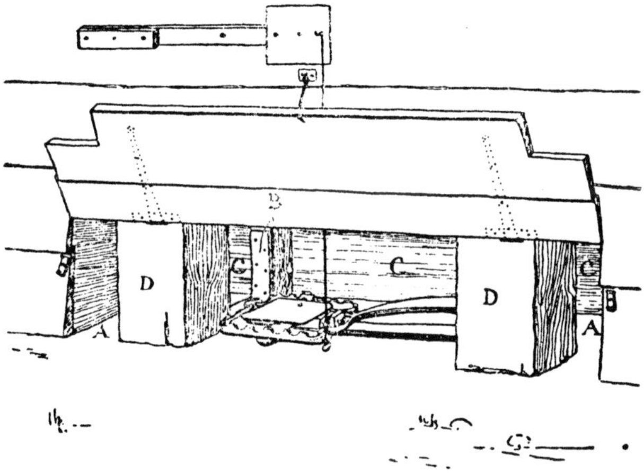

FIG. 28.—Arrangement for setting inside a building, a steel trap which is accessible from the outside. A, entrance. B, inner buttress; C, inner wall of run; D, upright of building or stud.

Rats often obtain entrance to an outbuilding through the hole made for cats, at or near the bottom of the door. The hole for this purpose should not be less than 2 ft. from the ground. When so situated, a rat would most likely run past the hole without seeing it, for it would be almost directly above him. Rats usually keep close to a wall when going from one place to another.

RATS IN THE YARD.

IF premises are to be maintained free from rats, it is essential not only that traps should be kept set all the year round, but that they should be in the places where rats must pass in order to reach shelter.

Gates leading into a yard often have a space beneath them, either in consequence of the threshold having become worn, or from the gates having been hung high from the ground, and it is through such entrances that rats often obtain access to premises. When the aperture cannot be blocked, a "Terrier" Death Run trap or a "Terrier" Signal Run should be placed on each side of the yard, a short distance from the gate, so that a rat on entering will have a trap in front of him no matter to which side he turns.

It is well not to place the trap too close to the gate, particularly if the wall or fence in which the gate is placed forms part of a corner. A rat sometimes passes across a corner to reach the side wall, and in that case might miss the trap.

Sometimes the floor of a coach-house or outbuilding is below the general surface of the yard, and consequently the doors do not reach to the floor or they would not be able to clear the higher ground over which they must pass when opening outwards. The best method for closing the space between the bottom of the door and the floor is to have a hinged flap on each door. This must be affixed to its inner surface.

A block of wood about 2 or 3 in. in thickness should be fastened to the inner surface of each flap, flush with its inner edge, to prevent an opening being formed if one of them does not fall completely. This might happen if the hinges became rusty or were clogged by paint, or if the lower edge of a flap rested on a twig or stone. An aperture on the outer edge is prevented by the proximity of the side surface of the door-post.

The flaps may be kept from rising when the doors are closed, by fixing a block to the door-posts immediately beyond them.

Rats may be found under the kennel of any dog, other than one of the terrier class, especially when the kennel is in a corner or built into an outhouse. It is advisable, therefore, to examine the space beneath a kennel when when taking steps to free a yard from rats.

Mr. Barkley, in his book entitled "Studies in the Art of Rat-Catching," gives an account of finding a rat living under the kennel of a dog who was, the owner assured him, "as keen as mustard" on rats. Yet the only access which the rat had to its place of concealment was through a hole in the floor of the kennel, so that not only had the rat to pass the dog, but actually enter the kennel in order to go to and from its retreat.

Walls made with loose stones around a yard should receive attention; all the interstices ought to be filled with mortar. This is not as expensive a matter as might at first be supposed, for any labourer or intelligent lad can do the necessary work. The proportions suitable for making thc mortar for that work arc :—

Lime	... ...	1 part
Sand	... ...	4 or 5 parts.

Care should be taken that the holes and crevices are thoroughly wetted before the mortar is put into them.

Occasionally it happens that a hole appears in the ground within a foot or so of the same spot, the place usually being over or near an old brick drain. When this is the case there is generally a hole in the wall of the drain through which the rats work their way. If from any cause it is inexpedient to trap the drain where it enters and leaves the premises, as mentioned in the Section "Rats in the House, Shop, Warehouse, &c."; and if the drain does not convey sewage or objectionable matter, the hole in the ground may be left open, since if closed it is sure to be re-opened.

Sometimes a hole of this description is made in the vicinity of a stone-ware pipe drain. In this case, there is either a broken pipe or an old brick drain close by, the existence of which is unknown; or the rats have burrowed along by the side of the pipes for some distance.

A hole of the kind just mentioned may be used only occasionally, but it should be kept trapped; because the rats emerging from it may be seeking fresh quarters and have no intention of returning to the drain. Some of the rats caught near a hole of this kind on the premises referred to in the preface, have apparently been in search for a home for the family shortly expected.

The simplest way to trap such a hole is to place an inverted box over it and put a "Terrier" Signal Run, such as is described in the Section "Traps," against the box, an aperture corresponding to the entrance to the Signal Run having been previously cut in the side of the box. Every rat then attempting to leave the drain will be captured, since he must pass over the trap, which should be placed with its jaws facing the box.

In the vicinity of many farmyards there is a pond with trees and bushes growing along a portion of its edge, and where this is found the owner or tenant may be heard to remark: "There are always rats by the pond," as if the rats were as inseparable from the pond as the water forming it.

On inquiry it may be learnt that a number of young chickens and ducks are killed by the rats in the course of the year, and for this reason they are "kept away from the pond as much as possible."

The holes made by the rats in such a situation, although they can be seen from a distance, are often difficult to reach, and are sometimes almost inaccessible, not only on account of the trees and bushes occupying the edge of the bank, but because the upper part of the bank overhangs the lower.

The roots of the trees and bushes form with the bank a sheltered run along which the rats can pass in comparative safety, and these conditions, being in proximity to water, create an ideal abode.

A pond colony should be exterminated by ferreting, poisoning, and trapping, the details for which are given in their respective sections. The low projecting branches and bushes should be cleared away, all the holes filled in, the overhanging portion of the bank broken down, and the surface made smooth. Traps should afterwards be kept set around the pond throughout the year.

In some yards there are drains that discharge into a pond through an open end. When this is the case, a grating should be placed against the end of the drain so that no rat can enter it. If any solid matter passes along the drain the grating may be hinged, so that any material collecting against it may be cleared away.

Before fixing the grating it is as well to put a sanitary inspector's smoke-ferret into the drain, and temporarily to close it. This will show whether or not the stable or other drains which run into it are trapped; if they are not, rats may use the drain as a place of concealment.

Rats frequently lie in a stack of faggots, and when clearing premises of rats, the faggot stack should be carefully ferreted.

It must be remembered that rats often lie in the faggots above the level of the ground, and that therefore it is sometimes best to put the ferrets in at the top of the stack and let them work downwards.

Nobody can say whence the rats will bolt, so it is best to put a net round the stack at a few yards distance. A rat escaping from a ferret often jumps from the faggots above the level of the ground, so that unless the net is well back it may be cleared in the jump.

Subsequently one or more "Terrier" Death Run traps, or trapped "Terrier" Signal Runs, should be kept permanently against the faggot stack, and it is well to keep some wheat or maize in them, and occasionally to place a drop of oil of aniseed on the traps.

When fowls are kept or fed in a yard rats are sure to go to it, and "Terrier" Death Run traps, which should be kept under a cover, or trapped "Terrier" Signal Runs, should therefore be in position against the walls all the year round.

There is no risk of the young chickens being caught in the traps, for chickens do not readily enter a darkened passage, and the low entrance to the covers or Signal Runs which, for this purpose should be only 2 in. high, is sufficient usually to keep them out. To meet exceptional circumstances and thereby ensure their not entering it, a prolongation may be made outside the cover or Signal Run, but in continuation with it. The top of the extension should be made movable, so that it can be lifted off to clear away leaves or any other material blown into it.

To clear a yard of rats Mr. Sharpe's method may be employed—see Section "Trapping." The tub in which the platform will be fixed should be sunk to the ground level against a wall and the earth around the tub rammed until quite firm. Wire-netting with a 2½ in. mesh should then be fixed around it at a sufficient distance to prevent the poultry reaching the water, and also over it at a height of not less than a foot.

Rats often frequent the goods yard of a railway company. Some hide by day in the space beneath the goods shed floor, and others under the adjacent sheds or in the banks near, if the yard is in the country, whilst at night still more come from their holes under the station platform.

Many rats live below the platforms of railway stations, the entrance to their holes being through the apertures that have been left in the brickwork to allow the escape of water that otherwise would collect.

If in the future more openings were made with a maximum width of three-quarters of an inch, instead of fewer with a space of 2 in. or more, the drainage of water would be as thoroughly provided for, and the passage of rats through the brickwork would be prevented. The existing holes could be easily narrowed by fixing pieces of tile in them.

If "Terrier" Death Run traps in covers, or trapped "Terrier" Signal Runs were kept in the goods yard throughout the year, the number of rats would be materially reduced with but little trouble.

RATS IN THE STABLE.

Rats in a stable do more harm than by merely undermining the paving, and eating or damaging the corn; they keep the horses from resting properly. No horse can sleep while rats are running over the straw which forms his bed or gnawing woodwork near by. Many horses would be in much better condition and even able to do more work if their rest at night were not disturbed by rats.

To clear a stable of rats, the measures mentioned in the Section "Rats in the Outbuilding" must be adopted. The thresholds must be made good, and should be fitted with a piece of iron, fastened to the sill and posts, for the door to shut against. This will keep it from becoming worn again (see fig. 26). All holes in the outside wall should be stopped, and measures taken to prevent rats entering from adjoining buildings. Those already in possession must be got rid of by flooding, ferreting, blocking, or trapping as fully described in the sections dealing with these methods of destruction.

Where gutters are used for drainage, a hinged grating should be affixed to the outer side of the wall through which the gutter passes, so as to cover the outlet; otherwise rats will enter by this opening.

It is necessary for the grating to be hinged, so that it can be raised to remove any straw or other material which may have been carried against its inner surface, and also to prevent it from obstructing the flow of water when the stable is washed down.

The grating should be suspended by two suitable iron loops as shown in fig. 29. They can easily be made by a blacksmith and attached to the grating. Fasten them to the wall by staples driven into a plug wedged between the bricks after the mortar has been cut out with a small cold chisel to receive it.

FIG. 29.—Grating for closing an aperture for a gutter.

The plug must be made of soft wood, and the holes for the prongs of the staples should be bored with a gimlet; otherwise there may be difficulty in driving them in as far as is wished.

In some cases two pieces of chain will be found more suitable for supporting the grating; and in some instances a nail with a large head may be used for fixing the upper end of each chain, the wall having been plugged previously with wood to receive the nail.

The grating should so hang that the upper edge of the lower border of the frame is on a level with the bottom of the gutter, or even slightly below it. Failing this, the frame of the grating will obstruct the flow from the gutter. The bottom of the grating should be about half an inch above the level of the gully or surface on to which the gutter discharges ; if too high, the rats might raise it and creep under into the stable.

A piece of wood projecting about 2 in. from the wall should be nailed on each side of the grating about half an inch from it, so that if the grating is temporarily prevented from falling flat against the wall, in consequence of some straw or other material having got underneath its edge, the aperture at the side, resulting from the grating projecting slightly from the wall, will be blocked by the pieces of wood. Thus the entrance of a rat through it will be prevented.

When a stable is built on a slope, and the gutter in consequence passes through the wall above the level of the ground, a grating should still be hung over the opening, as above described, even though it be a foot or more from the ground. Rats find out such an opening, probably by means of the escaping emanations from the stable, and obtain an entrance as may be seen in some instances by their footmarks. Where the grating is hung above the level of the ground, there should be a piece of wood below the grating as well as on each side.

Trouble would be saved, if iron founders were to cast a frame projecting forward 2 in., and fitted with a hinged grating for covering these openings. If the frame had a flange turned outwards, the frame could be fixed easily to any wall.

It often happens that rats have a run in a stable behind the boarding which covers the walls of the stalls and loose-boxes, and usually there is an opening from it, close to the manger. Where this is the case and there is reason to suppose that there may be a hole in the wall, it is well to take down the boarding and fill up all holes found. When this has been done the woodwork should be replaced, and all openings by which access to the space between it and the wall had been previously gained should be closed.

Doors and thresholds inside the stable and outbuildings connected with it should be repaired in the manner previously mentioned, so as to keep any stray rat which may gain an entrance through an open door, or by other means, from obtaining a full run of the building. Sound doorways enable a rat to be killed more easily when discovered, as he must be sooner or later if the premises are in use, provided all holes have been stopped in the manner above described.

Rats frequently lie in the space between a ceiling and the floor above it, and it is important not only that they should be cleared from this position before the holes in the floors are stopped, but also that means be taken to prevent other rats getting there.

It is best to begin by clearing the loft, and anything too large to be taken away should be put as near the centre of the floor as possible.

The board against the wall on each side of the floor should then be taken up, so that the walls may be examined, and any holes found must be temporarily stopped with hay, paper or any other suitable material ; both ends of each space between the joists should also be plugged. When this has been done, a ferret should be run between the joists, beginning at one end of the loft and working regularly along it, the opening at the ends of each space being unplugged to allow the ferret to enter and the rats (if any) to bolt. As soon as the ferret comes out, and before it is put between the next joists, the ends of the space which has been ferreted should be plugged again.

A small sack or net may be placed at the opposite end to that at which the ferret is put in, so that the rats may run into it when driven out by the ferret.

Dogs are liable to run from the floor on to the ceiling and break it down, and therefore they should not be used to kill the rats.

When all the spaces between the joists have been ferreted in this manner, every third or fourth board across the loft should be taken up, and the space cleared of the hay, straw, or other material which has been carried beneath the floor. The walls at both ends of the boards should be carefully examined, and if a good view of them cannot be obtained through the openings made by the removed boards, additional boards must be taken up to enable a thorough investigation to be made.

When all the holes in the walls and ceiling have been stopped, so that no aperture exists through which rats can get under the floor, the boards may be replaced and the floor made good. The holes on its surface can be stopped with wood or galvanized sheet-iron (gauge 24).

If the boards which form the floor of the loft are tongued and grooved, dust will not fall through.

RATS IN THE COW-HOUSE.

In cow-houses rats frequently lie under the mangers, which are often set low, and sometimes have the space underneath them boxed in, making a safe retreat for vermin, and providing them with comfortable quarters in which they can make their nests. Where this is the case and it is not desired to alter the construction of the mangers, the space between the bottom of the manger and the floor of the cowhouse should be filled in with concrete, or bricks and mortar.

RATS IN THE FOWL-HOUSE.

WHEN rats are in a fowl-house, measures must be taken as already described in Section " Rats in the Outbuilding" to make good the doorway and stop all holes in the walls. Any holes in the floor should be flooded or ferreted, and when this has been done, the holes must be filled in immediately and the ground around them well rammed.

If the fowl-house nests are on the ground, or so close to it that rats can remain underneath without being seen, they must be raised to not less than a foot from the floor, so that the space beneath them can be swept and kept clean. It is best for the nests to be movable, merely resting on supports, so that they can be taken away to be lime-washed. These movable nests enable the wall behind them to be kept clean.

When a fowl-house is made of wood, there are usually spaces on the inside formed by the intervals between the supports, called studs, to which the boards are nailed. Care should be taken that the back of the nests does not rest against these supports where they join the horizontal piece at the bottom which holds them in position; if the nests are so arranged, a cosy space will be formed in which rats can lie. By raising the nests from 4 to 6 in. above the bottom of the spaces between the uprights, the recesses will be too exposed for rats to stop in them.

The following illustration will make the matter clear.

If from any cause the nests cannot conveniently be placed otherwise than in front of the recesses, the latter should be boarded in or filled with bricks and mortar to the level of the top of the nests.

Rats frequently reach a fowl-house through the entrance made for the fowls, but if this aperture were made with its lower edge not less than a foot from the ground

FIG. 30.—X shows the recesses in which rats might lie if the nests were placed in front of them. A, Alighting board outside nests; N, nests; S, uprights of building or stud; W, boards forming wall of building.

the fowls could still pass in and out freely, while a rat would most likely run past the hole. As it would be almost directly above him, he would probably fail to see it, for rats usually keep close to a wall whilst going from one place to another.

When a fowl-house is situated in a range of buildings and rats enter it by running inside the rafters along the walls from the next building and climb down into the fowl-house, the best way to keep them out permanently is to fix a 9-in. board by its upper surface all round the fowl-house at the upper part of its vertical walls, at a right angle to them. The space between the boards must be filled in with wire-netting to prevent the fowls getting on to them and steel traps kept always set by an arrangement such as shown in fig. 31.

If a wide aperture exists between the edge of the boards and the wall, it must be blocked with mortar to which some cement has been added, the mortar being kept in position by nails previously partially driven into the boards and walls at the places which the mortar will cover.

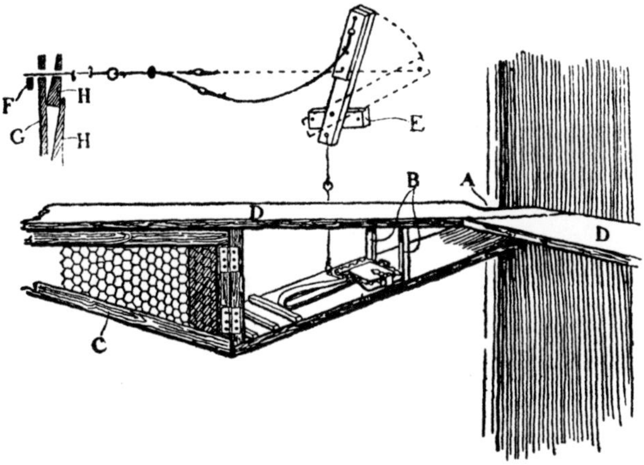

FIG. 31.—A steel trap connected with a signal. An arrangement for catching rats entering from the upper part of a building. A, hole for rats to reach trap; B, buttress; C, door to protect trap; D, board to prevent rats passing down into the fowl-house; E, block to which the lath is pivoted; F, stem of signal; G, lath to allow signal to slide along building; H, wall of building.

For detailed arrangement for signal see "Signals," Part II.

It must be remembered that rats frequently move from place to place, and if premises are to be kept free from them, a trap must be ready at every place to which they are likely to go.

RATS IN THE PIGSTY.

WHEREVER pigs are kept, there sooner or later rats will be found. Many pigsties are infested with rats, because destruction has never been undertaken in a systematic manner, nor have measures been adopted to prevent the vermin from obtaining an entrance to the sty. On the contrary, in many places they have been allowed to come and go as they please, to fatten on the pig's food, and incidentally to breed and largely increase in numbers.

The first step to be taken here, as elsewhere, with the view to destroying the rats frequenting the sty, is to flood or ferret all the holes. Even when the holes have been ferreted, if there is not a dog that can be thoroughly trusted to show that "all are out," it is advisable sometimes to flood the holes as well, before filling them in. Sometimes an old rat will stand at bay and the ferret will retreat and leave him in possession, but when the hole is filled with water that rat is obliged to bolt.

Before the ferreting and flooding are begun, the ground outside the sty should be cleared of any wood, empty cases or other articles which may have been placed there, and any coarse vegetation that may facilitate the escape of rats should be cut with scythe or hook.

If there are pigs in the sty, it is best not to use poison anywhere near it, lest they should eat some of the rats that have been poisoned.

When the ground around the sty has been cleared and

all the rats have been driven from their holes, the next procedure should be to re-make the floor of the sty, and stop all the holes in the walls leading into the covered or inner compartment.

If the floor of this inner covered compartment of the sty is made of wood and has a space underneath it sufficiently deep to allow rats to lie there, it is best to entirely remove the floor and fill the hollow space with earth or brick rubbish to a suitable level. After this has been well rammed, a foundation for the new floor should then be prepared by making a bed of concrete 3 to 6 in. in thickness according to the area which has to be covered.

When the cement or concrete surface has set, and if thick pieces of wood, such as old railway sleepers, are not used for the pigs to lie upon, a new wooden floor may be made by nailing boards on to cross-pieces not more than an inch in thickness. These, although holding the boards firmly together, will not allow space for a rat to lie between them and the concrete on which the new wooden floor rests. The boards should be nailed at a right angle to the fall of the concrete, and the cross pieces to which they are nailed should be parallel with the fall, otherwise they will obstruct the flow of any water that may find its way between the boards. If the flooring is made in sections about 2 ft. wide, these can easily be taken up from time to time, and the cement swept clean, for dirt and fragments of the bedding are sure to get through the crevices of the flooring and to collect beneath it.

A hole about an inch in diameter made with a centre-bit through the flooring, sufficiently far from each end to be clear of the cross-piece, will enable the boards to be lifted up easily by a finger passed through the hole.

There must be a fixed threshold across the doorway somewhat higher than the movable flooring to prevent the pigs displacing it.

The inner part of the sty having been put in order, attention should now be given to the yard with the object of making it rat-proof. The threshold must be made good, and if necessary, protected with iron as described in the Section "Rats in the Outbuilding." If the walls are made of brick and no holes exist through them, all that is required in the future to keep the sty free from rats is to place one or more "Terrier" Death Run traps, or "Terrier" Signal Runs, described in the Section "Traps," against the outside of the walls. Better still, build as a fixture one or more single or double runs.

When there is a hole through the wall to allow the drainage to escape, a grating must be hung over the aperture as described in the Section "Rats in the Stable."

When the walls are made of wooden uprights with spaces between them, a couple of 9-in. boards, placed one above the other, should be nailed against their inner side all round the sty, so as to make the walls of the sty rat-proof to that height. If the sty is not paved, a row of bricks or some concrete may be placed under the edge of the boards to prevent the rats from burrowing beneath them.

A run built against the sty as a fixture is in the end less trouble than one which can be shifted about, and in which the trap is liable to be sprung if accidentally disturbed. If this latter plan is decided upon, a run with one or two traps according to the requirements of the situation, may be constructed in the following manner, either along the front or at the side of the sty, the position selected being that to which a rat is most likely to come first. With a range of sties there may be a run in the front of the range, and one on the outer side of each end sty. The number decided upon, and their position, must be determined by the number of rats that are likely to enter the premises, and the direction from which it seems likely that they will come.

Where there is plenty of room, it is usually better to place the run outside the sty, as the traps can then be reached more easily.

The simplest plan is to place on edge a 9-in. board about 4 ft. in length, leaving a space of 7 in. between its inner surface and the outside of the sty-fence, fastening it securely to pegs driven in the ground and filling in each end of the space with wood to within 3½ in. of the ground.

A run thus formed is fitted with buttresses at each end similar to a "Terrier" Signal Run if both of the 5-in. rabbit-traps are to face outwards, but if one is to face inwards so that its signal may engage the fixed jaw, the outer surface of the buttresses for this trap ought to be about 10 in. from the inner surface of the corresponding end of the run, for in this case they are placed on the spring side of the jaws.

The top is made of a loose piece of board and a signal attached as described with a "Terrier" Signal Run. A hole may be made from the centre of the run into the sty to catch any stray rats that may have climbed the fence.

On the premises referred to in the preface, a 5-in rabbit trap in a single trapped run of this description fixed inside the sty which for many years guarded the rats' entrance to it, has never been found with a rat caught as he was leaving the sty. From this it may be inferred that when an opening exists by which rats think they can enter, they do not attempt to climb the wall or effect an entrance by another way. The practicability of this point may be considered to have been thoroughly tested, since the death-roll for which the above mentioned trap is responsible is shown by the records to be a very large one.

If a more elegant arrangement is wanted it may be made as shown in fig. 32.

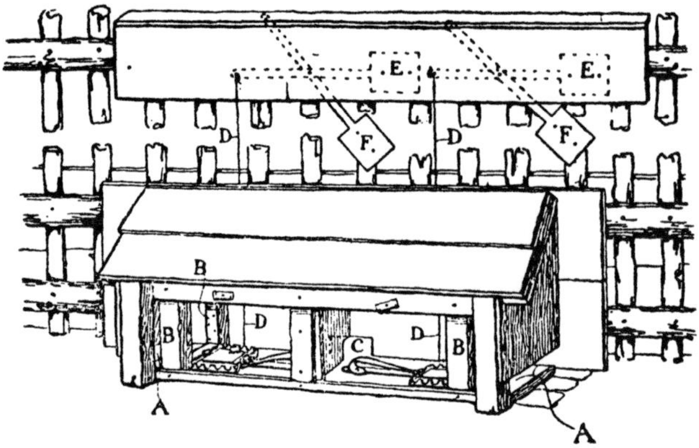

Fig. 32.—A double trapped run with signals. A, entrance to run; B, buttress; C, entrance to sty; D, wire connecting signal with trap; E, position of signal when trap is set; F, position of signal when trap has been sprung. The movable fronts have been removed to show the interior of the run.

One or more "Terrier" Death Run traps, or trapped "Terrier" Signal Runs (figs. 4 and 3) according to the situation, should be kept throughout the year in close proximity to the pigs' tub. If the tub is kept against a wall or a wooden fence through which there is no hole, a trap may be placed against the wall on each side of the tub. If it is kept in the open, there is a good way of placing the traps, so as to ensure that any rats which may come on attempting to pass through them shall be caught. The method is as follows :—

Set 9-in. boards on edge around the tub, so arranged as to form three sides of a square and fasten them to stakes driven into the ground, the trap being put at the end of each side so as to form part of the central barrier, the inner end of the cover or run being flush with the board. For preference the jaws of a steel trap should be towards the area in which the tub is kept. Any rat disturbed while feeding around the tub will go into the Run Trap or "Terrier" Signal Run for shelter, and will thus be caught. It is unnecessary to examine the traps daily, the signal attached to each will show by its position when a capture has been made.

There has been a considerable increase in the rat population throughout the country since the introduction of the system of open-air pig keeping, for not only has there been plenty of food for the rats attracted to the area, but also for succeeding generations as they came into existence. Ample housing accommodation has been provided for them, where buildings were not available, by the banks and the ground in sheltered places.

The quickest way to clear these areas of rats is by the use of water-carts described in the Section "Flooding"; but when this method is inconvenient, systematic ferreting should be adopted, all the holes in both cases being carefully closed as soon as their occupants have been evicted. As, however, rats will continually be drawn to the premises by the smell of the pigs, their numbers will soon increase rapidly again unless every hole is flooded or ferreted as soon as it is discovered, and traps are kept set in Signal Runs throughout the year. It must not be forgotten that at night rats often travel a considerable distance from their home to obtain food.

All fences leading to the pig enclosure should be trapped, but if it is wished to place traps inside the enclosure, the best position for them is between a bank or rat-frequented area and a feeding bin, as in this case a rat will go to the run, on account of the cover which it affords, on its way across the open space.

The run is best placed lengthways with the line of route, with the jaws of the trap facing the bank, but in all cases the runs must be fastened to pegs driven firmly into the ground and every precaution taken to prevent the run being shifted and the trap left exposed.

RATS IN A GARDEN, GREENHOUSE OR VINERY.

WHEN the measures described in the previous sections for clearing premises of rats have been adopted, rats seldom give trouble in a garden. After all the banks have been ferreted, the holes stopped, and after they have been dislodged from their old haunts in the sheds, the garden is left in peace.

Sometimes, however, the rats come from neighbouring buildings; and when this is the case, "Terrier" Death Run traps, or "Terrier" Signal Runs should be placed where they are likely to pass.

If rats dig up the seeds, peas, beans, or newly planted potatoes, additional traps should be placed on the ground in which these are sown, but the traps guarding the approaches should not be moved.

There are but few walled gardens with wooden doors into which rats have not gnawed an entrance, provided there was not sufficient space beneath, or a hole between the door and posts large enough to admit them. Before trapping those that may be in the garden, the thresholds, doors, and posts, if defective, should be made good, either by renewing them, or repairing them as described in the Section "Rats in the Outbuilding."

When the ornamental is substituted for the useful, when wooden doors to a walled garden are replaced by open ironwork gates, that let in the winds that walls were built and solid doors specially made to exclude, it is much more difficult to keep rats out of the garden.

The best plan is to place a "Terrier" Death Run trap or a "Terrier" Signal Run on either side of each gate, and to fasten fine wire-netting to the lowest 2 ft. or more of the gates. This forms an obstacle to entrance, and renders it probable, that while searching for an opening into the garden and before proceeding to climb the obstacle, the rat will enter one of the traps.

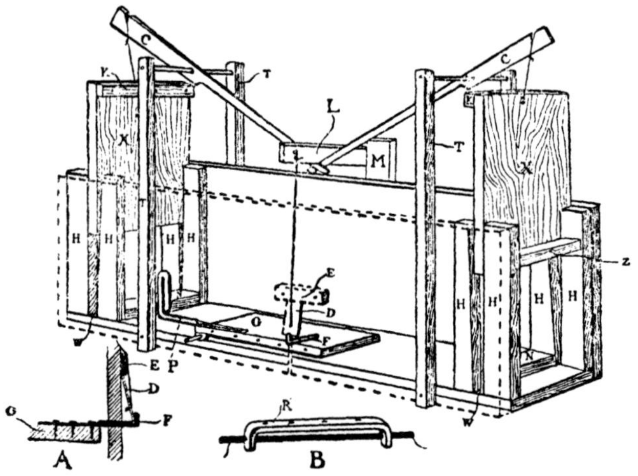

FIG. 32*.—Combined Rabbit and Vermin Trap.

Rabbits are very fond of getting into a garden, as they find pinks, carnations, and the various kinds of vegetables, a pleasing change to their ordinary fare; when they have obtained an entrance they often do a considerable amount of damage.

It is practically useless to attempt to keep them out with wire-netting, unless it is buried deeply and is sufficiently high, for not only will they burrow underneath it, but they will also climb over it, and they can jump much higher than many persons suppose.

The best way to keep rabbits out of a garden is to have a wire-netting fence not less than 2 ft. high, with its lower part buried about 6 in., or bent to about the same length or more at the bottom, away from the garden. The fence should have openings through it at intervals, and a Run trap, such as shown in fig. 32* and described in the Section "Traps" and Part II, kept set against each opening, the trap being on the garden side of the wire-netting.

A rabbit before burrowing under, or climbing over a fence always runs along by it trying to find an opening through it. In this case, while so doing, it will come to the inlet guarded by a trap and will be caught on attempting to pass through into the garden. The author has employed this method for many years and found it most successful. Not only have all the rabbits attempting to enter the garden been caught, but a number of rats, stoats, and other vermin have been taken annually. On this account, a galvanized sheet-iron lining for the traps around all the openings is recommended.

Each trap should have a signal attached to it, so that it can be seen from a distance whether it is set or sprung.

When a garden is near a wood or other place where there are always a number of rabbits, it is a good plan to have another fence of wire-netting about 6 ft. or more nearer the wood.

The outer wire-netting fence will keep back all rabbits not bent on leaving the wood. The others, when they have burrowed under the netting or got over it, will still be separated from the garden by the inner fence.

The ground by the side of the wire-netting should be examined from time to time, and any hole that is found should be filled in.

Access to a vinery is frequently obtained through the holes left for vines. To prevent this in the future, the holes should be filled with hay from a hay-band, and afterwards covered with wire-netting about half-inch mesh.

When the vine enters the vinery through an arch, the ground should be made up so that the top of the arch is several inches below its surface, or the arch may be covered by a piece of thick board laid against the outside of the wall, so that its lower edge is buried several inches. If the stem of the vine is near the surface, the board should be sufficiently notched.

The thresholds of vinery and greenhouses must be made good, as described in the Section "Rats in the Out-building." The hole in the wall through which the heating pipes pass, must be carefully closed round with brick and mortar, so that a rat cannot pass through it by the side of the pipes.

When a vinery or greenhouse is over or near an old brick drain, rats are very liable to work their way into the one from the other. If holes are being made frequently in the floor by rats, the proximity of an old drain may be suspected, and the holes should be traced in the manner described in the Section "Rats in the House, Shop, Warehouse, &c."

RATS BY THE RIVER, STREAM OR ORNAMENTAL WATER.

THE fondness of rats for the vicinity of water is well known; in the summer they like to take up their quarters near it. When passing from one locality to another they often follow the course of a river or stream, so that banks and hedgerows adjoining water should always receive special attention when the destruction of rats is undertaken.

It must not be forgotten that the brown rat will take to water freely, and not only swim across a stream but also dive readily into it. When an animal the size of a rat is seen to dive off a bank, do not assume hastily that it is a water-vole.

Although rats are fond of water, they prefer to cross a stream or wet ditch by a plank, or by a strong rail if one is near. When selecting the position for a trap, advantage may be taken not only of this habit, but of another, that of running near the edge of the water.

For permanent trapping, a run with a 5-in. rabbit trap in it is the best way to catch rats that travel by the side of a stream. As mentioned already, the trap may be placed in a run without being concealed in any way, but a piece of wood should be laid under one side of the cross-bar of the frame to prevent rocking.

It is obvious that the precise plan employed to guide a rat to the run, must depend upon the shape and nature of the bank on which the trap is set. If the bank is more or less steep, with about a foot or more of slightly sloping ground between the steep part and the water, a run may be placed at the water's edge. In this case the space between it and the vertical portion of the bank should be blocked with a low wall made of sods or boards.

If there is a long shelving bank to the water's edge, and the water-level is constantly varying, two 9-in. boards may be nailed to posts driven firmly into the ground and a run placed at the end of the barrier above the water-line.

When a run is placed at the edge of water too deep for a trap to rest on the bank, it may be placed on a board cut out to receive it, as advocated by Mr. Sharpe. (See Section "Trapping.") It is best to cover the board with earth.

When ornamental water is fed by a stream, it is well to place a run on either side of the stream, and also on each side of the channel which carries off the overflow. This is in addition to the runs placed on the edge of the water.

When a stream runs through a covert, advantage should be taken of a rat's inclination to cross it on a pole by placing some poles about 2 or 3 in. in diameter, across it about 3 in. above the water, with a trap on each with its jaws against a barrier which may be made of sticks as shown in fig. 33. The rail should have a piece of wood a foot or more in length nailed transversely to each end and resting on the ground to keep it from revolving, and narrow flat pieces of wood nailed to its upper surface for the frame of the trap to rest on.

Any space that exists between pole and bank must be

filled in, so that vermin cannot pass through it. If the bank shelves, some strong pegs must be driven into the edge of the water on each side of the pole, and the ground raised with turf to the pole's level.

All plank and foot bridges across a stream ought to be trapped at one end, if not at both, but the trap must be placed on a support separated by one or two inches from the bridge, otherwise the vibration produced by a person crossing over will be liable to spring the trap.

FIG. 33.—This diagram shows a trap set on a pole across a stream with a barrier in front of it. The turf cover to the trap has been left out, and the cross sticks on which it would rest have not been sketched, so as to show more clearly the construction of the barrier, and the frame set up to support the turf roof.

A simple arrangement, and quite sufficient for a plank across a ditch or a stream in a covert, is to place across the plank a piece of wood an inch or more in thickness, and about 9 to 12 in. high.

Keep it in a vertical position by fastening it to two pieces of wood nailed to, or for preference let into, the opposite sides of the plank, so as to be flush with its edge. By this arrangement they are more firmly fixed and kept rigid.

For a larger and frequented bridge, it is best to have a step to bar the passage-way of vermin. This is more easily crossed by passengers than a vertical piece of wood which must be stepped over.

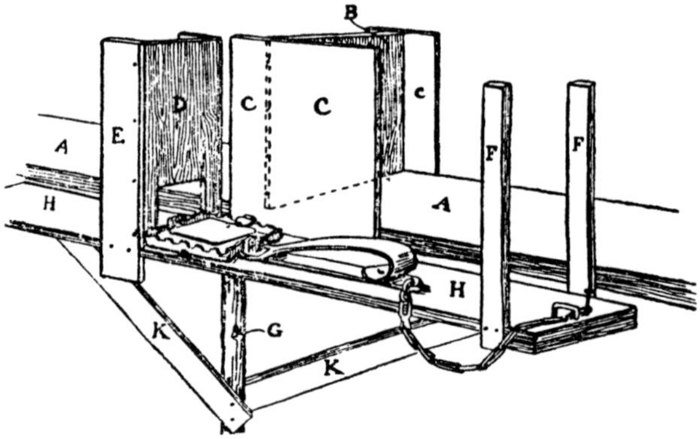

FIG. 34.—Arrangement for trapping a plank bridge. A, plank bridge; B, barrier across bridge; C, supports to barrier; D, barrier for trap; E, support to barrier for trap; F, back supports for roof to cover trap; G, pole supporting board on which trap is placed; H, board on which trap is placed; K, supports to make board more rigid.

The banks of a pond or a wet ditch are a favourite resort of rats, and many may be caught by placing traps in the runs, especially where the run passes through shallow water or comes so close to the edge that by removing a little earth a trap just covered by water can be placed in the run. When so placed, a trap need not be concealed, although a little of the neighbouring vegetation or some dead leaves from the bottom of the pond may be lightly strewn over it. If the water covers the trap only to the depth of the thickness of a piece of cardboard, it is quite sufficient to stop any smell that may come from the trap.

Another method is to place a trap against a run which comes close to the edge of the water. The jaws end of the trap is against the run, supported by a peg beneath the front corner of the fixed jaw near the bank end. Another support is fixed beneath the cross-piece of the frame of the trap which is beneath the loose jaw. The tail of the trap is kept in position by resting on a peg about an inch in width, the peg being adjusted so that the water just covers the trap.

As an inducement for rats to cross the trap, a piece of bait that has not been handled, such as cheese, a crust covered with dripping, or other food of which rats are fond, may be fixed on to a sharp nail at the end of a stick stuck into the bottom of the pond in a sloping direction. So place it that the bait is immediately above the water, just beyond the end of the loose jaw. This ensures a rat passing over the free end of the treadle or the part which will enable the trap to be sprung by the least weight. If a hole, sufficiently deep to submerge a trap and its victim, is made below and beyond the spring end of the trap, no trace will be left of any rat which may be caught.

The following arrangement will keep the cross-piece of the trap from falling between the bank and the peg which supports it, a mischance which would prevent the trap from slipping into deep water. Place the vertical peg rather deeper and drive a horizontal peg into the bank for the cross-piece of the trap to lie on, resting it on the vertical peg, the lower part of the horizontal peg being cut into a flat surface to give it a firmer bearing.

The trap may be fastened to a submerged peg by a piece of string sufficiently long to allow the trap when sprung, to slide into the hole prepared for it.

For trapping wet ditches under bush and bramble, the trap can in some cases be handled most conveniently for setting from a board laid across the ditch from the clear side.

Many rats make a highway of a shallow wet ditch. The run in these cases is either in the centre of the ditch or along its sides, according to the depth of the water, and many rats may be caught by placing traps in these positions, immediately below the surface of the water. It must be remembered that with running water the footprints of rats are often obliterated, but their habit of making use of such thoroughfares must not be forgotten. In some cases a row of vertical pegs may be stuck into the bed of the ditch to ensure a rat passing over the treadle of a trap, but in most cases this is unnecessary.

Another useful way of catching rats is to lay a pole across a ditch about 2 or 3 in. above the water, with a stick nailed transversely at each end to prevent the pole revolving. Then make a turf barrier across the pole a few inches from the water's edge on the opposite bank to that in which the rats' holes are situated, placing a trap on each side of the pole in the space formed.

Several poles, a few yards apart, may be laid across the ditch simultaneously, and trapped after the rats have become accustomed to cross the ditch on them.

Immediately after a flood has submerged the banks of a river, stream, or ditch on which there are trees, and also the adjacent land, so that the trees are surrounded with water, rats may often be found on the trees. The pollarded top of a willow is a likely place for them to be concealed.

If rats are known to have been in the banks, a visit to the trees immediately the water has risen may result in a large number being killed. A small terrier that can be lifted on to the trees, provides the quickest and surest method of ascertaining whether any rats are lying on the top of a pollarded tree amongst the branches. It is well at the same time to have one or more dogs below, to catch any rats that may jump into the water. Stick and gun will help further to ensure that none escape.

RATS ON A SHIP.[1]

It is probable that rats have infested ships since the days when the latter were made sufficiently large to afford the necessary concealment. But although rats in a ship do, and always have done, damage in varying degrees, (sometimes to a very serious extent), yet, until recently, no organized plan for their destruction has been carried out. As a rule, vermin have been regarded as an ill that must be endured. In olden days when an excessive amount of damage had been done to the cargo, the ship might be fumigated with sulphur as soon as the holds had been emptied; but beyond this, little was done to keep the vessel even comparatively free from rats. It is probable that nothing will be done in the future on a thoroughly comprehensive scale, until it is made compulsory for a ship to be fumigated at regular stated intervals, and destruction of the rats on a vessel coming into a port is dealt with as a matter of routine.

For some years past, Messrs. Elder, Dempster and Co., the well known ship-owners, have systematically destroyed the rats on their vessels. The procedure is for a professional rat-catcher to board each ship as it comes into

[1] The author is indebted for much of the information contained in this Section to an interesting paper by Dr. Carl Prausnitz on "The Destruction of Rats on Ships" in the *Journal of the Incorporated Society for the Destruction of Vermin*, vol. i, No. 4, July-October, 1909.

port, and set traps under the supervision of the company's officials. In addition to this, the crew are encouraged to trap during the voyage; a remuneration of twopence was paid by the company before the war for every rat captured by their employees.

As a result of this system, many thousands of rats have been caught on the company's steamers; and it is greatly to be regretted that the excellent and most useful work undertaken by this company is not universally adopted.

The systematic destruction of rats on ships is extremely desirable, not only on account of the damage they do to the cargo, but as a preventive measure against their leaving the ship and entering the warehouses on the quay. The Elder, Dempster system also lessens the danger that exists to-day of rats carrying plague to this country from distant ports, and thus causing an outbreak here.

Although continuous trapping on board a ship will assist materially in reducing the number of rats, yet, in order to clear a ship, a more wholesale method of destruction must be employed.

This may be effected by closing the hatches and stopping up all the apertures leading to the holds, and then filling them with a gas or fumes that are destructive to life.

Several methods have been employed, but the best is the Clayton method in which the gas used is sulphur dioxide. This method was invented by Mr. T. A. Clayton in conjunction with Dr. S. R. Olliphant, the President of the State Board of Health, Louisiana. It has been extensively employed both for purposes of fire extinction and of fumigation. Experience has conclusively shown it to be a valuable method for the destruction of all kinds of vermin, and also for obtaining a good surface disinfection.

The apparatus consists of a half-cylindrical generator in which the sulphur is burnt, a cooler, a pump supplying the water required for the cooler, and a blower to provide the air required for the combustion of the sulphur, and to drive the sulphur dioxide fumes into the hold. The pump and blower are driven by a steam-engine, oil-engine, or electric motor of 1 to 15 h.p. according to the size of the machine.

The apparatus is worked as follows: There is a suction orifice connected by a flexible tube or hose with the air in the upper part of the hold, and a blower is connected by another hose with the same hold, as far from the suction pipe as possible, and at a rather lower level. The generator is charged with roll sulphur, which is ignited by a little methylated spirit after the hose connections have been made and the engine started. The air sucked from the upper part of the hold enters the generator where part of it is converted into sulphur dioxide by the combustion of the sulphur, the resulting high temperature destroying any bacteria that may be carried in the air. The fumes leaving the generator, pass through a radiator into a main cooler in which they are reduced from a temperature of more than 1000° F. to one of about 60° F. The rest of the air from the suction pipe is then mixed with the cool gas and forced by the blower back to the hold. The gas passed back to the hold has the same volume as the air that is drawn out, but is heavier; the action of the blower, therefore, is to keep up a constant circulation of the air in the hold through the generator, so that theoretically the entire atmosphere of the hold should ultimately be replaced by air that has passed through the generator and become impregnated with the fumes of sulphur dioxide. Any air escaping this circulation will become saturated with the fumes by diffusion, in such a manner that the gas will come into contact with every article in the hold.

It has been estimated that 1 lb. of sulphur will supply about 370 cubic feet of a gas containing 3 per cent. of sulphur dioxide. For fire extinction, 10 per cent. is used, but for the destruction of rodents and other vermin, such as mosquitoes, flies, fleas, bugs, &c., as well as for a reliable surface disinfection, much smaller percentages suffice.

The principle of the Clayton apparatus has been adapted so as to fulfil various requirements. Thus both a stationary and a portable apparatus have been constructed; the stationary apparatus being suitable either for installation in the engine room of a ship, or for installation on special harbour boats. Vessels of the latter type are used by the Port of London Authority. A large number of steamers belonging to various shipping firms have been fitted with different types of the apparatus, the majority being designed principally for the purpose of fire extinction. Many ports in different parts of the world are provided with types of apparatus suited specially for the destruction of vermin.

As a result of an exhaustive investigation undertaken on behalf of the Local Government Board, by Dr. Haldane and Dr. Wade, and supplemented by a careful

[1] Report of the Medical Officer of the Local Government Board 1903-4.

study of the sulphur dioxide method by Dr. Wade,[1] it is recommended that the air in the holds, while they are being disinfected, should contain 3 per cent. of sulphur dioxide gas. The gas should be pumped continuously into a 500-ton hold for eight hours, or for ten to twelve hours into a hold containing 1000 tons or more. This will ensure all reasonable requirements being fulfilled in regard to disinfection generally, as well as the destruction of rats and rat-fleas, and the disinfection of the rats' excreta.

The necessity for leaving the gas in a loaded hold for a lengthy period is due to the absorption of gas by the cargo; some materials take up a large quantity. Thus woollen goods absorb about ten times their volume of the gas, whilst hemp, corn, and flour absorb four times their volume. Moist articles take up relatively more of the gas than dry, since one volume of water absorbs fifty volumes of sulphur dioxide.

Although this process is thoroughly efficacious for the destruction of rats, it must be borne in mind that for certain wares the method is not harmless. Thus fresh meat (not frozen meat), vegetables, and fresh fruit absorb considerable quantities of the gas and become unpalatable. Some articles while absorbing the gas, allow it to escape on subsequent aeration; but moist flour retains it to such an extent that it becomes useless.

The simple method of fumigation with sulphur has long been practised on board ship for the destruction of rats and mice, flies, mosquitoes, fleas, bugs, and other vermin, and this method is still used in some ports as a

[1] Report of the Medical Officer of the Local Government Board, 1906.

preventive measure before lading the vessels. It can of course be employed only in an empty hold, owing to the danger of fire. The usual practice is to take about 1 lb. of sulphur and 2 lb. of charcoal per 1,000 cubic feet of hold space and mix them together; the mixture is then placed in braziers and allowed to burn with a slow flame. The hatches being battened down and the ventilators closed, the flame extinguishes itself as soon as sufficient charcoal has been burnt to produce 2 to 3 per cent. of carbonic acid in the air. After ten hours the hold is opened and ventilated.

An apparatus for pumping carbon monoxide into the holds of vessels was constructed by Dr. Nocht, the Medical Officer of Health for the Port and City of Hamburg, in conjunction with Dr Giemsa, and was in routine use in the Port of Hamburg for all ships carrying plague-infected rats. The composition of Dr. Nocht's mixture of gases is as follows:—

Carbon monoxide	...	5 per cent.
Carbonic acid ...	...	18 " "
Nitrogen ...	...	77 " "

The specific gravity of carbon monoxide being 1,085, the gas is readily diffusible, mixes well with the air in the hold, and passes into the remotest nooks. It even destroys rats hidden in mattresses, bales, sacks of flour, &c., its action paralysing them before they have time to escape. The products of combustion are arranged to contain not more than 5 per cent. of carbon monoxide. The gas having been generated for two hours, the hatches are opened and it is allowed to escape by natural ventilation; this procedure being aided in some cases by supplying fresh air from the ventilator to the hold through a tube. After six hours, cages containing mice are let down through a ventilator, and if they remain alive, the hold may be entered safely.

This method, however, has some serious drawbacks. The first of these is the danger of persons inhaling the gas which is quickly fatal. Further and serious disadvantages of the method are that it does not serve to destroy insects or other vermin, and that as a disinfectant it is useless, so that secondary disinfection becomes necessary. On the other hand, the method has the considerable advantage of cheapness and efficiency and does not harm any goods. In these respects it is greatly superior to the sulphur dioxide method, and is useful for warehouses. Possibly a combined method might remove or greatly lessen the drawback associated with either process when used alone.

The large amount of damage done by rats to certain cargoes and to goods stored at the docks is well known; and as mentioned already there is always the ever present danger that plague may be conveyed by rats from a distant port. Rats on a ship frequently come ashore, and those on shore go on board if the position of the vessel permits the passage to be made easily; while as before stated in Section "Poisoning," there is a constant passage of rats between docks and the adjacent town.

With the knowledge of these facts, not only should the destruction of rats on board ship be made compulsory, but a permanent staff should be appointed by all port sanitary authorities to see that the measures are properly carried out.

Although at most large ports rat-guards are placed on the hawsers, and precautions are taken to prevent rats leaving or going on board ship, yet there is laxity and even total neglect at many small ports.

Every ship should be fumigated as soon as its holds are empty ; it should be compulsory for all hawsers to have rat-guards of an approved pattern applied to them as soon as a vessel comes into port.

The "Terrier" Blocking trap (fig. 7) described in the Section "Traps," will be found invaluable at all ports. It should be the duty of the watchman to spring the trap several times during the night, and then to remove and drown any rats caught. Such a regular system of rat destruction in conjunction with the measures mentioned previously, if combined with continuous trapping and poisoning in the warehouses and on the quays, (see Section "Poisoning") would lead to the destruction of most of the rats concealed in cargoes soon after they had been brought ashore. At the same time rats which had come from the neighbouring town would not return.

The Port of London Authority introduced some time ago the following by-laws :—

"(1) All rope and mooring tackle for securing any vessel either to the shore or to mooring buoys shall be fitted with such effective guards as will prevent access of rats from the vessel to the shore. For any breach of this by-law the master of the vessel shall be liable to a penalty not exceeding £5.

"(2) All possible means shall be adopted for catching and destroying rats during the stay of any vessel in dock. All empty cases and barrels shall be examined before being landed, to ensure that no rats are contained therein. Any rats caught on board the vessel shall be killed, then placed in a bucket of strong disinfecting solution, and afterwards burnt in the vessel's furnace. No rats, alive or dead, shall be removed from the vessel. For any breach of this by-law the master of the vessel shall be liable to a penalty not exceeding £5.

"(3) When the discharge of cargo, or the landing or embarking of passengers is not proceeding, one gangway only shall be permitted to afford means of communication between any vessel and the shore. The end of the gangway near the vessel shall be whitened for a length of 10 ft. For any breach of this by-law the master of the vessel shall be liable to a penalty not exceeding £5."

It must not be forgotten that the prevalence of rats on board ship is due chiefly to the escape of a certain number when measures for destruction are undertaken. A contributory cause is that rats come on board when the ship is in port; many of them obtain entrance by the gangway.

The rapidity with which rats increase in number is readily realized when it is remembered that the period of gestation is only twenty-one days. It is well to remember too that rats generally begin to breed when they are only three to four months old, and they continue to breed five or six times in a year, and even more frequently; that they have five to fourteen, and sometimes even more young ones in a litter. It is evident, therefore, that a ship is quickly re-stocked, if only a few escape the slaughter that takes place on arrival in a home port.

Now it is obvious from the number of rats killed on these occasions, (even when they are destroyed as often as the vessel returns home), that more efficient means than those now employed must be adopted if the number of rats usually on board is to be lessened permanently.

The present system employed by Messrs. Elder, Dempster and Company, of paying their employees for every rat caught during a voyage should be developed and encouraged, although it is evident that this plan falls far short of ridding a ship of rats, or even keeping them reduced to only a few. It is the few that must be killed, so that none are left to breed; and the only way to ensure this being done as far as possible is to keep Run-traps in covers fitted with a signal, (see "Terrier" Death Run traps) set throughout the year in all parts of the ship which rats frequent. Someone must be told off to attend to the traps, and to keep a record of the trap by which the capture was made, so that experience may be gained as to the area in which the largest number of traps should be placed. This is easily done (as mentioned in the Section "The Habits of Rats—Some Facts of General Interest") by numbering the traps, and noting the position in which each number is placed. By this system traps would always be at work, and their setting would not depend, as now, upon the aptitude for trapping of one or more members of the crew, or upon the spare time available to enable them to practise their craft. At the same time casual assistance would be valuable in helping to add to the number of rats caught, and consequently it deserves encouragement.

The great advantage gained from partially concealing a trap by placing it under a cover, must not be forgotten; nor the additional advantage of this method in so far as it protects the trap from injury and thus ensures its prolonged usefulness.

Rats might be almost entirely prevented from entering a ship by the gangway, by having a swing door placed in the centre of the gangway at dusk, and at other times when the quay is comparatively quiet and free from traffic. A strong light placed by the door at night would not only make the gangway less attractive to rats, but would enable the precise position of the door to be seen easily. For the description of a suitable door, see Part II.

Such a door could be fitted to any existing gangway and easily lifted on or off as required.

If it were made compulsory for ships to carry a gangway fitted with such a doorway, it could be used at ports at which such a gangway is not provided.

RATS ON A SHOOTING-ESTATE AND ON A FARM.

ALL game-keepers are not good rat-trappers. Some cannot be induced to refrain from touching the traps with unprepared hands. They appear unable to understand that for successful rat-catching this must not be done; and that a rat will avoid a trap set with hands that have the human smell.

So ingrained has the habit of handling traps become among keepers, that, incredible though it may seem, there are some who believe it to be impossible to set a new 5-in. rabbit trap without touching it with a hand, on account of the strength of the spring. There are others who have not even heard of a trap being set with two pieces of stick (see Section "Traps").

They often argue that they catch a number of rats in the traps which they set; and this may be true. The explanation is that, after a time, the smell of the hand passes off, and then the trap catches a rat moving from one place to another, and coming across the trap for the first time after the human odour has disappeared. But the rat that lives near the place when the trap is set, and has smelt the keeper's hand, will not go near the trap although it may remain set for weeks.

It is generally a mistake for all the keepers to undertake trapping, as in that case if the work is not well done, each keeper is inclined to shift the blame on to someone else.

It is best for one man on each beat to be set to do it and to be held responsible for the results. If the beat is large, one or two men may be deputed to assist; but each should be given a distinct area, and a clear understanding should exist as to who is to attend to the boundary fences dividing the beats. If rat-holes remain it is evident that the work is not being done properly, and if one man proves himself unfitted for the task he should be replaced by somebody who is competent.

The head-keeper, however, must be made responsible for the extermination of the rats. Unless this is the case, he may prevent a most willing and competent subordinate from doing the work by keeping him occupied with other duties.

The prevalence of rats on a shooting-estate is generally due to another cause than the improper manner in which the traps are set. All keepers will not take the trouble to destroy the rats; nor will they arrange for the coverts and hedgerows to be systematically ferreted and trapped by anyone else. Consequently, rats increase to an enormous extent.

Keepers of the class described usually advocate the destruction of the rats being placed in the hands of a rat-catcher who lays poison on the estate periodically. By this means, not only are they saved the trouble of doing it themselves, but they are absolved from blame when rats are found on the property.

It has been mentioned before, and it cannot be repeated too emphatically, that poison only lessens the number of rats. Unless flooding, or ferreting, and trapping as well, are systematically carried out irrespective of seasons, an estate cannot be kept even comparatively free from rats.

Not only must all the rats that have been bred on the property be killed, but also those which are constantly coming in from the country around. A rat's hole should be flooded, ferreted, or smoked as soon as it is discovered, and filled in directly its occupants have been killed. If this be done, no other rats can take it for their abode. Any hole may thus be made to indicate "Occupation by Rats."

When mentioning the centres on an estate towards which rats tend to draw, or where they may often be found in large numbers, the outbuildings and banks around the cottage of the average game-keeper must not be forgotten. Nor must the banks and ground in proximity to the pheasant pens under his charge be overlooked, or the hut in or beside the covert in which he mixes food for the pheasants. There rats often abound, and the thought arises naturally, if this condition exists around his home and the places he visits daily, what must be the state of the hedgerows and coverts on his beat?

When comment is made as to the number of rats which are about his cottage or the pens, the reply usually given is to the effect that he is going "to have a turn at them presently" when he is a little less busy. Yet whenever his premises are re-visited, it will be noticed from the well-used runs and the existence of inhabited holes, that his busy time is not yet over and that the rats are still enjoying themselves thoroughly and expensively.

The keeper's plea of want of time is a very feeble excuse; if he were keen on the destruction of the rats he would soon *make* the time to attend to the matter. It would take only a few minutes to place some poison in each hole, or if he had some terriers, to ferret or smoke the rats out and stop up all their holes; or he would find the time to make some run-traps and catch the greater part of the vermin.

If the *will* existed, the *means* to do it would be found, so that the presence of the rats is a conclusive proof of the keeper's indifference.

Every individual has a weak point, however much he may excel generally; and a gamekeeper although indifferent to the presence of rats, or deficient in the knowledge of how to get rid of them, may be good at rearing birds or in the other numerous duties that fall to his lot. Where this is the case, the destruction of the rats should, in the shooting interests of the estate, be placed in other hands. But if the keeper possesses no quality which more than counterbalances his want of keenness in the destruction of vermin, the question should be seriously considered as to whether or not a more competent man cannot be found to take his place.

As rats are sure to make their way to the buildings around a keeper's cottage, and to a pheasant pen on account of the food to be found lying about, several trapped "Terrier" Signal Runs or other run-traps should be kept in position on the keeper's premises all the year round. When the pens and feeding huts are in use, traps should be placed around them.

In consequence of the want of knowledge or supervision on the part of game preservers, or because of the deficient equipment or slackness of their subordinates, it is not the universal custom for keepers to ferret rats on the property under their care. Consequently comparatively few keepers are provided with properly trained terriers.

Terriers trained to ferrets for ratting should be considered as requisite to a keeper as his retriever or spaniel; they will be appreciated by any man who understands his work and does it thoroughly. A large number of keepers would welcome ratting terriers if they were provided, and if arrangements were made for their maintenance. It is not surprising that a keeper shows no keenness to keep them where he is left, not only to procure the terriers, but also to feed them at his own expense.

Many rats live in rabbit-holes, and while the rabbits are being ferreted a large number of rats might be destroyed if only there were terriers to kill them.

Special care should be taken during the nesting season to keep the hedgerows free from rats, but during this time of year very many keepers discontinue trapping entirely, and would not think of ferreting a rat's hole if they saw one.

The reason usually given for discontinuing trapping during the nesting season is that if it were done the birds would be disturbed. Yet they do not hesitate to walk close to the hedgerows when searching for nests.

Obviously, this traditional but thoughtless inactivity is wrong. Any rat-hole in a hedgerow ought to be flooded, ferreted, or smoked (especially when a game-bird's nest has been discovered) and a trap placed afterwards at each end of the hedgerow, so that vermin approaching from either direction may be secured before the nest is reached. What chance has a partridge of bringing off her young, when there is a colony or even a single nest of rats in the bank on which her nest is placed?

When ferreting in the spring of the year, it is best to walk a few yards from the hedge. Even at this distance, the place where rats have been working can be seen, and there are but few birds that would leave, or at any rate desert a nest, because someone with a dog passed within a few yards of it.

Supposing even that ferreting were to cause a partridge to forsake her nest, the action could still be defended as far as the shooting interests are concerned. The rats if left would undoubtedly have destroyed the nest and possibly killed the sitting bird as well; whereas the bird having forsaken her nest would, if not too late in the season, make another elsewhere.

It is well recognized that the destruction of vermin is one of the duties of a keeper, and that the damage done by rats on a shooting estate is very great. Yet all too frequently the owner or man in authority when walking with a keeper by the side of a hedgerow riddled with holes and showing clearly that a large number of rats are lying in the bank, makes no comment. It is not surprising in such circumstances that the keeper becomes even more lax in the work of vermin destruction.

A frequent cause of this neglect of supervision is the fact that many owners and lessees of shooting estates know but little about either game-rearing or preserving. They are compelled to leave everything to their keepers, who are thus practically master and servant combined; and consequently only do what suits their fancy and convenience. If the owner or lessee realized the amount of damage done by rats, he would wish to ascertain why there were so many on the property. The result of his inquiry would be a much larger head of game with the same or even less expenditure.

A business, however good it may be, will not continue

to be a success unless personal attention to detail is given by those in authority. The same principle applies to the destruction of vermin. If game-preserving is to be carried on efficiently, the owner of the property or his deputy must from time to time personally inspect the traps and runs to see that they are in proper order. He must also satisfy himself that trapping and ferreting are done systematically throughout the year, and that all holes are filled in after the occupants have been destroyed.

Some owners may say that they have full confidence in their keepers and that as such an inspection would imply a want of trust in them, they would not allow it to be made. This sentiment, although the outcome of praiseworthy altruism, cannot unfortunately be put into practice with advantage to its possessor. Human nature has changed but little since the sixth century before the Christian era, when Æsop is reputed to have said that there was

"No Eye like the Master's Eye."

Personal superintendence by the owner was necessary in those days; it is required no less in these. Moreover a keeper who takes an interest in his work and does it well, likes the results to be known and verified. He will take a pride in showing a run he has made, the means taken to protect it from injury, and the manner in which he has concealed a trap from the sight of a passer-by.

Provided the owner or his deputy uses his eyes and understands what he sees, time will prove generally that the right course was adopted when the keeper was dismissed, who resented having his work supervised.

On a large shooting-estate it would well repay the

owner or shooting tenant to employ all the year round a lad about seventeen, and a boy a little younger, to flood, ferret, or smoke out the rats in the farms and banks. An intelligent lad and boy working together would do the work very well, and their wages would amount to less than if two men were employed. They would of course be employed in other ways when not engaged in destroying vermin.

The lad should feed the dogs and have sole charge of them, for unless this is the case they will not readily obey his orders. This arrangement, however, need not prevent his work from being supervised.

As the farmers on the estate would benefit very largely by the systematic destruction of rats on their farms, they might reasonably be asked to make an annual contribution towards expenses thus incurred. Should a farmer decline to do so, care should be taken to keep the rats officer of the county informed of any rats which may be on his premises.

Many women excel in rearing poultry, and would probably succeed with game. It is not within the scope of this book to discuss the question as to whether or not it would be well in some cases to employ women to rear pheasants or to assist in rearing them, in order by so doing to give keepers more time to attend to other and less pleasant duties.

Foxes, as is well known, are particularly fond of rats, and where rats abound, they will hunt the hedgerows and banks systematically in search of them. It is extremely probable that many of the partridges' nests that foxes destroy are found while they are hunting for rats. Consequently, if the hedgerows on the estate were free from rats many nests would be saved, as the foxes would lose the habit of hunting the hedgerows for food.

Although in some parts of the country a large number of partridges' nests are undoubtedly destroyed by foxes, yet in many instances when a nest is destroyed it is probable that rats, and not foxes, are the real culprits. Obviously, a keeper will not acknowledge this to be the case, because such an admission would expose his want of thoroughness, even if not his actual negligence, in the destruction of vermin.

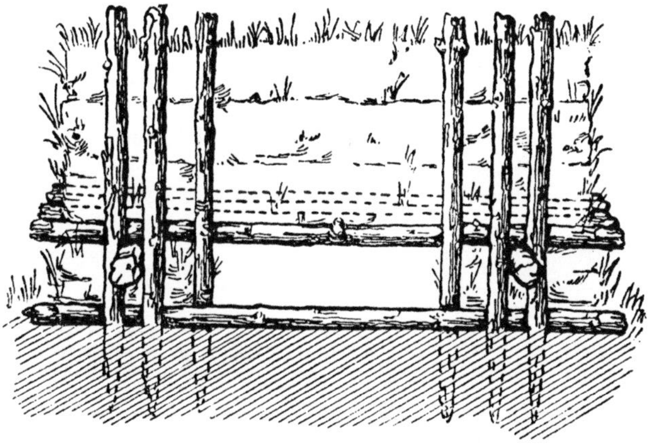

FIG. 35.—Entrance to turf run showing the arrangement of sticks and pegs for supporting the turf over it and for securing the threshold.

If the property is to be rat-freed, traps must be kept set all the year round, but it is no use leaving traps buried for a week or more. To be effectual, a buried trap must be re-set at least every third day, or it will get clogged and fail to be sprung by vermin passing over it. As previously mentioned, it is unnecessary to bury a trap unless it is set to catch vermin that are lying close by.

For trapping rats in hedgerows, &c., it is best to build a run of turf, but in a stone country it may with advantage be constructed partially, if not entirely, of stone.

In order as far as possible to guide all vermin passing along a hedge through a particular run, a board 9 to 12 in. wide may be placed on edge diagonally through the hedge, the end in the hedge being nearer to the direction from which vermin are expected to approach, whilst the opposite end is against the entrance to the run.

FIG. 36.—Side view of turf run showing trap in position.

The simplest way to get the board through a hedge when the latter is dense, is to pass a strong pole or iron bar along the ground through the place where the board is intended to go. Then lift its two ends simultaneously to the required height, and while the pole is raised and the branches are held out of the way of it, push the board through the passage thus formed.

Care must be taken to fill up all the inequalities in the bank from the side on which the stakes which hold the board in position, are placed. Failing this, vermin may pass under the board instead of running beside it until they reach the run. The board should be examined from time to time and any earth thrown up by moles, or leaves blown against it, cleared away.

It is well to keep a 5-in. rabbit trap set between each row of sitting boxes; for rats smell from afar the ground used for feeding the sitting hens, and come by night for any food which may have been left uneaten. If not killed, they will probably visit the rearing ground later, provided it is not too far off. Some runs with buried traps should be kept around both the sitting boxes and rearing ground, so that any rat that avoids an uncovered trap may be caught.

Care should be taken to keep coverts free from rats, and special attention should be given to the place where the birds are fed. It is well to build a turf or stone wall about 1 ft. or 18 in. in height on each side of the ride used for this purpose, and to make runs through it as previously described, with a 5-in. rabbit trap in each one of them, one end of the run being flush with the inner or ride surface of the wall. Boards placed on edge and kept in position by stakes driven firmly into the ground, may be used instead of a turf or stone wall. Each wall should be 20 to 40 yds. or more in length, and placed at intervals along the ride. If built on opposite sides alternately, the whole of the ride can be trapped with practically one wall. When the birds are fed in a field adjoining a covert, the wall need be only on the covert side of the feeding-ground.

To keep the signals from being disarranged by birds perching on them, a stout stick may be placed horizontally about 4 in. above the signal arm and fastened securely to uprights placed firmly in the ground.

To clear a large estate of rats when it is infested with them, is a work calling for organization and perseverance, but the task although difficult, is not impossible if properly undertaken.

Corn-stacks, barns, and farm-buildings must always be looked upon as centres to which rats will draw in due season. Most of the rats on an estate will be found in these places in winter, except when the weather is mild, and berries, beech-mast and acorns are plentiful. All corn, therefore, both in stacks that are not on high staddles, and in barns, should be threshed so as to destroy the strongholds and large breeding establishments and kill the rats collected. This ought to be done irrespective of the then market price of corn, for any profit due to a future rise will be counteracted by the amount destroyed in the meantime.

The farm-buildings should next be cleared. To drive the rats from their holes, employ water, as fully described in the Section "Flooding," or ferrets. All holes must be filled in immediately afterwards and the floors subsequently repaved or, better still, concreted.

All surface drains from a stable, cow-house or other building ought to be protected by a grating. (See Section "Rats in the Stable.") All doors, doorways, and walls should be repaired and all superfluous vegetation removed from around buildings. (See Section "Rats in the Outbuilding.") "Terrier" Signal Runs or run-traps in proper covers must be set around the buildings and pigsties to catch any rats coming to the premises. (See Sections "Traps," and "Rats in the Pigsty.")

On many farms the doorways and walls of the buildings are badly out of repair. When this is the case and until they can be put in order, it is best merely to stop all the holes leading under the floor, or behind boarding, or other structures which can afford concealment. This is to compel the rats to lie above ground, as when so doing they are more liable to be discovered.

There is an outhouse on some farms in which the pigs' food is kept, and where this is the case, rats usually go there at night to feed. When a farm is to be cleared of rats, this outhouse should be so prepared that all the rats which have gone to it may be killed during the night. To enable this to be done, holes in the floor should be flooded, or ferreted, and then filled in, and openings into the building stopped; leaving only a few which, from their position, it is advisable to keep open in order to enable the rats to enter the outhouse readily. When this has been done the place should be left quiet for a few nights to allow the rats to go there again regularly, and afterwards arrangements should be made for killing them, as fully described in the Section "Blocking."

After all the rats frequenting the outhouse have been killed, of which there will be proof if the finely sifted earth around the openings remains untrodden, several "Terrier" Death Run traps or "Terrier" Signal Runs containing a 5-in. rabbit trap, must be kept set all the year round in proximity to it. Remember that any rats which may be about are sure to be drawn there by the smell of the pigs' food. If from the position of the outhouse, traps cannot be placed conveniently outside it, the holes which the rats have used may be made to communicate with a run inside, as described in the Section

"Rats in the Outbuilding"; but if their position is inconvenient they may be stopped, and fresh holes made to communicate with a run in a more suitable place.

After all the holes in and about the farm buildings have been flooded, or ferreted, and filled in, the buildings put into repair, and traps set around them, the rats must be cleared from the rest of the estate; not forgetting the outbuildings and premises belonging to tenants' houses and the cottages.

The most satisfactory way to do this (a method that records the number of rats killed, and is probably also the quickest in the end) is to go round all the fences with a water-cart and flood the holes. (See Section "Flooding.") When the holes are filled with water, even the most ferocious rat must bolt, and there is no time lost as there so often is when a rat stands at bay or a ferret lies up. If the estate is to be cleared with poison, meal must be laid first, then two days later the poison, then a week later the holes must be closed, and later still, any holes still existing must be flooded or ferreted. Holes in an old bank with a broken surface, and with numerous thick roots on the surface, are often best ferreted at once.

The work ought to be done on a definite plan, and it is best to take as a starting point farm-buildings that have been cleared of rats, and work round and round them field by field in order, as far as prevention is possible, to stop rats from reaching them.

All banks and sides of ditches should have the superfluous vegetation removed year by year, so that any rat's hole can be easily seen; and special attention must be paid to banks near water, whether that water be pond, river, stream, or ditch. Those in charge should not forget to look for holes under the stems and roots of trees; for many rats live in these quarters, either in holes which they have made themselves or in a rabbit burrow, although probably in this latter haunt, the place in which they have made their nest is apart from that occupied by the rabbits. Beech-trees, by the arrangement of their roots, are easily adapted by rats to make comfortable quarters, where they sometimes store beech-mast in considerable quantities for winter use. The trees selected are not always on a bank or in close proximity to water.

In order to get rid of rats, the hole must be ferreted or flooded, and when they have been driven out it should be carefully filled in. It will be found in many cases that a considerable quantity of earth has been removed from beneath the stem. Some of this may be replaced and the earth banked up against the tree, so that any attempt to re-open the hole can be seen at once.

When near the level at which the earth will be left, a little tar may be poured close against the tree where the entrance to the hole has been, and the remainder of the earth then placed on the top so as to bury it. This will be found especially useful in keeping rabbits from reburrowing.

The ground around the trees under which rats have been found should be kept under observation. Rats, and mice too, frequently take up their abode in a place which has been previously inhabited by their species; and year after year may be found in the same place, although all those previously occupying it were killed.

To prevent rats frequenting barns, granaries, mills, and other places in which corn and other seed foods are stored or placed, the doorways and walls must be made rat-proof and the ground-floor concreted. Upper floors must either be concreted or left without a ceiling beneath them, because, otherwise, any rats which may be about are liable to lie concealed between the ceiling and floor.

Where there is a wooden floor, continuous strips of wood may be fastened to the wall immediately below the floor to prevent rats passing from one floor to another; they need to be sufficiently thick to completely close any opening which may, or might, exist between the floor and the wall. All the apertures between the floor and the wall must be filled in afterwards from above, with cement or other suitable material.

Both rats and mice multiply largely in a barn, even when cats have free access to it; because usually the cats are able to reach only the front and top of the corn stacked there.

To allow cats to more easily reach the rats and mice, a continuous passage-way may be made around each end of the barn, about 18 or more inches high, and about 12 or more inches wide, with each end open to the passage-way across the centre of the barn between the doorways.

If well made, the passage will last as long as the barn. The uprights to support the inner wall must be strong, and may have a shoulder cut to take the inner end of the support for the top of the passage, the outer end of this support being let into the wall, if of brick, and then wedged. The inner wall may be made of sheep-fold wire-netting or of board. In the latter case, when the boards forming the top are nailed to prevent them being taken away temporarily for other purposes, a space of

4 to 6 in. must be left above and below the side board to enable the passage to be cleared of cobwebs and swept from time to time.

With this arrangement, a cat can pass around the stored corn whether it be in the ear or in sacks, and will destroy a large number of both rats and mice in the course of the year.

When a large number of sacks filled with corn are stored, the number of passage-ways should be increased by piling the sacks in small blocks away from the corners and walls.

A strong rail, fixed about 9 in. from the wall and 1 ft. to 18 in. from the ground, might with advantage be placed around all granaries and places where food-stuffs are stored, to ensure sacks, &c., being kept away from the wall. This allows a passage-way for cats. The hole for cats in a door ought not to be less than 2 ft. from the floor, otherwise rats are very likely to enter the building through it.

The purchase of 100 yds. of Hessian or other suitable material, not less than a yard in width but wider for preference, with which to surround stacks while they are being threshed, will be money well spent. Wire-netting cannot be recommended for this purpose because it is too rigid, and in consequence when the ground is uneven apertures are created beneath its lower edge through which vermin can escape unless the lower part is bent and buried. The flattening and re-bending of the wire netting for the purpose of removal from place to place and re-setting, lessens its durability and causes it soon to get out of shape. Moreover, unless a fine mesh is used, mice escape through it; so that besides being more expensive, it is less effectual and less durable. For convenience of handling, the sacking is best divided into lengths of 20 yds. Eyelet-holes, of about half an inch placed along the top at intervals of 2 to 3 ft. facilitate the sacking being fastened in position. The escape of vermin through the joints may be prevented by having a parallel row of eyelets about 6 in. apart along each end, and lacing together the ends of two lengths of sacking around a post about 4 in. in diameter which has been driven firmly into the ground. Five posts may be pointed at one end and kept with the sacking for this purpose. The sacking is made much more secure if it is fastened to hurdles fixed into the ground. About 6 in. or more of the lower edge must trail on the ground and be carefully covered with earth to prevent vermin escaping under it. As even sacking may be torn with the points of a hay fork which is used to kill a rat or mouse, it should be examined and all holes mended before it is put away. It is best to suspend it from a beam when not in use, otherwise rats or mice are liable to gnaw holes in it. The sacking ought to surround the stack entirely, and be placed at not less than 4 yds. from the ends and the side away from the machine, to ensure rats that jump from the top of the stack alighting inside the enclosure. Unless the sacking is placed on the machine side also, rats and mice are almost sure to escape through this gap when the bottom of the stack has been reached, but as vermin usually bolt from a part of the stack which is away from the machine, the sacking may be placed much nearer to the stack than it is at the ends and on the opposite side.

It is convenient to have two parallel rows of eyelet-holes, 6 in. apart, across the centre of one of the sheets of sacking, so that a shorter length is available when required. It is best to begin by placing the sacking between the stack and the threshing-machine, the dimensions of the enclosure can then be arranged so that all the pieces of sacking used are stretched to their full length, and loose folds do not exist. Several pointed stakes kept with the sheets of sacking are useful to form corners when the joints in the sacking do not come there, or to create a bulge in the sacking when it is too slack. All stakes should be kept on the outside of the enclosure. The earth ought not to be placed on the lower trailing edge until the outline of the enclosure is completed.

When there are stacks close to the one which is to be threshed, it is advisable to surround them also with sacking, for when this has not been done rats often leave them and run into holes in the adjoining bank, even while the threshing is in progress. Terriers should always be present while stacks are being threshed, for they kill on such occasions far more vermin than boys do with sticks. When sacking is not available lamb-folding sheets may be used.

To prevent rats and mice escaping unseen, tie a sack, containing a little loose straw to keep its sides apart, to the enlarged end of a 4 or 6-in. drain-pipe, and place the free end of the drain-pipe at each corner of the sacking enclosure, taking care to fix the sacking close to the pipe with earth. Mice escaping from the stack may also be caught by the following method, which, however, is not so good as the former, as that collects and retains the rats and mice until the end of the day's work. At each corner formed by the sacking or sheets, and at the centre of the side and ends, a hole is dug sufficiently large to hold a bucket with its upper edge on a level with the ground. After the bucket has been placed in it, and the edge of the sacking tucked around the pail, the hole is carefully filled in. Mice missed by the dogs while escaping from the stack will run along beside the sacking and fall into the nearest bucket, which should contain water to the depth of 3 or 4 in. A boy should be stationed to kill and remove the mice from the buckets and to watch the sacking or sheets to keep them clear of straw that falls or gets blown against them.

Many rats and mice are often left in their holes in the ground beneath the bed of straw or faggots on which the stack rested, the holes often going to a depth of 18 in. or more. To destroy these vermin the ground should be forked up in a systematic manner before the sacking is removed and then rolled with a heavy roller previously placed near by in readiness for the horse of the water-cart to be attached to it. Five or six men, according to the width of the stack, digging in a line with four-pronged forks, will soon turn over the ground on which the stack rested, and in doing so may bring to the surface not only some of the rats and mice which have escaped into their holes, but also their nests and young ones. The usual practice of jobbing the ground around the entrance to the holes with a hay-fork does but little good, as the ground is not disturbed to a sufficient depth.

When there are rats' holes in a bank close to a stack which is about to be threshed, it is advisable not to disturb the fence, so that the rats may continue to go into them at night during the intervals of the threshing; the bottom of the sacking next the bank having been fastened up at the end of the day's work to allow them to do so. Immediately after the stack is down, and the ground on which it rested has been cleared of the rats and mice which have escaped into the underground holes, the fence should be trimmed to expose the holes and prevent vegetation facilitating the escape of the rats. It is best to surround the part of the hedge occupied by the rats by leaving the sacking which is next to it in position, and placing on its other side and at the ends of the area the sacking which was on the opposite side and at the ends of the stack, and then to flood the holes, beginning with the one nearest to one end of the occupied part of the bank; all available water-carts having been brought to the place in readiness to ensure a continuous flow of water. (See Section "Flooding.") If there is not time to flood the holes on the day the threshing is finished, the vegetation should be left undisturbed until the following morning, so that the flooding can be done directly the bank has been cleared.

It would well repay farmers to build all their corn stacks on staddles. In many cases the cost of placing staddles throughout the whole of the rickyard would be more than repaid in one year by the amount of corn saved. (See Section "The Habits of Rats—Some Facts of General Interest.") It would, in the long run, even repay those farmers who persistently destroy rats throughout the year. Although they succeed in keeping the number down, there are always some that travel from place to place, and these take shelter in a corn-stack when it is built on the ground.

The reason why staddles are so frequently found to be ineffectual is because they are much too low. They have been designed by someone who is unacquainted with the habits of rats, and who does not know the distance to which they can jump, or the manner in which they can climb round a projecting surface where a foothold can be obtained.

No staddle barrier should be less than 3 ft. from the ground. If it were 3 ft. 6 in. to the horizontal projecting surface which prevents the rats climbing any higher, or to the upper edge of the unclimbable surface around the upright supports, a decided advantage would be gained. This lesser height is mentioned by the American Department of Agriculture as the lowest which ought to be allowed, and this advice is undoubtedly sound.

The material of which a staddle is made is of no consequence, the essential part is an unsurmountable barrier. In the north and in parts of Cornwall and in other places where stone is plentiful, staddles may be built of stone with a large stone projecting horizontally at the top. Several smaller stones placed close together may take the place of one large stone. In other parts of the country wooden posts may be used, provided they have an unclimbable surface at the upper part.

The additional 4 to 5 ft. in the height of the stack created by the staddles and supports is no real objection to their use. The sheaves can be raised on an "Elevator," "Traveller," or "Feeder," as it is called respectively in different parts of the country, or by a grip, or cradle which can be easily raised by a long pole-lever pivoted to an upright of suitable height, or arranged so that the level of the pivot can be raised together with the lever as the height of the stack increases.

Another reason why staddles are rendered useless, is

the custom of converting a stack on staddles into a roof, and putting implements and various articles underneath the stack to keep them dry. When this is done, rats climb up the things under the stack and jump from them on to the stack.

Another way by which access is obtained to a stack on staddles, is by climbing up a ladder or pole which is resting against the stack. When a pole is wanted as a support it should be placed as vertically as possible, and a piece of galvanized sheet-iron or zinc, fastened round it about 2 or 3 ft. from the ground, the joint being made on the underside of the pole. A piece of metal thus placed will prevent rats obtaining sufficient foothold to pass over it.

The erection of staddles is not a costly matter, and if, when done, the woodwork is kept tarred or otherwise preserved it will last for many years.

The loose boards or poles laid on horizontal supports to make the flooring on which the sheaves rest, can be removed and placed under cover as soon as the stack has been threshed. When building a stack, the outer sheaves should be laid so that they project six or more inches beyond the woodwork to keep it dry.

For details for making a rick stand on staddles, see Part II.

When a permanently roofed but open building, Dutch barn, as it is called, is erected to save the expense of thatching stacks each season, it would well repay the farmer to make it with a floor for the corn to rest upon, so that rats and mice could not reach it. This could easily be done by bolting transverse horizontal supports to the main uprights, with their lower edge at 3 ft. 6 in.

from the ground for the floor to rest on, taking care to render all vertical supports unclimbable.

Such a floor could easily be added to existing buildings, and the slight additional cost of the flooring would be repaid many times over in one year in rat-infested districts from the corn saved by keeping the stack free from rats and mice. For the same reason the cost of erecting another Dutch barn to compensate for the stack space lost by the raised floor would soon be repaid.

When such a floor is made, it is important that it should occupy the whole barn area and no space be left for the roof to cover a part used as a shed for carts, implements, &c. If these latter are housed there, sooner or later, the means are sure to be found by which rats will reach the raised floor.

Another method of keeping rats out of a stack, especially applicable to Dutch barns, though less effectual than staddles and more costly in the long run than making a raised floor, is to surround it with galvanized iron sheeting for about 3 ft. above the ground. When sheeting is corrugated, the corrugations for preference should be vertical, and each corner should have a piece of a sheet bent at a right angle to overlap to the required length. When used for a stack built to stand in the open, the size of the stack to be put up can be regulated by the length of the sheets of iron, and if four stakes be driven into the ground to mark the position of the corners, the area which the stack is to cover will be known to the men who are engaged in building it.

It is stated on authority that rats do not burrow to a greater depth than 30 in, but it is unnecessary for the sheeting to be sunk to this depth when stacks are kept under observation, for if rats burrow under an untrapped barrier they must leave the stack for water, and can be caught while doing so. If there are rats about, they should be killed and not left to go elsewhere.

Another but less durable method is to sink a wide board and leave it projecting about 3 in. above the ground, to enable the lower edge of the sheeting to be screwed to its outer surface. The upper edge of the sheeting can be screwed or tied to stakes driven into the ground between the sheeting and the stack, a block the thickness of the board in the ground having been previously nailed to the front of the stakes. Obviously, a stake must not be put against the outer surface, or the rats will climb up it and get into the stack over the barrier intended to bar their progress.

When the sheeting has been fixed, a "Terrier" Signal Run should be kept against each side of the stack outside the iron sheeting, so that every rat approaching the stack may be caught. Note that a rat always runs round a structure on the chance of finding a hole before attempting to climb or burrow into it.

Unless the stack is watched and trapped, the money spent on the iron sheeting, and in fixing it, will in many instances have been thrown away.

When iron sheeting is thus used to keep rats out of a stack, it must be fixed in position directly the stack is built, and not at some later period which may be considered more convenient, for by that time rats may have found their way into the stack: the rapidity with which they multiply has been already noted.

Another way to lessen the number of rats on a farm is to go round the buildings and ricks at night with a gun, and carry a powerful bull's-eye lantern or an acetylene bicycle lamp. Any rats which are about, on seeing the light, will run to the entrance of their hole, or a foot or more up a stack, and there remain motionless watching the light, and while in this position can be easily shot. The more quietly the rats are approached, the larger the number that will be seen of those running about; for preference, therefore, boots with india-rubber heels or shoes with continuous india-rubber soles should be worn. Only felt wads must be used in the cartridges, for if paper is put to keep the powder and shot in position, it is liable to set fire to the rick. A dark windy night is best for this work, as under these conditions the light from the lantern is more blinding, and footsteps and the report of the gun are less audible. While blinded by the light, rats can often be killed with a stick or by a dog.

A large number of rats may be destroyed on a farm which has not been poisoned or ferreted recently, by hunting the hedges at night with terriers. When the order in which the hedges are to be worked has been arranged, it is advisable in some cases that someone should go forward by a circuitous route with one or more dogs to where the first side fence joins the one to be hunted. He then works back towards the advancing party, so as to intercept any rats which may be escaping.

If the fields are small and the hedges short, several of the hedges may be hunted simultaneously towards the same place, but the manner of working must depend upon their character and position.

It is best to hunt hedges in this way on a moonlight night. Not only is it easier then to get about from place to place than if it is in darkness or semi-darkness, but dogs can be kept under better observation. A powerful bull's-eye lantern is often useful, but it is best not to show the light unless hunting a hedge.

It is very important that there should be no talking or noise of any kind, and the more quietly the dogs work the better. A yapping dog is unsuitable for this purpose. A dog accustomed to the work will sometimes go forward 30 or 40 yds. or more, and there wait for any rats driven towards him by the other dogs which are working by the side of those in charge of them. The rats thus killed are partly those that are moving from one locality to another, and partly those that have travelled a distance from their holes in search of food. The dogs thoroughly enjoy the work, and very soon understand what they have to do.

RATS IN SEWERS.

It is well known that a large number of rats live in the sewers of cities and towns; and in places where the street drains are not properly trapped, as frequently occurs abroad, they may be seen running to and fro at night and at other times when the streets are quiet.

Rats frequently obtain entrance to houses and premises by working their way through a broken trap that has become dry, or through a broken or improperly laid drain pipe, and they burrow thence to the surface. An entrance is also obtained to house-drains from a sewer when the plug has been left out of the cleaning arm. On these occasions their footmarks may be seen in the inspection chamber.

Formerly the presence of rats in sewers was looked upon as a matter of necessity. They ate up the large amount of vegetable and animal matter which is daily washed from scullery sinks and elsewhere. Now that a flushing system is in vogue in most cities and towns, the necessity for their presence for this purpose exists no longer.

It is obvious that if cities and towns are to be kept free from rats, they must no longer be allowed to exist in large numbers in the sewers; their destruction, therefore, must be undertaken in a systematic manner by the authorities.

This task is not an easy one, as special conditions require special modifications in the usual methods of destruction.

POISONING.—Although this method may be carried out on an extensive scale, the time for doing it should be carefully arranged. Either the dead bodies of the rats should be immediately collected for disposal in a destructor, or the poisoning should be done immediately before a prolonged flush that will carry the bodies of the dead rats out of the sewers into the sea, or into a large river on the outgoing tide. Obviously, the collection of the bodies is preferable.

Poisoning alone, as mentioned in the section dealing with that subject, merely lessens the number of rats and does not exterminate them. Recourse therefore must be had to other measures, if the number of rats is to be reduced permanently.

Traps, if merely placed at random, will be practically useless, as the number caught in them throughout the year must be comparatively small. The only way for traps to be efficient is permanently to trap the ends of sewers where they enter main thoroughfares or leave special areas. This can be done by placing a horizontal board for the traps to rest on, transversely across the sewer immediately above the usual level of the liquid. Arrange, resting across it on edge, a board a foot or more in height, having openings in it extending upwards from its lower edge through which the jaws of a 5-in. rabbit trap can be passed midway, so that every rat on attempting to pass through any one of the openings may be caught.

The traps should be fastened with chains, and the board also secured by a chain, to prevent them being carried away by a flood. Should an aperture exist between the horizontal board and the liquid, or a space be considered advisable to allow of the rise of the liquid, it may be blocked, as far as rats are concerned, by a strip of wire-netting or some other arrangement that will not obstruct the flow.

DRIVING.—The method by which the largest number of rats in a sewer can be destroyed, is by systematically driving them into specially constructed bags as shown in fig. 37, laid temporarily on boards placed immediately above the level of the liquid. The portion of the sewer above the bag is blocked by a piece of sacking held in position by the apparatus shown in fig. 39. The method of working is to block each entrance to an area with a bag and sacking, and then deal with the cul-de-sac of the house-drains as hereinafter described.

Each bag is about 6 or 8 ft. in length according to requirements, its width depending upon the size of the sewer; and for a large sewer, two bags placed side by side are recommended in preference to one of double their dimensions. For details for making expanding frames, see Part II.

On a man entering a sewer the rats will run away and either continue to run along the sewer until they come to a cross street guarded by a bag, or else they take shelter in the cul-de-sac which each house-drain forms by its extension between the trap placed on the street side of the house and the sewer.

The simplest way to drive rats out of this part of house-drains, is to pass a caged electric lamp attached to a stout flexible wire or jointed rod to the end of the cul-de-sac, and then to turn on the light. This will cause the rats to bolt towards the sewer, where they may be caught in a canvas bag resting on a board laid across it. While the rats are bolting, the light from the hand lamps which the men are carrying should be kept away from the open end of the pipe.

The mouth of the bag is fixed open by being fastened to a stout iron ring somewhat larger than the diameter of the pipe, bent backwards towards the bag near the top and then forwards so as to form a cleft for the passage of the electric-light rod. Three inches behind the ring,

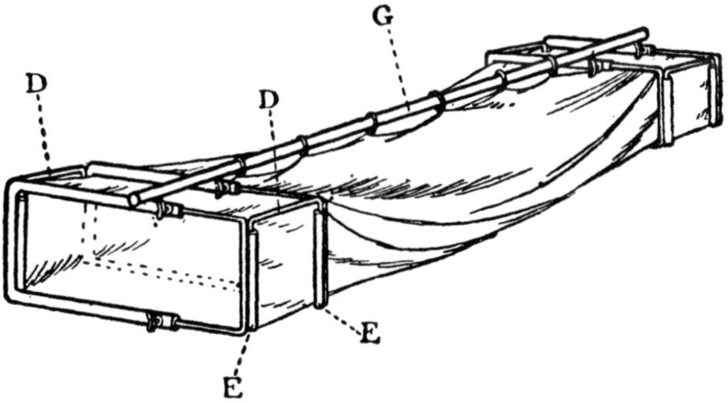

FIG. 37.—Bag attached to expanding ends for capturing rats in sewers.

and firmly connected with it by sheet metal, is an iron ring 3 in. in diameter, so that the two rings and the intervening metal form a funnel leading into the bag.

The rats that have bolted into the bag can be immediately killed while in it, and removed by untying the cord which closes it and is run through eyelet-holes around the bottom of the bag.

A handle attached to the outer ring enables the bag to be used more easily.

In the Paris sewers rats have been electrocuted by a live wire about 4 in. above the level on which the rats travel with bait hanging at intervals close above the live wire. A rat, on attempting to reach the bait, touches the live wire and is killed.

SOME NOTES ON PLAGUE.[1]

THE black rat, still the indigenous rat of the East, and formerly the common rat in this country and throughout Europe, has been from time immemorial a distributor of the plague, but the brown rat, which has now largely taken its place in Europe, has always been equally capable of carrying the disease. It is to be regretted that this truth is not more generally recognized.

Dr. Louis Sambon, in a paper published June 2, 1924, in the *Journal of Tropical Medicine and Hygiene*, deals with the supposed entry of rats into Europe, and the author feels that he cannot do better than quote Dr. Sambon's own words. He says: "From recent publications I notice that naturalists and archæologists continue to perpetuate the erroneous notion that the black rat (*Rattus rattus*) was unknown to the ancient Greeks and Romans, and that it came to Europe during the twelfth century in the ships of returning Crusaders. On several occasions, during the last twenty years, I have endeavoured

[1] The author is largely indebted for information contained in this Section to a very able paper by Dr. Louis W. Sambon in the *Journal of the Incorporated Society for the Destruction of Vermin*, vol. i, No. 1, October, 1908, and to Dr. Sambon's letters in the *Times*, January 30 and February 4, 1911. Use has also been made of information contained in the *Times* of December 22, 1910, February 6 and 20, 1911, and March 13, 1914, and of Dr. Sambon's paper in the *Journal of Tropical Medicine and Hygiene*, June 2, 1924, from which illustrations have been taken with his permission.

to show that the black rat has inhabited Europe from time immemorial. To the ancients the rat was merely a large mouse, and, indeed, even the early mediæval Bestiaries describe and picture a *Mus major* (rat) and a *Mus minor* (mouse). I have drawn attention to the innumerable and excellent representations of rats in ancient Greek, Etruscan and Roman works of art, and especially to works portraying them in actions more appropriate to rat than mouse, such as gnawing ship cordage, as on Etruscan bronze votive boats (Etruscan Museum, Florence); feeding on mussel-beds, as on the silver coins of Cumæ (*circ.* 490-480 B.C.); spreading the bubonic plague, as on a Roman colonial coin struck at Pergamum (between A.D. 161 and 169). I laid particular stress on the raging of plague in Rome three centuries before our era, because, in the light of modern knowledge, it clearly reveals the presence of the rat. Indeed, outside the permanent Asiatic plague-area in which the Bobak marmot stands as reservoir, plague and rat necessarily are inseparable.

"As to the brown rat (*Rattus norvegicus*), a similar error survives. Naturalists persist in asserting that it did not reach Europe before the eighteenth century, and give figures purporting to be the exact dates of the first arrival of brown rats in different countries—Prussia, 1750; Norway, 1762; Faroe Islands, 1768; Sweden, 1790; Switzerland, 1808—as if they had actually stamped their passports. We know from Pallas that in 1727—a 'mouse year' in the Caspian region—vast hordes crossed the Volga and swarmed into Astrakan, thence spreading westward across Russia; but the fact that, whilst travelling in Southern Russia, a distinguished naturalist had witnessed the migration of a great rat army does not prove that the brown rat first came to Europe at that particular moment. Ælian, in his work, 'De Natura Animalium,' written in the second century A.D., undoubtedly refers to the brown rat when he states that 'Caspian rats' at times migrate in countless hosts and bridge the rivers, forming live rafts, each rat holding by teeth to the tail of the rat in front. Among ancient bronze representations of rats found in Italy, while some show the large ears, sharp muzzle, slender build and long tail of the black rat and, therefore, often are confounded with mice, others portray most faithfully and unmistakably the small ears, blunt muzzle, heavy build and shorter tail of the brown rat, proving that both species were available as models to the Italian sculptor of at least twenty centuries ago."

It is probable that plague is primarily a disease of rats which is from time to time communicated to man. For many centuries it has been known that the great human epidemics of plague have been usually heralded by similar outbreaks among rats. Since the discovery of the cause of plague, viz., the *Bacillus pestis*, it has been possible to prove that the outbreaks amongst rats are due to the same cause as the human epidemics. It has also been shown that in the intervals between epizootics (pestilences prevalent among animals corresponding to epidemics among mankind), some rats suffer from a peculiarly chronic but still infective form of the disease.

Experiments carried out on a large scale by infecting rats with plague bacilli, have demonstrated great differences in the susceptibility of individual rats to the disease. While the majority die within a few days, some may linger for weeks and remain "carriers" of plague bacilli. It is probable that in outbreaks of plague the same conditions occur. The more resistant infected animals survive, at any rate for a time; and some of these, owing to the disease running a more chronic course, are not severely ill. They therefore mix freely with healthy rats and go on excreting plague bacilli, and thus remain sources of danger to the rat community. It also seems likely that as time goes on and new generations of rats are born susceptible to the disease, the danger increases until at length a fresh outbreak occurs.

The researches of the Indian Plague Commission have shown that the spread of the disease among rats is largely due to the rat flea. They have further proved that this flea attacks man, and certain other animals, and that it may thus serve to transfer plague from the rat to man. Probably two-thirds of the cases of human plague—viz., the bubonic cases—are caused in this way. The remaining third, the pneumonic and septicæmic cases, appear as a rule to be spread directly from man to man; but many of these may probably be referred to an infection originally transmitted from the rat or some other animal.

Some years ago, a Russian scientist suggested that fleas and bugs might be plague-carriers; but it was the Indian Plague Commission that first conclusively showed the rôle played by fleas in the transmission of this disease.

Although *Xenopsylla cheopis, Pulex pallidus, Ceratophyllus fasciatus*, and other rat fleas cling the longest to their normal rat host, after his death they are the great plague carriers from rat to rat, and may be regarded as the more frequent carriers of plague from rat to man, yet other fleas are to be found on rats, such as *Pulex irritans*, the human flea, *Ctenocephalus canis*, the dog flea, and *Ctenocephalus felis*, the cat flea. These very soon leave a dead rat, and probably forsake a living one as soon as a more congenial host is found.

It is most important when rats are killed in a plague-infected area, that their bodies should be immediately submerged in an insect-destroying solution, or placed in a bag, so that the fleas may be imprisoned and subsequently burnt with the bag and its contents. If insect-powder is sprinkled over the interior of the bag the imprisoned fleas become stupefied and are less likely to escape. Obviously, however, a combination of these methods is best. Unless measures of this kind are adopted directly a rat is killed, it will be found when the bodies of the dead rats are collected subsequently, that the fleas have left. They have gone in search of a new host.

During an outbreak of plague in Japan, the practice of putting the dead rats into bags at once and subsequently burning the bags and their contents, was carried out with the most satisfactory results.

In plague-suspected areas the authorities would do well to have a smoke-ferret containing sulphur placed in all rats' holes before they are closed, so as to ensure the destruction of the fleas in the rats' nests.

It may be mentioned that it was known thousands of years ago that rats were the cause of plague, but knowledge of this kind, together with much more that is extremely valuable, is apt to become lost in process of time, and has to be rediscovered.[1]

That it was known thousands of years ago that rats were the cause of plague, is clearly shown in the First Book of Samuel, chapter v. Here we are told that the Philistines were smitten with "emerods," or in other words, with plague buboes (glands enlarged by plague

[1] In the present day, a most valuable art and one that is fast becoming lost, is the knowledge of the medicinal properties of certain fresh herbs. The knowledge is becoming lost, because the medical profession as a body regards such a matter as being beneath its notice, although there are very many individual members who are fully alive to the benefits to be derived from such measures. Unfortunately it is no one's business ro revive this knowledge, and there is no sum of money devoted to obtaining information on this subject. This art of healing, therefore, is fast sinking into the sole possession of a few herbalists with whose death the area of knowledge becomes seriously diminished. They may leave instructions to some relative, but with the lessening knowledge of each succeeding generation the art will soon cease to exist. To give a single case. Most herbalists are aware that in treating whooping-cough if "cloves" of garlic, as the segments of the bulb are called, are cut into thin slices and placed under the sole of the foot between two pairs of socks, so that the juice gets pressed out during standing or walking, the whoop in very many cases will be quickly modified and the virulence of the disease will disappear.

The remedy is unpleasant, because the smell of garlic can be detected in the breath shortly after the slices have been applied and continues to be in evidence so long as the garlic is in use. The smell, however, is of but little consequence when compared with the distress and even fatal result produced by the disease. It is important that the slices should not be placed in contact with the skin as great local irritation would result. The cloves are also sometimes cut up and

infection), and in the following chapter we learn that their priests told them to return the ark of the God of Israel with a trespass offering of five golden images of emerods, and five golden images of "your mice[1] that mar the land."

In the Septuagint version of the Bible, the association between plague and rats is more clearly indicated, 1 Kings,[2] chapter v, verse 6, "And the hand of the Lord was heavy upon Azotus, and He brought evil upon them and it burst out upon them into the ships, and mice sprung up in the midst of their country, and there was a great and indiscriminate mortality in the city." Chapter

eaten with bread and butter or with breadcrumbs to which milk has been added.

Garlic juice, sweetened with treacle or syrup, can be taken by the mouth, 5 to 60 drops of the juice being given two or three times a day according to the age of the sufferer. If in addition to using garlic, as already mentioned, the root of the tongue (the continuation of the upper surface which dips down the throat out of sight) is painted with a strong astringent, the cough will cease. The cough is caused by a collection of tissue in this region, called the tongue-tonsil, becoming swollen and tickling the edge of the valve which guards the entrance to the windpipe. When the swollen tissue has been shrivelled up by the astringent application, the tickling sensation is removed and, therefore, the cough stops. Painting the back part of the tongue is best, but gargling with alum or another astringent is of use.

[1] It is clear that rats are here alluded to and not mice, for it is mentioned that the evil burst out upon them into the "ships," and as will be seen further on, when referring to the animal depicted on coins which might be taken for a rat or mouse, a coin is referred to which shows the animal eating a mussel.

[2] In the Septuagint version of the Bible 1 and 2 Books of Samuel are called Kings 1 and 2.

vi, verse 1, "And the ark was seven months in the country of the Philistines and their land brought forth swarms of mice."

Verse 2, "And the Philistines called their Priests. . . . and they said, If ye send away the ark of the covenant of the Lord God of Israel, do not on any account send it

FIG. 38.—Roman bronze votive offering of the 1st and 2nd century B.C., representing brown rat, similar to the gold rats given by the Philistines. (The base is modern.)

away empty, but by all means render to it an offering for the plague."

Verse 4, "And they say, what is the offering for the plague which we shall return to it ? and they said according to the number of the lords of the Philistines five golden emerods, for the plague was on you and on your rulers and on the people; and golden mice, the likeness of the mice that destroy your land."

There can be no doubt that the rat was an inhabitant

of Europe from the remotest ages, and there are fossil remains of this rodent and many monuments bearing its effigy. In Asia Minor, the ancient Greeks worshipped Apollo as "the destroyer of rats" and on monuments their god was represented treading on a rat.

Dr. Sambon in his paper states: "Many bronze and terracotta votive offerings in the shape of buboes and rats have been found recently in Palestine, the Troad and Italy. Strabo, in his geography, written some years before our era, says that in Iberia (Spain) rats frequently

FIG. 39.—Colonial coin of Lucius Verus struck at Pergamum about A.D. 161-169.

give rise to pestilence and that the Romans issued a proclamation offering bounties for the destruction of rats in one of these plague outbreaks in Cantabria (Northern Spain).

"A colonial coin of the Emperor Lucius Verus, struck at Pergamum during a plague epidemic, bears, on the reverse, Æsculap in himation with a snake-encircled staff and a rat at his feet, whilst on his left stands a small naked figure with right-hand raised in attitude of supplication and with a bird in his left. The Roman god of healing here replaces a local plague deity, Apollo Smintheus, the destroyer of rats, 'whose arrows spread the plague.'"

It is clear that the animal depicted on ancient coins commemorating the plague is a rat, and not a mouse, for on a Roman coin, as already remarked, one of these animals is represented feeding on a mussel. The habit of visiting a mussel-bed is peculiar to rats and not to mice. While at Bognor, Dr. Sambon saw in the night rats visiting the mussel-covered rocks at low tide, just as their forebears had done 2,000 years before.

In Roman times, Æsculapius replaced the more ancient God of Medicine, and in all the temples of Æsculapius snakes were kept. When in the year 291 B.C., Rome was devastated by the plague, the Sibylline books were consulted, and it was decided to despatch ten ambassadors to Epidauros to confer with the priests of the Temple of Æsculapius. Valerius Maximus mentions how the tribune Quintus Ogulnius, chief of the embassy, returned with the snake sacred to the god of healing, and how a temple to Æsculapius was subsequently erected on an island in the Tiber. A beautiful medallion of Antoninus commemorates this event. A galley is represented passing beneath a bridge, and from its prow a snake moves towards the figure of the Tiber-god who stretches out his right-hand in sign of welcome. This legend doubtless refers to the introduction of rat-snakes into Rome for the purpose of destroying rats and thus stamping out the plague.

From the above, it will be seen that the present day emblem of medicine, the snake-entwined staff of Æsculapius, refers to the use of the snake as a destroyer of rats, and in consequence a means of prevention against the deadliest and most terrible of disease scourges.

Although for several centuries there has been no serious epidemic of plague in Great Britain, yet for some years past there have been a number of small outbreaks from time to time, even quite recently, in several English ports. There was an outbreak in Glasgow which produced thirty-six cases and sixteen deaths; and in the following year there was another outbreak there which produced ten cases. No infected rats were found upon the first occasion; but after the second outbreak, rats infected with plague were found in the city from time to time for nearly two years. Most of these epidemics were proved conclusively to have originated from rats. In all probability, every such case that has occurred here or in Continental ports within recent years is referable to them. In man plague develops in less than eleven days after infection. No plague-infected harbour is less than eleven days' journey from England. These facts and the very efficient control exercised by our Port Sanitary Authorities, have afforded sufficient protection down to the present time against the introduction of the disease by infected persons. But the possibility that rats suffering from acute or chronic plague on board a ship, may infect persons on the same ship, or other rats in a harbour, is one of the great perils to be guarded against.

Rats infected with plague are from time to time found in British ports, but the systematic destruction of rats in the warehouses, &c., usually prevents human beings becoming infected, and stops the spread of the disease among the rats themselves.

The necessity for a very complete extermination of the

rats on board ship, is emphasized by the fact that they do not appear to mix freely with one another ; it being thus possible for a few infected rats to remain hidden unless a very careful search be made. It is not an uncommon experience to find infected rats in only one of the holds, whilst the remainder are in good health. The rats in the rice or grain holds appear to be particularly liable to infection, a fact that has not been satisfactorily explained hitherto. In one instance on record, out of several hundreds of rats on a steamer coming from an infected port on the Levant, only one rat was found to be infected, whilst examination showed that many others had suffered, but recovered. The infectiousness of such rats is evidenced by the following occurrence. In a steamer from Bombay, the Port Authorities at Hamburg found a large number of plague rats, although no case had occurred in man during the journey. The rats were completely destroyed and the ship was disinfected. Yet one sailor developed the disease in a few days after leaving the harbour. This man had only been chartered in Hamburg, where for years before and after, no case had occurred. But it was afterwards shown that in spite of precautions, he had managed to get on board before the process of rat destruction had been completed. There can be no doubt that he was infected at this time, either by handling articles soiled by the rats, or perhaps as the result of his having been attacked by rat-fleas.

In India the cases of plague are almost entirely bubonic (affecting the glands), a form of the disease which is rarely transmitted from man to man, and which is almost invariably produced by contact with the rat-flea. The mortality among natives who have contracted the disease is about 80 per cent., and among Europeans about 30 per cent.; but in Hong-Kong the native death-rate has been as high as 96 per cent.

The large number of deaths occurring annually from plague in India is hardly realized by people living in this country, as many years have passed since there was a serious outbreak of this disease in the British Isles.

In India[1] alone, during ten years, 6,473,704 persons died from plague; a figure that, for its better realization, may be contrasted with the total population of Ireland 4,381,957, or of Scotland 4,759,445 in the same period. The *Lahore Press* (April, 1924) states that during the preceding month 25,000 persons died from plague in the Punjab.

Only 2 per cent. of the cases in India are usually the purely pneumonic or the lung variety. This is the most deadly form of the disease, and is directly infectious, whereas the bubonic form is not. In a pneumonic case, the patient's breath carries the bacillus, and mere inhalation of such breath from some distance away may set up infection. The intervention of the rat-flea is no longer a necessary condition. Doctors and nurses who tend pneumonic cases ought to wear over their mouths and nostrils a mask of germicidal gauze moistened with some oily product, and the patients should do the same.

To illustrate the serious nature of pneumonic plague which was the disease causing the large loss of life (68,595) in London in 1664-1666, let us refer to some modern instances. Only a few years ago eight persons

[1] "Prevention of Plague in Madras Presidency," by Colonel W. G. King, C.I.E., I.M.S. (*Journal of State Medicine*, February, 1912).

living about a quarter of a mile from the river Orwell were attacked with pneumonia (inflammation of the lungs), and six of them died within a month.

The semi-detached cottages where this occurred are in Shotley, in Suffolk, near the southern bank of the river Orwell, opposite to the place at which the larger ships anchor to lighten their cargoes into barges, to enable them to proceed up the river to Ipswich. The illness, however, was not at the time attributed to plague, although viewed in conjunction with a subsequent outbreak of plague at Freston, which is only about six miles distant, there is but little doubt that this was the cause.

Three and a half years later, on September 13 at Freston, a girl, aged 9, was taken ill and died on the 16th. Her mother, aged 40, was taken ill on the 21st, and died on the 23rd, and her husband, aged 57, was taken ill on the 26th and died on the 29th. A neighbour, Mrs. P., aged 43, who nursed the girl's mother on the night of the 22nd and 23rd, was taken ill on September 26 and died on the 29th. All these individuals died of pneumonia, and bacteriological examination showed that the deaths were due to plague.

Investigation as to the cause of the outbreak elicited the fact that a great many rats were dying in the neighbourhood; and on bacteriological investigation many of these, as well as a hare and a cat, were found to have plague. It was noticed that after the six deaths at Shotley previously alluded to, there had been an undue mortality amongst rats. It would almost appear as if there had been a chronic condition of plague among rats in the district since that time—a condition usually preceding such an outbreak of plague amongst human beings, as has been previously mentioned.

During the two months following the outbreak of plague at Freston diseased rats were found in six districts in East Suffolk; one was found in West Suffolk and one in Essex.

Three years after the outbreak of plague at Freston a dead rat found at Harkstead in Suffolk was sent to the Local Government Board, whose experts reported the rat to be infected with plague bacilli. Harkstead is about three miles distant from Shotley and Freston as the crow flies, and forms the apex of a triangle of which those places are the base corners, thus showing that the disease was still prevalent among the rats of the district.

As another instance of the infectious nature of pneumonic plague it may be mentioned that on September 17 at Gudur,[1] Madras Presidency, a schoolmaster was taken ill with pneumonic plague and died on the 20th. He was much respected and was frequently visited during his short illness. By September 24, seventeen of the people who had come to see him were attacked with pneumonic plague.

The origin of the pneumonic form has not as yet been fully determined, but the history of most cases, according to Sir William Simpson, is that the person attacked has been dealing with an infected animal, and the disease has been most probably contracted from the animal. The first Freston case was that of a little girl of nine years of age, who may have contracted the disease from fondling a neighbour's cat, which was found dead from plague two days before the child's illness began. A cat also was

[1] "Prevention of Plague in Madras Presidency," by Colonel W. G. King, C.I.E., I.M.S. (The *Journal of State Medicine*, March, 1912.)

the cause of the outbreak on the S.S. "Friary" from Alexandria, at which port it was stated plague at that time did not exist. A stray cat went on board the vessel at Alexandria, evidently sick and ailing; it mixed freely among the firemen and sailors who were those afterwards attacked by plague. There was an outbreak of plague at Hull on the arrival of this vessel.

There have since from time to time been cases in the Thames and other British Ports; and if the Sanitary Port Authorities were less vigilant, a serious epidemic might ensue from the landing of plague-infected rats.

The pneumonic form of plague generally reproduces the same variety, and may occur in any country and in any outbreak. In an outbreak on the West African coast about 50 per cent. of the cases were of the pneumonic type. In Sydney this form was not encountered until the sixth outbreak.

Plague epidemics, however deadly, are usually preceded by cases without fever, but characterized by enlargement of one or more lymphatic glands. The merit of having drawn attention in recent years to these cases is due to Sir James Cantlie, now practising in London, who was struck by the unusual prevalence of glandular swellings previous to the plague outbreak in Southern China.

For many years it was thought in India that the white races were practically exempt from plague. That, however, is a delusion. Except for the general improvement in the stamina of the race, the Englishman is just as liable to contract plague to-day as he was in the Middle Ages, so far as his physical organization is concerned. The reason why Englishmen have rarely contracted plague in India is that they seldom come in contact with rats; and the chief protection of Englishmen at home is absence of contact with rats. The majority of people in this country never see a rat from one year's end to another. But all these advantages would immediately disappear in the presence of a serious epidemic of pneumonic plague.

As it is sometimes extremely desirable to isolate a house, market, or stores in a plague-infected area, it is useful to know that this has been done effectually in India. The method employed is making a line around the place to be protected, with a mixture of commercial sulphuric acid and *crude* gas tar, as received dried from the retorts.

This plan being mentioned to Colonel W. G. King,[1] as having been successfully employed for a long time for the protection of stores of grain, he tried it with great success. Finally he introduced it as a routine measure after disinfecting and cleansing houses in which plague had occurred.

He also found, that provided *all* the holes were treated with a sufficiency to ensure the smearing of the feet of any rat attempting to get away, not only were the rats got rid of, but they were prevented from returning for a period varying from a fortnight to six months. This result was probably due not only to the irritating nature of the preparation to the skin, but also the prolonged throwing off of gases to which rats object.

Dr. Hubert Marshall, D.P.H., who had charge of a large plague-hospital camp at Jollarpeth, Madras, where

[1] "Plague and the Destruction of Rats," by Colonel W. G. King, C.I.E., I.M.S. (Retired), late Sanitary Commissioner for Madras. (*Journal of the Royal Institute of Public Health*, December, 1910.)

rats were intrusive and troublesome, also carefully undertook experiments with this preparation with the result that by its use the whole camp was kept free from rats.

Care should be taken that the mixture of the tar with the commercial sulphuric acid is only made when about to be immediately used; and that it is not laid on wood or other substances that sulphuric acid will destroy.

With regard to the part played by domestic animals, poultry, &c., in spreading plague, the facts recorded by Dr. Sambon in his letter to the *Times* of January 30, 1911, are of great interest.

He says: "However valuable cats and dogs may be in keeping down the rat population during ordinary times, when plague breaks out they become, for this very reason, exceedingly dangerous to man. That cats do contract the plague there is no doubt whatever. In India this was noted in Bombay, Karachi, Bandra, and in particular at Ahmednagar, which was overrun with cats having open buboes in their necks. Dr. Hunter records an outbreak of plague among cats in a warehouse in Kowloon, Hong-Kong, in which rats had been previously dying of the disease. Dr. Ashburton Thompson saw plague in cats in Sydney. In the South African epidemics at Port Elizabeth, East London, and King William's Town, numbers of cats were proved to be suffering from plague. Sir William Simpson in his admirable treatise, mentions an interesting case of direct infection communicated by a cat; this occurred in the Cape Town outbreak. The Rev. Mr. Gressley, who took up his residence in the Health Camp and voluntarily performed the duties of Chaplain, was attacked with plague under the following circumstances: a cat of his became sick and after a few days died; examination proved that the cat's illness and death were due to plague. One peculiarity of the bacillus, however, was it being stained by Gram's method. A few days afterwards Mr. Gressley was attacked with plague, his infection being attributed to the cat. Curiously enough the bacillus in Mr. Gressley's bubo (gland enlarged by plague infection) also possessed the characteristic of being stained by Gram's method.

"Dogs are less susceptible than cats, but the danger lies not only in the fact that dogs and cats may contract the disease, but that even without falling sick themselves, they may convey to man infected fleas from rats or other lower animals. The famous Jesuit, Athanasius Kircher, who examined the blood and pus of plague patients under the low-power microscopes of his day to look for an animate causative agent of the disease, writing in 1658, says:—

"'Cats, dogs, pigeons, fowls and the like, dwelling within the precincts of an infected house, at the very first contact with the things infected take the contagiousness which breeds contagion; and even if by a kind of contrariety of nature, they are not affected internally by it, they nevertheless do carry it into the neighbouring houses and spread the plague they have caught throughout the city. Therefore, in time of plague, the slaying and extermination of dogs and cats and such like domestic animals is prescribed. Examples beyond all count show how great is the danger from such animals when a house is stricken by plague.'

"The reality and gravity of this danger were so fully recognized in bygone days, that from the remotest antiquity both in the Levant and in Europe, on the outbreak of plague all cats and dogs were either shut up in cages or destroyed. In Palermo, in the year 1576, upwards of 20,000 dogs were killed and buried within two days, and all cats, dogs, fowls, and pigeons were destroyed, not only in the Town, but for a radius of four miles all round it. A like extermination of cats and dogs was enforced by the magistrates in Padua during the epidemic of 1630, and in Turin the year after. The Turin edict orders that, 'having killed all cats, dogs, fowls and pigeons, arsenic be prepared for the rats.'

"In the same year, in Bologna, Cardinal Spada issued the following order:—

"'Seeing that dogs and cats easily contract the prevailing sickness and may infect persons and houses, His Eminence orders that these animals be either killed or placed under confinement, and he gives permission to anyone to kill other people's dogs and cats found wandering about the town or entering other people's houses, and for every dog killed in the streets, provided the animal belonged to others, the killer shall receive three soldi, the reward to be paid by the owner of the dog.'

"Also in England on the outbreak of plague, cats and dogs were destroyed. In the London epidemic of 1543 the plague order enjoins:—

"'That all persons having any dogs in their house other than hounds, spaniels, or mastiffs, necessary for the custody or safe-keeping of their houses, should forthwith convey them out of the city or cause them to be killed and carried out of the city and burned at the common lay-stall, and that such as keep hounds, spaniels, or mastiffs should not suffer them to go abroad, but closely confine them.'

"Again, in 1665, we read in Hodge's 'Loimologia':—

"'That all occasion of propagating the Pest might be cut off; the Magistrates did not unadvisedly command Dogs, Cats and likewise Pigeons, to be killed: lest, perchance these animals wandering here and there in all places, and birds flying about on all sides, should carry with them the pestilential seed, and become conveyors of the Contagion.'

"Plague is not a disease of the rat alone. We know that it attacks many other animals, such as monkeys, cats, dogs, ferrets, bats, squirrels, marmots, mice, jerboas, porcupines, guinea-pigs, hares, rabbits, cattle, sheep, deer, pigs, geese, ducks, turkeys and fowls. The predominance of the rat is merely due to its migratory habits and to the fact that it comes into close association with man; lives in his houses, travels in his ships. Locally, the other animals more or less susceptible to plague, play an important part in keeping up the infection. It is this wide zoological distribution that makes it so difficult to stamp out the plague when once it has taken a footing in any place. The disease spreads from one set of animals to another, and not infrequently, among several simultaneously. In each set, specific factors come into play, and the passage of the microbe through certain animals may attenuate its virulence, the passage through others may exalt it.

"Laboratory experiment has shown that the plague bacillus can be increased in virulence by passage through the bodies of guinea-pigs, and attenuated by continued passage through rats. The law appears to be that increase of virulence is relative to the susceptibility of the host, and that as a rule, young animals are more susceptible than adults."

FLEAS.

Now that the flea is recognized as the chief cause of the spread of plague, it is essential for the efficient dealing with an outbreak of this disease, that the life-history and habits of a flea should be known, and what takes place when the plague bacilli have entered a flea. This is described in a most interesting paper[1] by Dr. Millian which deserves to be much better known.

He says :—

"The biology of the flea has been exhaustively investigated by Drs. Bannerman and Kapadia, and their results are published in the fourth volume of the Plague Commission Report. According to these observers, the flea undergoes several complete metamorphoses; that is to say, it lays eggs which give issue to a larva, this larva surrounds itself with a cocoon, whence by and by the fully developed insect finds its way. It lays its eggs at all times of the year, varying in number from one to five, spherical or ovoid in shape, and of a pearly-grey colour. These are deposited in the interstices of the floor or carpet.

"The egg gives issue to a worm-like larva provided with organs of mastication. It feeds on vegetable or animal detritus and inhabits sand or dust. The larva is quite small, whitish in colour, and not easily distinguished from the various other larvæ that are met with in the floors of dwellings.

"In about a week the larva reaches its full size. It then becomes lazy, ceases to eat, and weaves for itself a cocoon of fine white silk.

"The fully-developed insect comes out of the cocoon in from seven to fourteen days, having accomplished its evolution in about three weeks.

[1] "The Natural History of the Common Flea, and its Connection with Communicable Diseases," by Dr. G. Millian, Physician to the Paris Hospitals. *Journal of the Incorporated Society for the Destruction of Vermin*, July—October, 1909.

"The young flea can do without food for a week or two, so that it lies in wait for a favourable opportunity of obtaining a supply of blood.

"The average duration of the life of a flea is—on a rat forty-one days, on a guinea-pig twenty days, and on man twenty-seven days.

"Much moisture is inimical to the development of the flea, and the same may be said of the other extreme—dryness.

"Fleas reproduce their species all the year round, but with less zeal in the month of June. A temperature above 80° F. and especially above 90° F. hinders flea reproduction and delays the development of the larva."

The fact that certain human and animal fleas may under certain circumstances inhabit the rat, justifies the assumption that vice versa they may pass from rat to man. This at any rate is the case with the Kirgus (Nomad tribes in Siberia which are very subject to plague). They live crowded together in filthy, miserable huts, the soil of which teems with human, and especially dog fleas.

Verjbitski demonstrated that fleas captured on rats dead or dying of plague, contained the plague microbe in a virulent state. The same is the case with respect to human and animal fleas that have fed on a moribund plague patient.

The excreta of infected fleas also contains the bacillus, and the inoculation of a rat with these dejecta gives the plague just as does the inoculation with the culture.

In appearance the plague microbe depends on the character of the medium in which it has been grown. In smears from an inflamed abscess, or infected tissues, the bacilli are as a rule short thick rods with rounded ends, or in other words the shape of a dumb-bell. When slightly stained, the ends are more coloured than the middle portion; that is to say, the bacillus is a bi-polar staining body. On the other hand, the bacillus assumes different shapes according to the character of the medium on which it is grown. Thus it sometimes occurs in long chains of very short bacilli, looking like chains of bacilli streptococci; at others times it assumes the shape of yeast cells, and it often appears in flask shape, i.e., rods with one end swollen out. The flask shape form of the plague microbe is not unlike the anthrax microbe in the spore stage, but the former is aerobic and the latter is anaerobic.

The plague bacillus evidently multiplies in the flea's intestine, since the number goes on increasing up to the fifth day. In all probability the disappearance of the bacillus from the flea which survives is due to a process of phagocytosis (cell devouring) by leucocytes (white corpuscles in the blood) introduced in the fresh blood; for the bacillus multiplies more freely when the flea fasts after sucking infected blood, than when it is subsequently fed on healthy blood.

When the plague-stricken rat dies, the fleas quit the body and it is then that they are most dangerous. This has been shown by actual experiment. If a rat dying of plague is placed in a cage along with a healthy rat, the two being separated by a partial wire gauze screen, as soon as the sick rat dies the fleas are seen to make their way on to the healthy rat, which promptly develops the disease.

Xenopsylla cheopis is the common Indian rat-flea, but is practically unknown as a rat parasite in Great Britain.[1]

[1] The *Times*, December 22, 1910.

It is however the chief rat-flea in Sydney, Brisbane and Manila, it is also very prevalent in San Francisco and at the docks in Marseilles. It does not remain always on the body of the rat, but like all rat-fleas frequents the rat's nest, only seeking the rat when it wants to feed. *Xenopsylla cheopis* seems quite invulnerable to plague. When it sucks blood from an infected rat, it may imbibe as many as 5,000 plague germs into the stomach where they multiply enormously. When the flea feeds again, it may transmit infection to a healthy rat if it takes blood from it. A single flea can infect a rat, but more than one bite is usually necessary.

Although the Indian Plague Research Commission discovered it was the rat-flea that spread plague, the precise manner of communication remained for a long time a mystery. It was known that the plague bacilli passed into the stomach of the flea, but the germs were never found anywhere save in the stomach and rectum (lower part of the intestines) and it was not understood by what method a flea with bacilli in its stomach and alimentary canal infected a wound which it made for the purpose of abstracting blood by suction. This problem,[1] however, was solved by the patient work and investigation of the late Mr. A. W. Bacot, entomologist to the Lister Institute, and Dr. C. J. Martin, F.R.S., director of the Institute, who bred fleas and studied at the Lister Institute the method of transmission of plague by fleas. They noticed that though certain plague-infected fleas sucked vigorously at the shaven abdomen of rats, no blood entered their stomachs. That discovery led to the solution of the mystery.

[1] The *Times*, March 13, 1914.

It may be mentioned that a flea has at the orifice of its stomach a chamber called the proventriculus, a sort of valve covered with tooth-like cells, which closes during the process of digestion.

It was found that when plague-germs enter the stomach of a flea they soon form jelly-like masses of bacterial culture, which for a time completely fill and block it. Now when a flea gets thirsty while its stomach is blocked with bacterial culture it sucks vigorously at fresh blood and tries in vain to satisfy its cravings, but as the stomach is blocked, the only effect produced is the distension with blood of, what for simplicity of description may be called, the gullet. The distended gullet pulling on the orifice of the proventriculus, opens it sufficiently to allow blood to enter, and the distending process now having extended to the proventriculus, the orifice of the stomach becomes in its turn slightly forced open, and some of the bacterial culture escapes back into the proventriculus and gullet, and thus contaminates the fresh blood in these cavities. When the flea relaxes its efforts, some of the blood it has sucked surges back by recoil from its distended gullet into the puncture made in the man or rat. This blood, having become infected by admixture with the jelly-like mass from the stomach, carries plague germs with it on its return. Such is the simple explanation of a process of infection which has perplexed experts for so long. It has required a vast amouut of minute investigation to place proof beyond doubt, although the theory of regurgitation was first advanced speculatively long ago.

As stated already, fleas desert a dead rat at once; and if no other rats are near when the flea wants to feed once more, it will bite an available human being and may infect him. It is by this process that the bubonic form of plague, the variety most frequently met with in India, is usually transmitted among mankind.

It was formerly believed that a plague-infected flea underwent a cleansing process after a certain number of days; and if it did not again bite an infected rat, became free of plague germs. It is now known that this belief is only partially correct. The flea does after a time dispose of its lumps of bacterial culture by auto-digestion, and the way to its stomach may possibly become cleared; but the process of obstruction is liable to recur, and on the whole a flea once infected has very little prospect of future happiness. In a cool, damp atmosphere, it may live a long time; but a starving flea with its gullet plugged up is soon killed by heat. Deprived of fresh fluid, the insect shrivels quickly in a hot dry climate. Thus, it is believed, we know at last exactly why in Northern and Central India plague epidemics cease abruptly when the hot weather begins. How, then, does it reappear with the next cold weather? The probability is that it lingers during the hot months among rats and fleas below ground. The fleas are fewer; the rat mortality is much smaller and not visible above ground; but when favourable conditions recur plague may blaze up again, and in due course, as the rats die off, the thirsty, infected fleas bite human beings. As has been previously mentioned, an epizootic among rats invariably precedes, occasionally by a period extending over weeks, an epidemic among human beings.

A large amount of data goes to prove that bubonic plague is rarely transmitted from man to man. The agent is almost invariably the rat-flea, and the infection is from rat to man by means of the flea.

Ceratophyllus fasciatus is the most common English rat-flea, as it is the flea that lives on the brown rat, and it is also found all over Northern Europe. It was proved years ago in the Punjab where a few of the species are found, to be a suitable host for plague germs. Most people thought—though experts had their doubts—that *Ceratophyllus fasciatus* would not bite human beings in Great Britain. This is a delusion. Given similar conditions, it will bite human beings as readily as *Xenopsylla cheopis* bites mankind in India.

In the Report of the Local Government Board dealing with the outbreak of plague in East Suffolk it is mentioned that *Ctenophthalmus agyrtes*, the flea which infests the long-tailed field mouse, was found on brown rats which inhabit hedgerows in almost as large numbers as *Ceratophyllus fasciatus;* but as far as the experiments went it was found not to bite human beings. A few giant fleas (*Hystrichopsylla talpæ*, about one-fifth of an inch in length), whose host is the mole, were found in rats' nests.

On the brown rat (*Rattus norvegicus*) in East Suffolk no human fleas (*Pulex irritans*) were found, and no mouse-flea (*Ctenopsylla musculi*), no cat-flea (*Ctenocephalus felis*), and no dog-flea (*Ctenocephalus canis*).

Fleas may be destroyed by sprinkling the ground infested by them with pyrethrum roseum (Insect Powder) and, after waiting about twenty minutes to allow the fleas to become stupefied, brushing up the dirt which contains them and immediately burning it. Turpentine sprinkled over the infected area is said also to stupefy them. Subsequently the ground should be thoroughly sprinkled with carbolic acid or some other germicidal powder.

SAINT ROCH.

It is not generally known that in Westminster Abbey there is a statue of Saint Roch, the Patron Saint of Plague, who was said miraculously to have stayed the pestilence; although he ultimately contracted the disease, from which he recovered.

The Statue is in King Henry VII's Chapel, the centre of three figures placed several feet from the ground on the left-hand wall of the alcove immediately to the right of the east window, and directly above the monument to Antonius Phillippus, Duc de Montpensier. In the centre of the alcove is the monument to Dean Stanley.

Saint Roch was born in Montpellier,[1] his parents being wealthy and owning property to which he subsequently succeeded.

About 1348 he went into Italy, where the plague was at that time raging; but before leaving home he placed his affairs in the hands of his uncle, who was then Governor of Montpellier. At Aquapendente, at Rome and Piacenza, he tended those who were afflicted with plague. It was stated that wherever he went he miraculously expelled the plague by the sign of the cross, and healed the plague-stricken by thousands and tens of thousands. At Rome he was well received by the Pope, and he made the sign of the cross on the brow of a Cardinal, leaving the mark so deeply impressed that it could not be removed.

Whilst tending the sick he became infected with plague, and was found by a dog in an isolated hut, alone and untended. The dog brought him food daily from a nobleman's table, and noticing that the dog went away

[1] "The Lives of the Saints," by the late Rev. S. Baring-Gould, M.A.

FIG. 40.—Statue of St. Roch in Westminster Abbey.

with food in his mouth the nobleman followed and thus discovered Saint Roch, whom he looked after until his recovery.

About 1350, a man without apparent means of subsistence and unable or unwilling to give a satisfactory account of himself, was taken up by the authorities of Montpellier and cast into a dirty cell of the common gaol, where he died, partly from neglect.

On the removal of the body for burial it was discovered to the surprise and dismay of everyone, that the reputed vagabond was Roch, the nephew of the Governor, the identification probably being effected through some papers or documents found on him.

A piece of the spine of Saint Roch is shown at St. Jacques in Antwerp, and other relics are in the hospital of St. Julian in the same city. In 1478 the body of Saint Roch was stolen from Montpellier and taken to Venice, where a church was erected to receive it.

The city of Arles also claims to possess relics of the Saint. The shrine containing them was melted at the Revolution, but the body itself was preserved. The relics are at present under the charge of the civil and ecclesiastical authorities, each of whom possesses a key to the reliquary, so that it cannot be opened without the concurrence of both. "The body is almost entire." So is the one at Venice; innumerable other portions stated to be of Saint Roch are dispersed throughout Christendom.

Saint Roch is usually represented as a pilgrim pointing to a gland enlarged by plague infection in his left groin; and by his side is a dog with a piece of bread in his mouth.

When he felt that he was dying, Saint Roch is stated to have prayed that all who should invoke him and rely on his merits should be delivered from the plague; and an angel from heaven appeared in the prison and wrote on a tablet: "Those labouring from the plague who fly to the patronage of Roch shall be healed."

In consequence of this Saint Roch is sometimes represented with an angel at his side touching the enlarged gland. The angel generally bears a tablet on which is written "*Eris in pesto patronus*" (You will be a patron saint in time of plague).

SOME NOTES ON CANCER.[1]

As investigation proceeds in the elucidation of cancer, the rat becomes more and more prominent as a possible factor in the complex animate and inanimate environment of the disease, and, probably, an important factor, on account of its close association with man and the domesticated animals. In any case, because of the frequency of cancerous growths in rats and mice, these rodents have been much used for researches and experiments in the elucidation of cancer.

Two forms of cancer, studied by Borrel and Fibiger respectively, throw considerable light on its natural history, and strongly support the theory of the parasitic nature of cancer.

Professor A. Borrel, of Strasbourg, studied most carefully the liver sarcoma (a non-inflammatory tumour of slow growth) of rats, and pointed out that very frequently the tumour arises about or over the very cysts enclosing the larval forms of the thick-necked Cat Tapeworm, which develop in the liver of rats and mice when these rodents have become infected by eating food

[1] For the information contained in this section the Author is very largely indebted to Dr. Louis W. Sambon's article in the *Journal of Tropical Medicine and Hygiene* for June 2, 1924, and facts are mentioned which he has directly communicated to the author. It is also due to his kindness that some of the illustrations which appeared in his paper are here reproduced.

contaminated by the excrement of cats containing the tapeworm's eggs.

Borrel's observations have been confirmed by numerous investigators in France and elsewhere. It is sufficient to mention those of the American investigators, Bullock and Curtis, in 1920. By feeding rats on the eggs of the cat tape-worm these authors obtained not only numerous

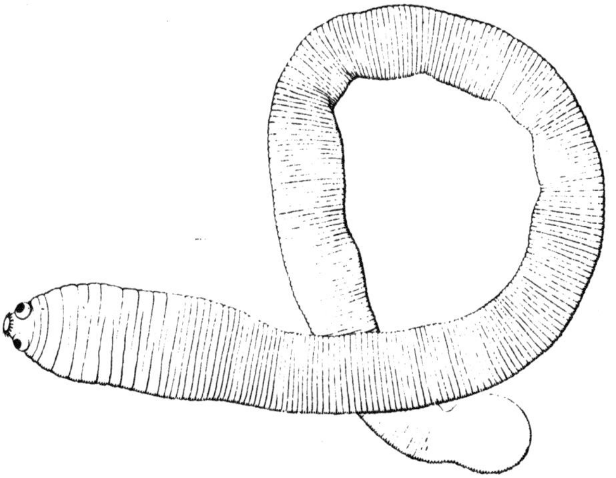

FIG. 41.—Larval form of cat tape-worm (*Cysticercus fasciolaris*) from liver of rat caught on ship at Albert Docks, London. (Sambon.)

bladder-worms in the liver of the experimental animals, but frequently sarcoma in the encapsulating tissues surrounding the larval tape-worm.

Professor Johannes Fibiger, of Copenhagen, studied another form of cancer in rats and mice, viz., a carcinoma which develops in the stomach of these rodents, and showed that this form is usually brought about through the agency of a round-worm : the *Gongylonema neoplasticum*, which burrows long galleries beneath the epithelium (surface cell tissue) lining the gastric mucous membrane. The larval form of this worm develops between the muscle fibres of the legs and prothorax of cockroaches,

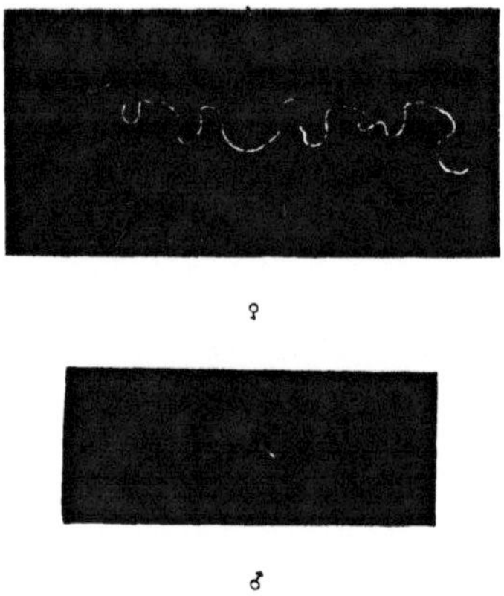

FIG. 42.—*Gongylonema neoplasticum*, female and male, both natural size. (After Fibiger.)

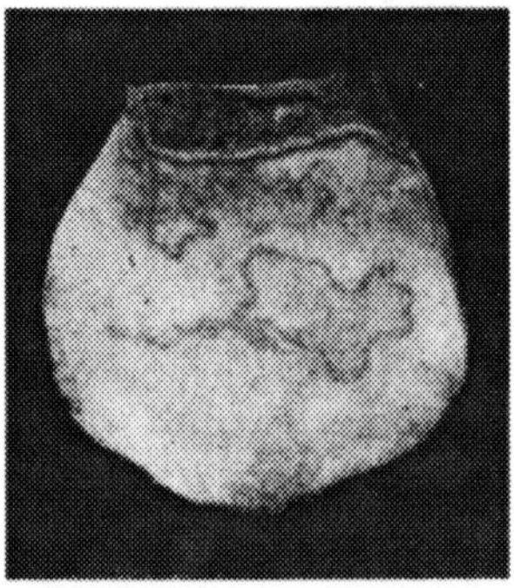

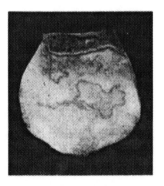

FIG. 43.—Gongylonema beneath epithelium of stomach of rat. (After Fibiger.)

the so-called "black-beetles" of our kitchens and pantries. The rat becomes infected by eating cockroaches, of which it is particularly fond, and the cockroaches acquire their larval parasites by eating food contaminated by the excrement of infected rats and mice.

Neither tape-worm nor round-worm is the actual cause of cancer, but both bring about tumour formation in their hosts, acting merely as predisposing factors, or as carriers of the causative germ.

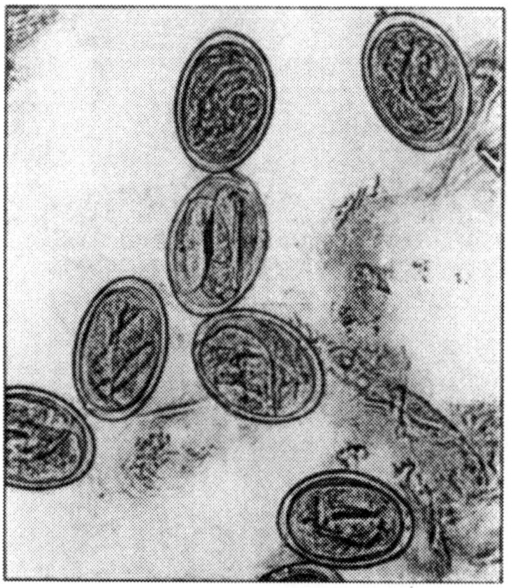

FIG. 44.—Embryonated eggs of *Gongylonema neoplasticum* found in rats' excrement. (After Fibiger.)

As pointed out by Dr. Sambon in his recent important paper on "The Elucidation of Cancer," these and other worms in man and animals only act as other lower organisms and even inanimate irritants, by preparing the soil for the essential cause of cancer which seems to be some as yet undiscovered micro-organism, probably ultra-microscopic as suggested by the experiments of Rous, who was able to reproduce experimentally connective-tissue tumours in fowls by inoculating filtrates from such tumours into healthy fowls.

Sambon points out that the prevalence of certain forms of cancer, and more especially their peculiar site incidence

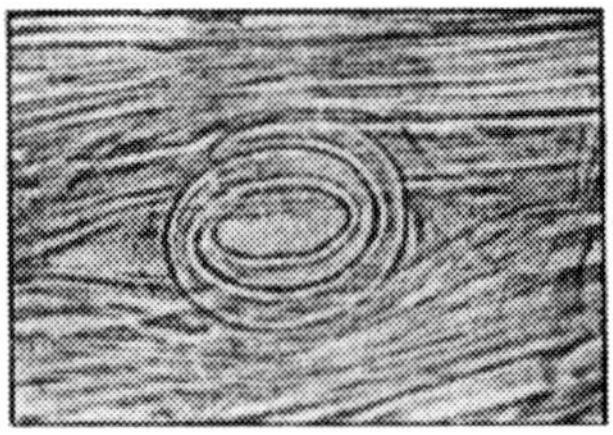

FIG. 45.—Larva of Gongylonema encysted in muscular tissue of cockroach. (After Fibiger.)

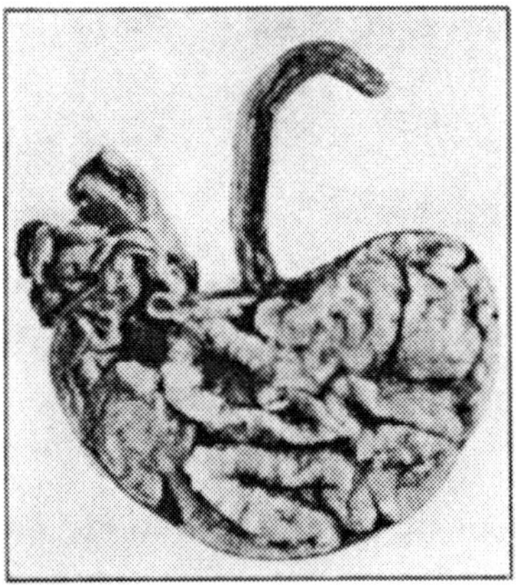

FIG. 46.—Cancer filling tomach of rat infected with *Gongylonema neoplasticum*. (After Fibiger.)

which differs somewhat in various places, are connected with some particular predisposing animate factor, just as the disfiguring tumorous growth, elephantiasis, is associated, in most tropical countries, with the well-known round-worm *Filaria bancrofti.* The filaria is not the cause of elephantiasis, but an important predisposing factor which determines its distribution and prevalence, the actual essential cause being a micro-organism which may give rise to the disease independently of the filaria. He further explains that, as in elephantiasis, a mosquito is the carrier and disseminator of the worm factor, so also in cancer we have to consider the intermediate hosts of the various tumour-inducing parasites. These may be of the greatest importance from a preventive point of view, because, as in the case of the mosquito in malaria, yellow-fever and elephantiasis, they represent the factor which may be successfully controlled.

COCKROACHES.

THE definite part that cockroaches play in the production of cancer in rats, as shown by Dr. Sambon, makes it imperative that this troublesome insect should be destroyed persistently by every possible means, especially as it seems not improbable that they may be a factor in the production of human cancer.

Dr. Sambon's recent visit to Italy resulted in one fact becoming established, viz., that "Cancer Houses," i.e., the houses in which members of successive families who inhabited them died of cancer—were badly infested with cockroaches, and that rats or mice, or both, frequented the premises.

Many houses are badly infested with cockroaches without the people who inhabit them being aware of it, for these insects do not emerge from the places in which they remain by day until about an hour after the kitchen or room has been in darkness, or in other words until those who occupy it have gone to bed.

When from time to time one or two cockroaches are seen, it frequently happens that no special attention is paid to them, because it is considered that there are only a few about, whereas, if the trouble were taken to go to the kitchen or room at night, it might be found that they existed in very large numbers.

Now that it is known that cockroaches are prevalent in houses in which cancer is contracted, perhaps more thought will be directed to them and trouble taken to lay poison until no more are to be seen at a night visit, and that poison will be laid ever after as a precautionary measure, although the premises may appear to have been freed from them. To those who are acquainted with the subject, it is well known that they reappear from time to time, and unless dealt with periodically in a thoroughly efficient manner they soon again become numerous.

Many new houses are infested with cockroaches, the first having probably arrived in the baskets which conveyed the washing from the laundry.

Dr. Howard, in his "Insect Book," New York, 1901, describes a migration of cockroaches he witnessed in Washington. He says: "New houses become stocked with roaches through migrations at night time from over-supplied adjoining establishments. On a dark day in Washington I once saw a migrating army of cockroaches, incalculable in number, crossing the street from a dirty restaurant towards buildings opposite. The majority of the individuals composing the army were females carrying egg cases, and the observation thus became one of psychological interest, since the migratory instinct seemed to have been developed by an appreciation of the fact that, while the restaurant might support the mothers, there would not be food enough for the coming children."

Cancer is known to have existed from the earliest periods, and so have cockroaches. It is a mistake to suppose that they have only been with us for the last few centuries. They are among the oldest known insects geologically. Their fossil remains occur abundantly in the early coal formations of Europe (Great Britain, Belgium, Germany), and the coal measures and millstone grit of America. Indeed, so abundant and generally distributed were they during the warm, moist carboniferous period of Palæozoic times that this period has been called the "Age of Cockroaches." They have been found also in the lithographic stone of Solenhofen and enclosed in brilliant and beautiful yellow amber. Notwithstanding their venerable antiquity, cockroaches have not departed notably from the early types, and thus form one of the most persisting groups among insects.

From what has been said it is evident that strict attention is urgently required to the state of bakeries, laundries and kitchens throughout the country. It is common knowledge that a very large number of bakeries swarm with rats and cockroaches, and as at present constructed, it is almost impossible to keep them free from these dangerous vermin. Many of them are in such a disgraceful condition that they ought to be condemned and rebuilt.

Considering the importance of the matter it would not be too strong a measure to insist—

(1) That the floor of all kitchens and places in which food is prepared or stored, is to be concreted, or made of some other rat and insect-proof material; if paved, that the slabs or bricks be pointed with cement.

(2) That all walls be cemented or covered with some hard material which cannot be eaten through, and in which any crevices can be obliterated.

As many cockroaches live behind a cooking-range, and emerge from between the wall and the range, some device is required to permanently prevent the chink which is so commonly met with. This might be done by making it compulsory for every range to have a flange attached to its circumference, either before or after it is set, which could be cemented into a groove in the wall and floor which had been cut to receive it.

The chink at the edge of ranges in position could be stopped by clipping a piece of thin metal on to the range and letting it into the wall.

Such regulations should apply to all hotels, restaurants, boarding-houses, and other places which cater for providing food, and the owners of many private houses would gladly avail themselves of a means of keeping these insects in check.

For destroying cockroaches the following powder which any chemist can make, will be found useful. It should be dusted from a dredger at intervals of a few nights, or more frequently, if that which has been laid has been eaten.

Take—Sodium Fluoride ... ½ oz.
Calcium Phosphate ... ¼ „
Flour ... ... ¼ „ Mix.

The author's family have used for the last sixty years or more the cockroach poison supplied by—

Mrs. Charles Penny,
83, Grafton Street,
Mile End, London, E.1,

or it may be obtained from her at

Reedham, S.O., Norfolk.

It has been found to be most effectual. It is sold, post free, in pots at 1s. 9d., 2s. 3d. and 3s. 3d.

As phosphorus is the poison used no cat or dog will eat it.

The phosphorus poison may with advantage be used simultaneously with the powder.

MICE.

HOUSE MICE are very prolific; they breed five or six times or even more in a year, and have from five to eight or more young ones in each litter. The period of gestation is twenty-one days.

Mice resemble rats in their habits. Always for preference they run by the side of a wall when passing from place to place, and they keep under cover when possible. For the former reason, therefore, a RUN-trap should always be placed against a wall, and all traps set in proximity to it.

Although a very large number of mice are trapped annually, a much greater number would be caught if their habits were better known. The popular belief is that a mouse-trap has only to be baited and set, to ensure the capture of every mouse that finds it. Consequently, when traps remain set and the bait untouched for a few days, it is supposed that there are no more mice about. This does not follow. Although mice are much less suspicious than rats, and the handling of a trap is usually of little consequence, yet occasionally some mice are met with, especially after a few have been caught, that may avoid a trap for many weeks, even though it be carefully and suitably baited. The trap-shy ones will not be caught, unless as much care and patience are exercised as are required to capture a wary rat. Sometimes a single mouse will defy trap and trapper for a long time.

It is best to place a RUN-trap against a wall at a distance of several feet from the hole, and not at the entrance to the hole, which is the popular custom. A trail of bait should then be laid from the hole to the trap and beyond it. Any bait that has been taken must be replaced immediately. Mice may take part of a trail several times in the twenty-four hours for a week or ten days or even longer, without venturing into or on to the trap; but if the trap and the uneaten portion of the trail are left undisturbed, the mouse will be caught sooner or later.

When mice are shy of a trap, it is a good plan to leave it unset or fixed in the set position—according to the kind of trap in use—and feed them on it or in it, as the case may be, until it is entered freely. Then when it is re-set, visit it frequently so that a mouse caught may be quickly removed.

As in the case of rats (see "Trapping"), when mice are suspicious, it is important not only to feed up to the trap, but also to place bait at the entrance, so as to accustom them to it. The amount used is not material; it need not be large, for mice do not eat at once all the bait they carry to their hole.

There is no better bait for mice than oats; and biscuit is often taken in preference to cheese.

If blood be spilt, it should always be carefully removed from a trap, and a drop of oil of aniseed or other essential oil may be put on the place.

The simplest way to ascertain whether mice are frequenting a room and avoiding a trap, is to keep a piece of biscuit or some other bait at the entrance to the hole. Alternatively it may be placed just inside the hole, but within sight; or in a trail if the trap is set. If removed, it should always be replaced at once.

When a trap is being avoided it is a good plan, where possible, to place a different kind of trap several feet from the hole in the opposite direction and make a trail of food to this as well as to the other.

Sometimes mice resort to a store-room or room that is visited only at intervals. In this case one or more traps may be placed un-set or fixed in the set position and a trail laid and plenty of bait placed on or in them. When the bait is taken, the trap properly set will probably effect a catch when the mouse returns.

Most of the numerous traps employed for catching mice are too well known to need description, but nearly all require to be baited and set, and catch only one mouse at a time.

It is often better not to bait a break-back trap, but to place it with its treadle-end against a wall at the entrance to a passage-way formed by drawing a box an inch and a half from the wall, or leaning a piece of wood against it. Bait should be kept in the passage-way and as a trail on the other side of the trap, to induce the mice to cross the treadle. If they appear to be suspicious of a bare trap, take it away; put down sawdust, chaff, finely torn paper, or some other suitable substance in its place and lay a trail across it. As soon as the trail is taken freely the trap may be concealed in the sawdust and a trail laid as before across the sawdust and over the treadle of the trap. The lid of a cardboard box makes a suitable receptacle for the sawdust, &c.

When setting in sawdust it is advisable to put a little wool around the treadle to prevent sawdust getting under it.

The risk of getting a finger caught in a break-back trap while it is being set, is prevented by raising and adjusting the treadle with a piece of stick about six inches long, flattened on opposite sides at one end and tapered to an edge.

When premises are overrun with mice, they may be cleared in about a fortnight or three weeks if sufficient trouble is taken and the proper method adopted.

It is a mistake to set only a few traps when such a condition exists; two or three dozen should be set simultaneously and distributed throughout the rooms and outbuildings. Break-back traps are suitable for this purpose; they should be placed facing the wall along which the mice run, and about a foot or more from it; and several feet away on each side of the hole by which the room is entered. When in position they should be left sprung, and food placed on and around them for a few days until it is taken freely. Then the traps may be set simultaneously at dusk, having been baited with bread, bread and dripping, biscuit or cheese, and visited at half-hour intervals to remove mice that may have been caught, and take away any trap that has blood upon it.

At the last visit all the traps should be sprung and a little bait, such as coarse crumbs of bread or biscuit or oats, sprinkled over and around the traps. The traps should be re-set at dusk the following evening and the same procedure followed, and thus repeated until it is found that the traps no longer catch.

As probably there are some mice that are trap-shy still left, bait should be placed behind a box or a piece of board leaning against a wall; and sawdust or other material placed on either side of it, as previously mentioned. The remainder of the mice may be caught by this method; and whether or not any remain may be ascertained by placing some bait near the entrance to the holes. The sawdust may be laid when the traps are first set, so that by the time it is wanted for cover, the mice may be accustomed to run over it.

The premises having been cleared, all that is required to keep them free in the future is for traps to be kept set all the year round in places which are visited daily, and to set the traps elsewhere, which have been placed in position but sprung, as soon as the presence of mice is noticed. It is unnecessary to bait traps which are kept set, nor is there need for bait to be laid near them; the traps merely require to be placed with the treadle-end against a wall at the end of a passage-way as before described. The passage-way may be kept by a lath of the required width being placed between the box and the wall.

For many years past the author has had house mice trapped largely with Hutch Traps (see Section "Traps"), made with a treadle about three inches long, pivoted transversely and counter-weighted. Some traps have been made with a single door, others with two doors, in both cases the door or doors being held open by whip-cord arranged as in the original Hutch Trap. The single-door traps have transverse wires across the last two inches of the further end of the trap and half-way down the front. The traps with two doors have two or three holes across the top of each door near the end, and also across the lower part of the vertical portion, for inspection when the trap has been sprung. The doors and edges around them, and the woodwork beneath the wires in the case of the one-door trap are lined with galvanized iron. The outside measurements are as follows:— Length, single door, 8 inches, two doors, 12 inches; height 4 inches; inside width 3 inches. These traps are not on the market.

Captured mice are dropped into a pail containing water to the depth of 3 or 4 inches and killed by a blow

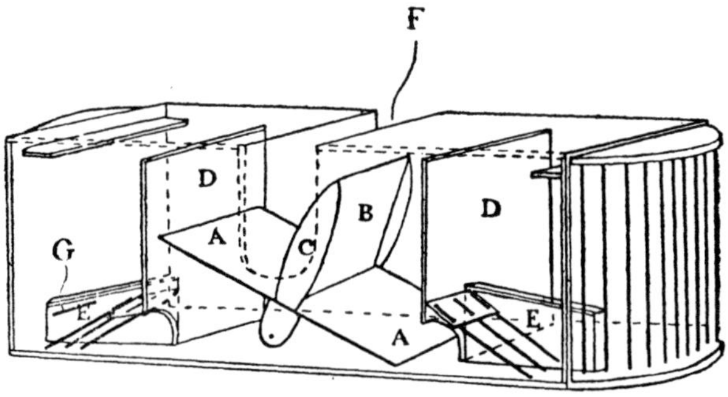

FIG. 47.—Colin Pullinger's[1] Perpetual Mouse Trap. The diagram represents the side of the trap removed so that the arrangement of the balance, &c., can be seen. The receptacle for the food and the bars at the left-hand end of the trap, together with the movable portion of the top to enable the food racks to be reached, have been omitted to make the drawing more clear.

with the back of a table knife; or drowned by placing another pail inside the one containing them, so as to submerge them. A dead mouse should be burnt immediately, to prevent sufficient time elapsing for fleas to leave it. A trap should never be made wet.

Many years ago the late Mr. Colin Pullinger invented a self-setting balance trap, which is fully described in Part II.

[1] Manufactured by Messrs. Duke, Waring, Crisp and Co., 139, Wardour Street, London, W.1.

The author has seen nineteen house mice in one of these traps, the result of a night's catch; but since the patent expired the trap has been altered in construction and rendered (in his opinion) almost useless. So that it may be again made in its original form, the proper measurements are given in detail in Part II, and the public are strongly advised not to buy a trap that is otherwise constructed. It is correctly made by the firm mentioned in the footnote.

The prevalence of mice is chiefly due to the practice of setting traps only when these vermin are heard or seen, or when inconvenience is caused by their presence. Bearing in mind the rapidity with which mice increase, much time and in some cases serious loss would be avoided if traps were kept set throughout the year.

To save time and trouble incurred by the setting and baiting of traps, the author has for many years kept Colin Pullinger traps in places frequented by mice.

The only bait used for many years was a drop of oil of aniseed placed on a piece of flannel in the bait rack; but after the war this bait failed to attract, for what reason is a mystery. A slice of cheese, the size of the bait rack and about an eighth of an inch in thickness has proved, however, to be an efficient lure.

When a balance-trap is used in a garden, it should be placed on a thick piece of wood about an inch wider than the trap, to keep the bottom dry. It should be covered with an inverted lidless box that is large enough to leave a space of two or three inches or more above and around it. The top of the inverted box ought to be covered on the outside with oilcloth or sheet metal to keep the trap dry. It should have a piece of wood, projecting about one inch and a half, nailed to the inside at each corner, to form the supports that keep the box raised from the ground.

Four traps kept for some years under such boxes in a garden with meadows and a wood around it, have caught annually 200 to 300 or more field-mice and voles. The only trouble incurred has been changing the position of the traps every few days, placing fresh bait in the bait-rack about once a fortnight, and removing the dead mice and voles. Both long-tailed field-mice and bank and field-voles die in a trap, although uninjured, a few hours after they have been caught. Most field-mice and voles are caught on a wet night. A good position for a trap is against a house, wall, building or hedge.

In the country mice and voles not infrequently obtain entrance to a house through air-gratings which are either broken or have the bars placed sufficiently apart to allow ingress. The defect is most easily corrected by fastening a sheet of perforated zinc over the grating. This is best done by passing a long loop of wire around a bar at each corner of the grating, and then putting the two ends of the wire through the perforated zinc at corresponding positions. The ends of each wire should be lightly fastened together when they have been passed through the zinc to prevent them slipping back. When the four wires are in position, the zinc may be placed against the grating and the wires shortened and twisted to fix it there.

A figure **4** trap (see Section "Traps") is often used in a garden; the **4** being made of wooden labels cut to the required width.

Break-back traps, when used in a garden, are best placed

under inverted flower-pots, tilted and rested on two stones or pieces of stick sufficiently thick to allow a mouse to pass under the edge in a position facing the treadle end of the trap. A piece of slate or tile about the size of the trap may be placed under it, and if the hole on the top of the pot is covered, it will darken the interior and help to keep the trap dry. It is advisable to fasten the trap to a peg, best placed behind the pot, with a piece of string having a large curtain-ring tied to its free end. Cheese is a good bait. Break-back traps will remain in a serviceable condition for several years out of doors, if the spring is kept oiled and the trap is soaked in boiled linseed oil before it is used.

A trap figured in some books which deal with vermin destruction is made as follows. A piece of galvanized wire about 4½ in. long (No. 18 or 19-gauge) is bent at each end with a curve in an opposite direction so as to form an **S** shape, its length when thus bent being about 3 in. A piece of cheese, or some soaked peas, is then threaded on to the wire near to its centre. Two bricks with a flat surface are then taken, one is placed on edge and the other laid against it, the ground, on which its flat surface rests, having been beaten until it is hard and smooth. The second brick is then raised and supported by the baited wire by resting one end 1½ in. from its upper edge, and the other against the brick on edge, placing the wire ¾ in. from the ground.

As soon as the bait is disturbed the brick falls and crushes the mouse. When set against a wall or other vertical surface, only one brick is necessary. Cheese is good bait. If the wire is kinked in the centre, the bait does not slip to the bottom. The drawback to this trap is that it catches birds.

When a garden is overrun with mice, some may be caught by sinking to the ground-level a receptacle, not less than twelve inches deep, with unclimbable sides such as a biscuit tin or glazed earthenware jar, and filling it with water to the depth of five or six inches. For bait, throw on to the water a handful of meal or float a crust against one of the sides. Both these baits may be used together. A drop of oil of aniseed on the tin will attract the mice.

When mice are living under a lawn or the paving of a stable or outhouse, they can usually be "flooded" out of their holes. A birch-broom is a handy thing for killing them (see Section "Flooding").

When mice are numerous in a garden, poison may be safely placed in the centre of agricultural pipes; the openings at the ends of the larger sizes being diminished, if thought desirable, with sticks placed vertically and forced into the ground. The poisons mentioned for rats are suitable.

Some farmers destroy a large number of mice in stacks by putting poisoned food into a small box without a lid scented with oil of aniseed, and then turning the box on its side and placing the open part of the box, formerly the top, against the stack. The box is kept in position by pushing into the stack a long pointed piece of wood, fastened to the inner surface of the side that has become the top. The poisoned food is kept from falling out by a piece of wood about two inches wide nailed along one side of the top of the box. This becomes the lower part of the side of the box when it is in position against the stack.

SPARROWS.

THE house-sparrow has his protectors and his friends. They are chiefly those who are not interested in agriculture, poultry-keeping, or gardening; and they like to watch his impudent, self-satisfied bearing and listen to his assertive chirp. Yet even they must admit that he does a considerable amount of harm. When the damage to crops and thatch is considered, and the constant theft of food provided for fowls and pigeons is estimated even roughly, it is evident that the annual loss due to sparrows throughout Great Britain alone amounts to a considerable sum. This is a fact not generally understood and it accounts for the sparrows' comparative immunity.

It is contended that sparrows do a great deal of good by destroying injurious insects. It is true that they feed their young on insects, but at other times of the year they live chiefly on grain, and they consume an enormous amount of corn in the fields before it is carried. The shape of their bill proclaims that they are not true insect-eaters.

The time has come when the number of sparrows should be reduced materially; and if every householder does his utmost to kill the sparrows on his premises, a very large number will be destroyed in the course of a year.

The cause of the large number of sparrows in the British Isles is similar to the cause responsible for the enormous number of rats, viz., the absence of continuous and systematic measures for their destruction. In the case of the sparrow, plans can be carried out with far less trouble than against rats; for sparrows are found chiefly throughout the year in cities, towns and villages, and around habitations. The area to be dealt with is consequently far less than it is in the case of the rat.

It is well known that sparrows drive away other birds. Those who systematically destroy sparrows have noticed that other species of birds not previously seen, make their appearance as the number of sparrows decreases.

The simplest way to prevent sparrows increasing would be for every householder to arrange for the eggs, or young, as the case may be, to be removed every week or ten days from nests that are easy of access. Nests situated in places that are difficult to reach should be destroyed.

Many house-sparrows build in trees, and it may here be mentioned that the best implement for removing a sparrow's nest from a tree, is a drain rod with the double screw attached; such as is used for dragging from a drain materials that have blocked it. If this rod end be twisted into a sparrow's nest, the whole structure is easily pulled down.

As sparrows frequently build in the same hole year after year, such apertures should be blocked with mortar, board or other suitable material. Every nest must be destroyed as soon as it is known to be deserted.

Poultry and pigeon keepers could easily kill a large number of sparrows annually and thus save a considerable amount of the food they now eat, by always feeding their birds in an enclosure, so arranged that the sparrows can have free access and egress until the time arrives for them to be trapped.

The trap is usually about three feet in height and it can be made to any size. If large, it is best to have

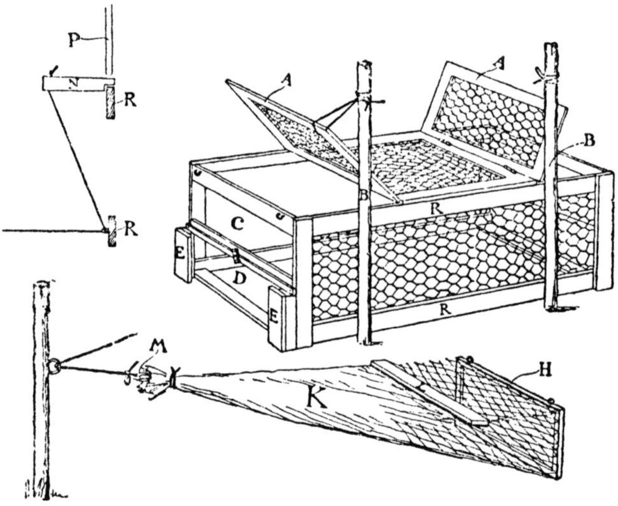

FIG. 48.—Feeding Enclosure Sparrow Trap.[1] The boards closing the entrance C and D, and also the netting at the opposite end and further side of the enclosure have been omitted to make the diagram more clear. A, lid; B, stake for supporting lid; C, aperture through which the sparrows are driven into the net; D, fowls' entrance; E, guide for groove to hold the board that closes the fowls' entrance; H, wooden frame to which the string net is attached; K, string net; L, piece of wood fixed to the net to ensure the top of the net falling quickly to close the space C when the sparrows are in the net; M, metal ring attached to the end of the net to which the string is fastened; N, movable piece of wood on which the lid prop is rested; P, prop for lid; R, top and bottom of the side frame.

the sides, ends and top separate, and arranged to hook together. Oblong is the best shape. There may be a lid at each end, as shown in the illustration, or one in the middle. It is convenient to have a door in the

[1] Manufactured by Messrs. Charles Orfeur and Co., Colne Bank Works, Colchester.

middle of one side when the lids are at the end. The aperture at the small end of the net, kept tied when the net is in use, is made sufficiently large to admit a hand easily. The aperture C is kept closed by a board hinged at the bottom to open inwards. The frame H, which with net attached is made to cover the aperture C caused by unfastening and pushing inwards the hinged cover, is held in position by a screw-eye at each upper end which catches on to a hook placed to receive it. It is secured below by a button placed on a lath, the thickness of the frame H, and fixed to the lower half of the cross-rail which separates the fowls' entrance from the space C. For catching, the bait—nothing better than oats—should be placed as far as possible from the lids.

A large number of sparrows may also be destroyed by going at night with a bat-fowling net (sometimes called a bat-folding net) and a bull's-eye lantern along walls covered with ivy or creepers, round shrubberies, and the eaves of buildings and stacks where sparrows will be sleeping. The light is thrown on to the surface covered by the net as soon as it is in position and the birds then driven into it. This may be done once or more a week at first, and at longer intervals as the number of sparrows diminishes. The best kind of bat-fowling net has a number of small pockets distributed throughout the net, as well as a large pocket at the bottom.

A good trap, serviceable throughout the year, is the old-fashioned brick trap. It may be propped open without the fork being used to accustom sparrows to feed inside before it is set to capture them. A percentage gratuity to a boy may produce a large death-roll.

The simplest way to remove the birds from a trap of this description, is to have a net, weighted along its edge, and sufficiently large to cover the trap and enable the fallen brick to be raised whilst the net is over it. Pieces of a small-sized composition gas-pipe threaded on to a string and fastened to the edge of the net, are convenient weights for this purpose; or short pieces of rope with their ends almost touching may be used. A continuous piece is apt not to lie flat.

FIG. 49.—A Brick Trap. A side brick has been removed to show the interior of the trap and arrangement of the peg, fork, and prop when the trap is set.

The various forms of trap with a **V**-shaped approach and small entrance at the apex, or with a well-shaped entrance on the top acting on the same principle, are useful chiefly for catching young birds. Old birds may be caught in traps of this description when food is scarce, or in the early morning. It is advisable to keep the trap in the same place throughout the year, and to spread food round it at first so as to accustom the sparrows to feed near. When set in a poultry-yard, it should be placed on a platform several feet from the ground so as to lessen the likelihood of the fowls finding and eating the bait. A large number of sparrows may be caught in wire-cage rat-traps baited with a crust.

Bird-lime is useful if smeared on a perch similar in appearance to the one on which the sparrows are accustomed to alight. The disadvantage of this method of bird-catching is that the perch must be watched, and the birds taken as soon as held by the bird-lime.

If every householder were to encourage boys to catch sparrows and take their eggs, the number of these birds would soon be reduced materially throughout the country.

At the same time it is necessary that all who trap sparrows should learn the difference between the harmful house-sparrow and the hedge-sparrow, the linnet and any other bird that may be trapped. It is of the first importance that only the house-sparrows should be destroyed.

CONCLUSION AND RECAPITULATION.

In this section some matters already mentioned are dealt with more fully and others have been introduced.

Annual Loss.

The enormous loss incurred through rat infestation has been pointed out from time to time for many years past, but until the passing of the Rats and Mice (Destruction) Act, 1919, no organized system had been put in force to deal with the matter. It is known that in Great Britain alone, the consumption of and damage to foodstuffs by vermin in stacks, granaries, mills, warehouses and shops; the damage to buildings, goods and merchandise of various kinds; the destruction of poultry and losses in other ways due to rats, amounts still to many millions of pounds sterling annually. The extent of the loss has been variously estimated from £15,000,000 to £75,000,000; the former calculation being pre-war, and even then generally considered to be very far below the real fact. There has been an enormous increase in the rat population since the beginning of the Great War, so that £52,000,000, or in other words one million pounds sterling per week, may be taken as an unexaggerated amount at the present time. However, supposing for the sake of argument that it is a smaller amount, it is sufficiently serious to show that the destruction of rats must be undertaken in a systematic and business-like manner.

Plague.

There is not only the very large annual waste of money to be considered, but the danger of loss of human life from plague and other diseases. Plague is almost sure to occur from time to time now that plague-infected rats have invaded the Eastern Counties. They must continue to obtain an occasional entrance at the ports—in spite of the very excellent work in rat destruction done by the Port Sanitary Authorities—unless a very thorough system of destruction is organized and carried out. Further measures are needed and must be adopted, particularly at the smaller ports, to lessen the possibility of rat invasion. More stringent regulations are needed for clearing rats from ships; especially when they come from or have touched at ports at which plague has occurred, even though the last recorded outbreak took place years ago.

Danger of Plague.

Many people are under the impression that the Great Plague of London which began in December 1664 and is stated to have killed 68,595 human beings (some authorities state as many as 100,000) was entirely ended by the Great Fire of London which raged between September 2 and 6, 1666; but this is not the case. Deaths from plague, in and around London, continued from time to time during the succeeding half century. All infected rats were not destroyed by the fire, and human beings became infected by the fleas that fed on them; perhaps in some cases, the fleas were carried from the rats to human beings by other animals. It is not unlikely that this history will repeat itself in the Eastern Counties and in the districts to which the rats suffering from plague migrate, unless the risk is removed by their destruction.

With the enormous number of rats now in the country and the absence of compulsory arrangements for their organized destruction, an epizootic of plague (corresponding to an epidemic among human beings) may occur at any time among them and spread with great rapidity, resulting in the infection of human beings. Should the outbreak be of the pneumonic form, as occurred at Shotley in 1906, at Freston in 1910 and in London in 1664, the death-rate may readily become very large.

Weil's Disease.

The recent fatal outbreak in Scotland of Weil's disease or spirochætal jaundice (infectious jaundice) has caused special attention to be given to this malady, which is a widespread disease of man, but which probably when it has occurred has not been always recognized. It is now known that it is a prevalent disease among rats and has been found in Japan, America, Germany, France, Belgium and also in several places in Great Britain. Further investigations will probably show that it exists among rats throughout the world. Infectious jaundice (Spirochætosis ictero-hæmorrhagica) is caused by an organism *Leptospira ictero-hæmorrhagica*, which was discovered in 1915 in the urine and kidneys of wild rats in Japan. The seriousness of the disease is shown by four deaths out of the ten individuals who contracted the disease in Scotland. As in the case of plague, an outbreak among human beings appears to be preceded by an epizootic among rats. As yet, the manner in which the disease is conveyed from rat to man is not definitely known; although it is thought that it may be by fleas or by contamination of food or water. It is said to have been transmitted by rat-bite. It is probable that the prevalence of this disease among rats varies in different areas ; but investigations in Great Britain show that it has been found in as large a proportion as 9 per cent. This disease most commonly occurs in Japan, but was met with frequently among the Allied troops in France during the Great War, the trenches being infested with rats.

Rat-bite Fever.

Rat-bite fever or "Sodoku," a relapsing fever of long duration which sometimes follows a rat-bite, has occurred in this country. It has been known for a long time in Japan, and has been described in the United States and elsewhere. The disease is produced by a protozoa, *Spiro-schaudinnia morsus muris* which lives in the mouth of the animal.

Rat Viruses.

Rats are subject to certain epizootic diseases which very closely simulate paratyphoid and which are sometimes intentionally spread by the use of various commercial "rat viruses," the use of which in a separate section has been referred to and condemned. It has been assumed and stated by the vendors of virus, that the causative organisms were harmless to man, but in recent years evidence has accumulated which indicates that serious sickness, and even death of man, may be caused by it.

Rosenau (1910) says "There is practically no difference between the *Bacillus typhi-murium* (rat and mouse typhoid fever) and the paratyphoid bacillus which is the well-known cause of meat-poisoning, and the *B. enteridion* of Jarbues, which is associated with intestinal disorders."

Favus.

Both rats and mice are at times affected by a favus (a form of ringworm encrusted on the scalp) which is occasionally transmissible to man, sometimes indirectly through cats which have preyed upon the diseased rodents.

Entamœbæ.

Of Protozoa, rats and mice not infrequently harbour pathogenic amœbæ, which very closely resemble the entamœbæ of man. In fact, recent experimental work, notably that of Lynch (1915) and of Brug (1919) have shown that rats may be infected by the *Entamœba dysenteriæ* from man and have strongly supported the view that in nature these rodents may be a very definite factor in the spread of these organisms.

Many workers regard the flagellate protozoan parasites *Giardia intestinalis* (*Lamblia*) and *Trichomonas intestinalis* of man as identical with species commonly found in rodents. The evidence is especially definite in the case of *Giardia*, which is now recognized as a fairly common intestinal parasite of man.

Tape-worm.

Of the grosser parasites, the rat harbours at least two species of tape-worm which are transmissible to man. Indeed, one of these, the dwarf tape-worm *Hymenolepis nana*, is the commonest tape-worm of man. On account of its small size, 10-15 mm. in length by 0·5-0·7 mm. in breadth, hitherto this worm had been very generally overlooked and had been regarded merely as a rare accidental parasite in man, until the extensive microscopical examinations of stools in connection with hookworm eradication brought it to light.

It is well known that rats are the chief agents in the propagation of the dangerous trichinosis (measles in meat). Indeed, it is highly probable that rats are the normal hosts of *Trichinella spiralis.*

Stiles, in 1910, wrote regarding trichinosis in man: "This disease will probably never be eradicated from man until rats and mice are practically eradicated, and any rational public-health campaign directed against trichinosis must take the rat into serious consideration. The eradication of rats and mice would be a very substantial contribution toward a reduction and eradication of trichinosis."

Legislation and Officials.

It is evident that if an organized system for the continuous destruction of rats throughout Great Britain is to be carried out efficiently, there must be really effective legislation, with Government and County officials whose business it is to see that rats are destroyed systematically. Summonses must be issued and proceedings taken against those individuals who harbour rats, and disregard the orders to destroy them or fail to fulfil the conditions necessary to reduce their number to a minimum. It has been shown already by the number of rats now in the country in spite of the Rats and Mice (Destruction) Act, 1919, and after all that has been seen and written with regard to the damage which they cause, that it is useless to trust to voluntary action in the matter. Even though they incur considerable loss by the damage done by rats to their property, many people remain careless and indifferent.

Supervision Welcomed.

Supervision with regard to rat destruction by officials of the right type, would be welcomed throughout the length and breadth of the land by all those who are doing their utmost to keep their premises and the area for which they are responsible free from rats. At the present time these men are very heavily handicapped and disheartened by the amount of work entailed, because though there are means of compelling the neighbours to destroy their rats, these means are not employed.

Tuberculosis Inspection Farce.

For efficiency, the organization and arrangements generally must be in the hands of those who have a knowledge of the ways of the world and have learnt something about human nature. Otherwise there may be a repetition of the farce which has been played with regard to the inspection of cattle for tuberculosis.

This matter was put in the hands of the Local Authority. Consequently the veterinary surgeon appointed by the Local Council, of which farmers and their friends may be members, has been expected to condemn the diseased cattle of such farmers, and thus cause annoyance and expense to those upon whose good-will he is dependent for retaining the post which he holds.

County Council.

Supervision of the destruction of rats should be in the hands of the County Council; it will be practically useless to entrust it to a Local Council. Many farmers are on the Boards, and some of them are the worst offenders in the harbouring of rats.

Government and County Council Officials.

The Government and County officials, to be thoroughly efficient, must not be hide-bound by officialism, nor chosen on account of scholastic attainments. They must be selected for their common-sense, tact and ability to deal with men, for they will have to contend with a considerable amount of ignorance, idleness, and deficiency of power in organization in those with whom they come in contact. It must be remembered that these failings are the principal cause of the enormous number of rats now in the country.

Revenue from Rat Destruction.

Unlike most legislation enforced for the benefit of the public, the measures necessary to ensure a systematic destruction of rats would not entail expense to the Government or County. On the contrary, they might become a source of revenue; for if effectually carried out, the fines imposed for disregarding the regulations would more than pay for the expense incurred.

Heavy Fines.

To ensure the Act of 1919 being systematically observed, it will be necessary to make the maximum penalties heavy. At the present time there are very many individuals who have never taken continued or decided measures to get rid of the rats infesting their premises, even if they have taken any steps at all, and many offenders do not know that there is an Act on the Statute Book.

It will be found that small fines, even frequently repeated, will have no lasting effect on men of this type. Only a heavy penalty and the fear of its repetition will rouse them from their lethargy, and make them understand that those who are in authority are determined that the Act shall be carried out.

Fines to Protect the Deserving.

In regard to fines, for whatever negligence imposed, it must be remembered that they are not so much for the punishment of the individual, as for the protection of his neighbours who are doing their utmost to keep their premises free from rats.

Injustice to Deserving.

Let A., B. and C. represent neighbours ; A. and C. are doing their utmost to destroy the rats on their property at considerable expenditure. B. does not trouble his head about vermin, and consequently the rats from his premises are continually passing on to those of his neighbours. It is unfair that A. and C. should not be protected from this rat invasion, and this protection can only be given by compelling B. to do his duty. The Act provides authority ; at present it is not being exercised.

Fines not Penalizing.

It is often stated that there is reluctance to "penalize," by imposing a fine, a man who does not destroy the rats on his premises or fulfil the requirements which are necessary in order to reduce their number to a minimum. It is however contended by the author that such a line of action would not really be penalizing him, but on the contrary, would be conferring a benefit on him. The rats on his property entail greater loss than would be represented by even a considerable fine.

The aspect that receives scanty attention, if any, is the injustice done to the public by not compelling the owner of premises to destroy the rats on them at his own expense. Yet this is the only method by which an efficient and continuous system founded on justice and common-sense can be carried out.

It is evident, therefore, that if there is to be a persistent and determined effort to get rid of rats,

> EVERYONE MUST BE HELD RESPONSIBLE FOR THE RATS ON HIS PREMISES AND THEY MUST BE KILLED AT *HIS* EXPENSE IF HE DOES NOT HAVE THEM DESTROYED.

Unless this is enforced under the Rats and Mice (Destruction) Act, 1919, there will be no permanent diminution in the number of rats in Great Britain.

Invasion by Rats.

From time to time, premises and even whole districts become invaded (sometimes to a serious extent) by rats which have gathered there as a result of a change in conditions elsewhere. It may be in consequence of the area which they inhabited being submerged by a flood, or because a host of rats has migrated ; or by reason of a large breeding ground in the vicinity, as frequently occurs when there is a municipal refuse-heap or other collection of material or food suitable for rats. In any of these cases it is unfair for the owner of the premises to be individually responsible for the destruction of the rats that have invaded his property. In such circumstances the Rats Officer of the county should avail himself immediately of the opportunity afforded for the wholesale destruction of rats, confined to a comparatively small area.

Rats Order, 1918.

The Rats Order, dated August 28, 1918, made by the Food Controller, under the Defence of the Realm Regulations, gave power to a Local Authority to go on to land or into a building infested with rats, when the owner or occupier had disregarded the directions given to free the land or building. He was empowered to enter within seven days or more of the notice being given, and to remove all rubbish or other materials likely to attract rats. The Local Authority was also empowered to recover from such owner or occupier any expenses incurred, so far as such expenses are directly attributable to the failure of such owner or occupier to carry out his obligations under these directions.

Inspection Necessary.

This Order was satisfactory as far as it went; but it did not provide for organized inspection to discover all the places to which the Order should refer. None can suppose that the occupier of town premises, or a farmer or land-owner will himself inform the Authorities.

Not enough Dogs.

Considering the many millions of rats now in Great Britain, it is evident that at the present time there are not nearly enough terriers available to kill them. Dogs are essential for rat destruction, but few farmers or game-keepers have dogs for this purpose, the cost of the licence being the chief reason for not keeping them.

Even when rats have been caught uninjured in a trap, or when they have been driven from their holes by water, a ferret, or noxious fumes, one or more dogs are required to kill them, for often two or three bolt from different holes almost simultaneously. In towns where they are trapped in a warehouse or cellar by a bag of sand being dropped over the hole by which they have entered, several dogs may be necessary. When the premises are overrun with rats, a considerable number may be imprisoned in the first few times that they are caught thus, and it would not be advisable to send only one dog amongst them.

Free Licence for Dogs.

If, therefore, there is to be a continual and determined war against rats, the keeping of terriers for their destruction ought to be encouraged by no tax being imposed on certain classes of individuals; the number of dogs allowed free from tax being not less than two.

Such an arrangement would not authorize unlicensed dogs, but merely create two forms of licence; one obtained by payment, the other, preferably of a different colour, free from tax and marked for rat destruction.

Magistrate to Control Free Licences.

Those who are allowed to keep terriers free from tax should be those on whose premises or arable or pasture land rats may be found; or those whose duties lead them to destroy vermin; or who, by keeping ferrets, have the means of destroying rats, and would do so either for pleasure or profit. Free licences should also be granted at the discretion of the Authorities to other individuals. Many boys throughout the country would ferret rats on every available opportunity if they possessed dogs trained to ferrets; but as neither they nor their parents can afford the dog licences, ferrets are not kept, ferrets being useless without dogs. Obviously there should be no hard and fast rule that these dogs must belong to one individual.

The spirit of the order would be complied with if they belonged to members of the same club, association, or family or its dependents, who often live off the premises. It must be borne in mind that what is required is the means to obtain two or more dogs trained to ferrets for the purpose of destroying rats. A magistrate, however, should be empowered to cancel this privilege, if the dogs are used for an improper purpose, or are not kept under sufficient control.

Licence Injustice to Rat-catcher.

A rat-catcher cannot do his work without dogs; they are as necessary to him as a sheep-dog is to a shepherd; it is therefore a gross injustice that he should have to pay for a licence for each of his dogs while sheep-dogs are untaxed.

Loss of Revenue, if any, Compensated.

It is obvious that dogs kept for rat destruction by those who have not kept dogs before would not produce a loss to revenue; but supposing for the sake of argument that some of the dogs for which a tax is now paid are retained for this purpose, the loss incurred by fewer licences might be compensated for by increasing the tax on dogs of other breeds, including toy-terriers; the term "toy" being determined by weight (say 8 lb.) at or below which a dog is in a condition which enables him to take active exercise. This would prevent the tax being evaded by dogs being overfed until their weight exceeded the limit. Toy-terriers might be specially taxed, as they are not kept for a useful purpose but merely as pets.

Loss of Revenue Comparatively Trivial.

It must be remembered that the object aimed at is to prevent the present annual loss calculated at £52,000,000.

So that if a loss of a few pounds were incurred to the Exchequer by the relaxation of the dog tax, the amount is very far below the gain to the country by the destruction of rats. It is also seen that the deficit might be made up in other ways.

Rats' Holes.

If it were made compulsory for rats' holes to be stopped as soon as their occupants had been driven out, an open hole would signify OCCUPATION BY RATS. The existence of the hole after warning would stand for HARBOURING RATS, and this should be considered a serious offence and entail a heavy fine.

Holes to be Closed.

The holes to be closed are all those that are out-of-doors; or in a detached building; or in a row or group of buildings; or in the door-ways or outer walls of an inhabited dwelling, whether detached or otherwise. Holes inside a house, or an outbuilding which is not detached, are often best left open; so that the rats coming to them from neighbouring houses or premises may be blocked and killed, or caught in a trap kept set throughout the year to secure them on their arrival.

Keeping Rats out of Buildings.

In very many instances it would entail only a small outlay to prevent rats entering buildings. A few square inches of galvanized sheet-iron nailed to the door is all that would be necessary; many other holes could be stopped in an equally simple manner. If this stopping were made compulsory, a sheet of galvanized iron would be kept on many premises and be cut as wanted. Indeed ironmongers would probably stock pieces of galvanized sheet-iron 3×2, $4\frac{1}{2} \times 2\frac{1}{2}$ and 6×3 in. with holes bored for nails, so that they could be easily affixed by anyone. These sizes would cover most holes gnawed by rats, and mend or protect the edges of doors and door frames. If a threshold had to be renewed, in most cases a new top to the existing one would be all that was necessary, the hollow being filled in with wood or cement, and if a piece of iron were fastened to its edge, as described in the Section "In An Outbuilding," it would last for very many years.

Traps should always be kept Set.

The necessity for keeping traps set throughout the year cannot be too strongly emphasized, for rats are frequently passing from place to place and will be caught on arrival before they have done any damage, if the traps have been properly placed. Poisoning large areas two or three times a year, and killing rats wherever they can be found by any suitable means is essential; but this alone will never suffice to secure the desired result. The premises around most small detached houses require half-a-dozen "Terrier" Signal Runs or "Terrier" Death Run traps, and in very many instances this number may be doubled with advantage.

Result of keeping Traps always Set.

The author keeps a dozen traps set throughout the year; and although no rats can be found on the premises, nor are there any houses or buildings in close proximity, yet the traps catch annually from 50 to 100 rats, generally at night. Such a large number would not be trapped if this simple system were adopted universally. Its utility is obvious. The traps are very little trouble.

The steel traps are sprung, and oiled, before being re-set, and the Death Run traps merely sprung and re-set on the first Monday in each month, and not visited otherwise unless the signal shows that a trap has been sprung. Many rats would be caught in most poultry yards if traps were kept continually set. This might be made compulsory. An individual who can afford to buy poultry can afford to buy traps, and it would be to his interest to do so. The number of rats will never be permanently reduced to a minimum until traps are kept set throughout the year in all places to which rats have been, or may go.

Trap all Pigsties.

Where there are pigs, rats will be found sooner or later; and a very large number of rats would be killed annually if it were made compulsory for traps to be kept set around a sty, the number being regulated by the size or number of the sties, and the nature of the surroundings. If pig keepers were registered and the sties inspected from time to time, the Authorities would be able to prevent the vicinity of a sty becoming a rat centre as is frequently the case at the present time.

First Quality 5-inch Rabbit-Traps.

For trapping, if steel traps are used, first quality 5-in. rabbit traps should be insisted upon.

Purchasing Traps a Paying Investment.

Money spent in keeping rats from buildings, and in purchasing traps, is not a useless expenditure; but a sound and well paying investment for the owner or lessee.

If the owner of the premises has traps of smaller size, he can of course set them; but they should be additional to a suitable number of 5-in. rabbit-traps and not used as a substitute for them. It has already been mentioned in the Section "Traps" that a 5-in. rabbit-trap generally kills a rat if the trap is kept properly oiled, whereas one of smaller size merely holds him a prisoner and therefore inflicts unnecessary pain.

Poison and Smoke-Ferrets.

It is desirable that coloured poisoned meal and smoke-ferrets should be procurable in every district; and the places where they may be obtained officially registered and made known. Many individuals would prefer to purchase poison ready-made, rather than have the trouble of making it for themselves, and would choose to buy their smoke-ferrets ready for use.

The regulations might contain a formula for all poisoned meal or food that is sold as the official preparation, and arrangements made for it to be sampled for analysis from time to time to prevent adulteration. The fines for departing from the standard might be made sufficient to cover the cost of the analysis and other expenses entailed; and if they were sufficiently heavy, it would not pay either to adulterate or depart from the official formulæ. The free use of this poisoned meal or food would be assisted further if its cost to the public were controlled, the price being marked on the tin; the sum named, however, allowing the retail dealer a fair profit for his trouble. Arrangements could easily be made for the public to procure the official preparations direct from a Government depot, County Council or authorized agent, in sealed tins at a fixed price. This would not interfere with the proprietary poisons now on the market, such as Ratinol[1]

[1] 80, Coleman Street, London, E.C.2.

and Londovus[1]; it would merely give the public a more extended choice. That some of the proprietary articles are too dear is shown in a striking way by a comparatively recent report. Some work done with poison prepared at the Government laboratory for less than £10, cost more than £100 when a proprietary article was used.

Simultaneous and Continuous Destruction.

Rats ought to be killed simultaneously and continuously in every city, town, and village, as well as in rural districts. Special attention must be paid to all ports, for rats are frequently coming ashore from ships; the food in the warehouses and on the quays offers a permanent attraction to them. No ultimate good will result from rat destruction in the rural districts only, for rats are constantly passing from cities, towns and villages into the country.

Importation of Rats.

The importation of rats would be greatly diminished if it were made compulsory for all ships coming into port to be fumigated in the most effective modern manner, and if measures taken to prevent rats coming ashore were strictly enforced even at small ports.

Blocking and Trapping for Cities and Towns.

As far as cities and towns are concerned, the work must be done almost entirely by blocking and trapping; and by far the larger number of rats will be destroyed by the former method. Obviously the areas suitable for ferreting and flooding are comparatively small; and it may happen that poisoning is inexpedient on account of

[1] The London Hygienic Chemical Co., Wansey Street, Walworth London, S.E.17.

the nuisance which might be created by decomposing bodies of the rats, and the trouble and expense incurred in removing them from beneath flooring and other places.

Blocking Trap.

Where rats frequent large yards in which there are boxes, crates, goods, or other materials which cannot be conveniently removed, blocking traps, fully described in the Section "Traps," will be found useful for reducing their number quickly. These traps will be found very useful also in markets, hotels, restaurants, on the premises of knackers, slaughterers, butchers, bakers, provision merchants, and in other places to which rats are being continually drawn for food.

Rat Destruction at Ports.

At ports, when the rats lie in inaccessible places, they may be caught in large numbers with very little trouble, in blocking traps. Where this can be safely done, it is advisable in the first instance materially to lessen the number of rats by poisoning. The poison should be put down after carefully feeding the rats for a few days in order to draw as many as possible to the places selected.

Public Knowledge Elementary.

Although most householders and occupiers of premises on which rats exist would be willing to take measures for their destruction, yet it must be remembered that the public as a whole, possesses only the most elementary knowledge as to the means to be adopted to gain this end, and this despite the information which has been conveyed in the past to Local Authorities throughout the country.

Organization for Blocking Out on a Large Scale.

"Blocking" is extremely simple both in the arrangements required for its effective working, and in the actual operation. Yet to insure its being carried out properly on a large scale, it would be necessary for an organized body of men or lads to show householders and others how to do it; and, when required, to fix the screw-eyes or staples.

Destruction of Fleas.

The men thus employed could explain to householders and others the advantage of working simultaneously a row or block of houses; as described in the Section "Rats in the House, Shop, or Warehouse." They could point out that it would be well to keep a pail or other receptacle containing a solution of izal, cyllin, or some other germicide, and to submerge the rats in it as soon as killed, so as to destroy the fleas and other insects infesting them. If this were done systematically throughout the country, it would largely assist in destroying the plague-infected fleas now distributed over a larger area than is generally supposed.

Municipal Refuse Heap.

A municipal refuse heap, or a railway company's dump of refuse matter, is usually infested with rats; and forms not only a large feeding-ground but also breeding-ground both for rats and flies.

It is now so well known that flies are the cause of outbreaks of infantile diarrhœa, typhoid fever and other diseases that from a sanitary point of view, the existence of a refuse heap ought not to be allowed. All the food in them, both for rats and flies; and all larvæ of flies, might be destroyed by keeping the refuse heap burning on the outside from one year's end to the other; treating it as if it were a heap of clay being burnt for ballast. The only difference is that no slack coal would be required to keep the fire burning on the outside of the heap.

There would always be a sufficient amount of cinders, particles of wood, paper, and other inflammatory material to ensure the destruction of the added refuse.

Collection of Refuse.

Instead of carts to collect the refuse, it would be necessary to have trolleys; on which were placed receptacles of a suitable size to be lifted from the trolley by a hand-crane to enable their contents to be shot on to the burning heap. A few air-shafts, which could be shifted day by day, would be all that would be necessary to keep the fire burning.

Poisoning Flies.

With regard to flies, it is greatly to be regretted that it is not made compulsory, during certain hot months of the year, for vendors of meat, fish, fruit, cakes, groceries, &c., to cover their goods with butter-cloth or other suitable material, and also to keep in proximity to the food exposed for sale, saucers holding some absorbent material which could be kept moist with a solution of formaldehyde of a definite strength (not less than 1 in 40), by means of some dripping arrangement.

Rats in Barns and Stacks.

A very decided step would be taken towards the destruction of rats throughout the country, if the places where they now congregate in large numbers to obtain food, were done away with, or were so constructed that vermin could no longer assemble in them or, having assembled, could be dislodged easily.

Away from cities and towns, by far the most important of these places are barns and stacks. The floor of all barns, and the ground floor of all granaries, mills, and other places in which food stuffs are stored or placed, should be concreted, and the doorways and walls made rat-proof.

In districts where concrete or cement floors are liable to sweat, the concrete must be covered with blocks of wood or boards, the latter, however, not as a raised floor.

Construction of Upper Floors.

The upper floors of granaries, mills, &c., ought to be made of rat-proof material, or without a ceiling beneath them; otherwise rats are liable to lie concealed between the floor and the ceiling. If tongued and grooved flooring boards were used, dust would not fall through.

It should be made compulsory for all stacks of corn, beans, peas, &c., to be built on staddles, unless the stack is threshed before a fixed official date.

Date for Threshing Stacks Built on the Ground.

November 1 would provide a good date limit within which all stacks built on the ground must be threshed. In most years many rats have left the hedgerows by that time and have gone to the stacks and buildings; after that date many more go to them week by week. In the case of high-lying districts where the harvest may be late, the last day for threshing stacks on the ground might be postponed until November 15 In the event of special circumstances arising to prevent stacks being threshed by the dates mentioned, the Authority responsible for the administration might grant an exemption.

Obviously no good will be done by making such a law, unless it is enforced. The penalty for leaving a stack unthreshed after the date fixed, and the additional penalty for each week that it so remains, should be made sufficiently heavy to outweigh considerably any possible rise in the market price of the stacked product.

Maximum Penalties Heavy.

It must be remembered that in some parts of the country corn stacks are built to a large size, and contain a considerable amount of grain; so that a rise in the market price adds considerably to the value.

Threshing-Machines.

At the present time there is a shortage of threshing-machines and engines in many parts of the country, and unless this condition is altered, a farmer might urge the shortage as a reason for his ground stack remaining unthreshed after November 1 or 15 respectively.

Although those who let out threshing-machines and engines make a profit, it is obvious that they can only do so by limiting the number kept to the supply of available labour, and the means of providing other employment for the men when not at this work. It frequently happens that a sufficient number of machines for the requirements of the district are not available, and the farmer must wait until a machine can be sent to him. As these labour conditions are unlikely to alter materially in the immediate future, the shortage will probably continue unless other measures are adopted.

Additional Threshing-Machines.

To remedy this defect, each Agricultural Executive Committee, County Council, or other authority dealing with these matters might place threshing-machines and engines at convenient centres outside the districts in which machines are kept; and when the engines are not required for threshing, they might let them out on hire for cultivating the land, hauling, winding, sawing wood, &c.

Men with Threshing-Machines.

The staff of men to go with the machines could be drawn from those permanently on the register of the County Council; and those engaged in ferreting or otherwise destroying rats, could take their dogs with them to kill any rats in a stack built on the ground. These men might supply at a fixed charge, and place in position the sacking that should surround every stack to prevent the escape of rats and mice while it is being threshed. To thus surround a stack should be made compulsory. (See Section, "On a Farm.")

Travelling Hut.

The question of a travelling hut (such as is used by road makers) for men engaged in rural work might be considered for the districts in which housing accommodation is not available. The men might be employed within reasonable walking distance of the hut for several weeks together.

Space below Stack on Staddles.

For the use of staddles to be effectual in keeping rats out of a stack, it would be necessary to make it an offence to place anything beneath the stack they support. There must be nothing to afford means for the invasion of the stack by rats or mice; nor must any article be left in close proximity to the stack to enable them to enter it.

Height of Staddles.

The height of staddles would be best fixed at three feet six inches from the ground as the standard level for the projecting rim which makes them unclimbable, or for the upper edge of an unclimbable surface. The United States Department of Agriculture wisely advises that the unclimbable barrier be "at least" three feet above the surface of the ground.

Advantages of Staddles.

If placing on staddles, stacks which are not threshed before the dates mentioned, and rendering barns, &c., rat-proof, were made compulsory, no farmer would have just cause for complaint. The money spent in erecting staddles, concreting the floors of all barns, granaries, &c., and making the doorways and walls rat-proof, would soon be re-paid many times over by the corn saved. Then again the corn in the stacks would mature better, because the bottom of the stack as well as the sides would be exposed to the air.

As but few stacks are built on staddles at the present time, and most of those in use are too low to be efficient, a large number would be required in the first instance. The country needs a number sufficient to raise all the stacks containing seed food out of the reach of rats, and thus remove their largest winter feeding and breeding grounds.

Material and Shape Unimportant.

The shape and material of which staddles are made are of no consequence provided the staddles are unsurmountable, and obviously their cost would be materially lessened if they were supplied in large quantities ready for use; either to be erected in the stack-yard or in the field in which the corn is grown.

Importation of Wooden Staddles.

In the case of wooden staddles, some might be obtained from the firms that send ship-loads of pit-props to this country, and might be distributed from the ports. They could be sold cut to the proper height, with a shoulder and surface for the upper and lower horizontal support to rest on respectively, and with holes bored for the bolts. The horizontal supports could be supplied at the same time. (See Section "Rats on a Shooting Estate and on a Farm.")

Two or three men going from farm to farm erecting the staddles would probably do the work better and more quickly, and therefore at less cost to the farmer, than men engaged locally who were without experience and had no pattern stand to guide them.

Standard Pattern.

If, however, the farmer prefers to do all the work during the slack season, it would be advisable for him to have drawings and measurements to work by. These could be kept in stock and supplied by the County Council.

Dutch Barns.

Dutch barns could easily be rendered rat-proof by bolting horizontal floor supports to the uprights and rendering the latter unclimbable; but unless it were made compulsory for the whole area to be thus treated, a portion might be left for carts, farm implements, &c.,

and rats might be able to climb or jump from these on to the floor.

Government Loan.

A Government loan at a low rate of interest would prevent the plea of "want of means" being raised as an excuse for not immediately undertaking alterations with a view to protecting corn from rats. Such work as is required at once is the concreting and preparing suitable barn floors. Staddles might be supplied by Government and paid for on the hire system.

The form for application for the loan and the money granted might be made obtainable at any postal money office. If the form were in duplicate and had to be countersigned by the Superintendent of Police for the District, or other responsible authority instructed to retain one of the forms, he would become acquainted with the purpose for which the application was made, and could see that the work was done within the prescribed period.

The amount of capital due, together with the interest to date, could be paid quarterly to the local tax collector.

Landlord to be Repaid.

In the event of the landlord being called upon to concrete and render rat-proof the buildings on his tenant's farm or other places, as the latter would benefit very materially by the amount of corn saved, the landlord ought to be empowered to add to the rent an amount which would repay within a given period the capital expenditure together with the interest on the money.

When all unnecessary openings into a building have been stopped as described in the Sections "Rats in an Outbuilding and in a Stable," it would not be difficult to kill the rats in it. With premises thus cleared of rats, and all stacks containing seed-food placed on staddles out of their reach, so that they could no longer take shelter in them, only those in the banks of the country around would be left to be destroyed. This work, if undertaken in a systematic manner with the conditions for doing it made suitable, would cause a very large decrease in the number of rats throughout any given district.

Superfluous Vegetation.

At the present time, however, it would be impossible to do this work efficiently. A very large number of hedgerows, banks, sides of ditches and of ponds and other places are covered with superfluous vegetation, in consequence of which rats cannot be easily dislodged. In many cases the brambles and other vegetation stretch from bank to bank across a ditch concealing the holes, and creating a covered way along which rats pass in safety.

Annual Clearance.

Legislation is therefore required to compel the removal annually of superfluous vegetation from all banks, ditches, and edges of ponds, streams, and other collection of water, in all places in which such vegetation has harboured or may harbour rats. Drainage Orders under the new Act are doing something in this direction, but are not working quickly enough. If the removal were effected between July 31 and December 31, the rats could be destroyed at the least busy season of the year and before new vegetation concealed their holes. This annual task would not be heavy after the first time it was done, but in some instances, to start with, the growth of many years would need to be removed.

Bad Farming.

It must be remembered that such conditions are generally associated with bad farming. Then most of the overgrown banks, &c., are a mass of weeds, the seeds from which are blown and carried by birds, not only over the farmer's own ground, but over that of his neighbours. It must be remembered that in some foreign countries farmers are punished for growing weeds that seed their neighbours' fields.

Fence one side of Ditch only.

The inspection of hedgerows would be rendered easier in many cases if a fence or bushes were allowed on one side only of a ditch—unless good reason could be shown.

In districts where labour is scarce, men specially engaged and provided with the necessary implements could go from farm to farm to do the clearing, and would do it more quickly and better than an ordinary farm labourer working at it occasionally. These men could also be employed to clear the hedgerows, &c., by order of an inspector when the farmer had undertaken the work, but failed to do it within the prescribed time. In this case the charge ought to be more than the usual rate, the extra payment going to the County Council. A small charge made for the use of the implements would soon repay the cost of purchasing and the expense of sharpening and keeping them in order.

Some Advantages of Rat Destruction.

As only loss is incurred by harbouring rats, let them be destroyed as quickly as possible, and let arrangements be made to ensure any future arrivals being killed without delay. If this were done, not only would the number of rats now in Great Britain be very materially reduced permanently, and the shocking annual waste of food-stuffs and pecuniary loss from damage be considerably lessened, but the danger from plague and infectious jaundice which now exists in a far greater degree than is generally realized would be averted. Measly pork from British-fed pigs would also become practically unknown, and the spread of horse-influenza, mange, distemper, ringworm, and "foot and mouth" disease and other ailments would be curtailed.

Summary.

To clear premises from rats and prevent them again becoming numerous:—

(1) Stop all unnecessary openings into buildings through which a rat can pass, and cover with a grating all openings that are required for use.

(2) Destroy all the rats that are on the premises.

(3) Keep traps set throughout the year.

To destroy existing rats they may be driven from their holes by:—

Water: Section "Flooding Out."
Ferrets: Section "Ferreting."
Noxious Fumes: Section "Fumigation."

They may be killed in a cellar, warehouse, &c., after the holes by which they entered have been

Blocked: Section "Blocking."

Their numbers may be reduced by:—

Poison: Section "Poisoning."

When there are only a few they may be

Trapped : Section " Traps " and also " Trapping."

Snared : Section " Snaring."

To enable rats to be easily destroyed in the future, and their number kept to the minimum, the following conditions are essential :—

Run traps, or steel traps placed in runs, to be kept set throughout the year against all buildings to which rats are likely to go or to pass while seeking food or shelter. No poultry-house, poultry-enclosure or pig-sty to be without traps always set.

Sections : " Rats in an Outbuilding."
" Rats in a Yard."
" Rats in a Fowl-house."
" Rats in a Pigsty."

To keep rats out of a building every doorway must have a suitable threshold ; and all thresholds sufficiently worn to give passage to a rat be made good. Thresholds must be kept in repair, and unnecessary openings into the building stopped.

Section : " Rats in an Outbuilding."

All necessary openings such as those for cellar windows, or stable or wash-house floor-gutters, must be covered with wire-work or a grating.

Sections : " Rats in a House, Shop, or Warehouse."
" Rats in a Stable."

To keep the number of rats down on a farm, all stacks containing wheat, barley, oats, beans, peas or other seed-food must be placed on staddles, unless threshed before November 1 or 15, as previously stated.

Section : Conclusion.

All staddles must be made with the unclimbable barrier or upper edge of the unclimbable surface not less than 42 in. from the ground.

Sections : "Rats on a Shooting Estate and on a Farm." Conclusion.

The County Council should insist upon having a stack which contains more than a few rats or mice threshed at once.

Section : "A Scheme for the Organized Destruction of Rats throughout Great Britain."

Superfluous vegetation must be removed annually from all fences, banks, ditches, and the edges of ponds, streams and other collections of water, in places in which such vegetation has harboured or may harbour rats.

Sections : "Rats on a Shooting Estate and on a Farm." Conclusion.

For the general destruction of rats, rat-catchers' dogs should be untaxed, and also other dogs kept for the purpose.

Section : Conclusion.

Terriers, to the number of two, owned by the landlord or lessee of premises on which rats may be found, or of arable or pasture land, or by a game-keeper or anyone who keeps ferrets, should be free from tax; the dogs not necessarily to be the actual property of these individuals, provided they belong to members of his or her family, or to dependents, or to members of a club or association.

Section : Conclusion.

APPENDIX.

The author has expressed already in the body of the book his grave doubts with regard to the efficient administration of the Rats and Mice (Destruction) Act, if controlled only by Government Departments. At the same time he realizes that criticism to be helpful must be constructive.

This is his excuse for presenting a long considered scheme of Rat Destruction that may serve to render the Act effective, if his fears of its inefficiency under Government control prove to be justified.

The County as the True Executive Basis.

For organizing rat-destruction the existing police force might be utilized, as the stations are usually in convenient centres. The extra work entailed on the superintendent would not be heavy, and could be compensated by a yearly payment from the fund created and maintained by the fines imposed.

Controlling Authority.

The inspection might be made by a constable selected on account of his intelligence and tact and, if thought advisable, he could also be given extra payment. Alternatively, the work might be done by an official not connected with the force. In any case a report would be made to the controlling authority when the regulations were not complied with. It might be desirable for the head of this special department to be a Port Sanitary or Public Health official, as far as cities are concerned; and a County official in each county outside city areas, with assistants if they were found necessary.

Permanent Staff.

There must be a permanent staff of men and lads for rat-destruction, and a list of those wishing to do this work could be kept at the police-station. There would be no difficulty in obtaining such a body, and there are a large number of police constables who would gladly earn additional money when off duty by devoting some of their spare time to the town branches of this work. With an organized staff for rat-destruction, and rat-catchers registered by the police, the public would be able to obtain what it has long wanted, viz., the services of men for rat-destruction, and of rat-catchers who are under official control.

Charge per Rat.

The charge per rat should be increased when the ferreting, trapping, or other measures of rat-destruction are done under a compulsory order of an inspector. This would be an inducement for a rat-catcher to be employed voluntarily at the usual lower rates, if the owner of the property did not otherwise arrange for the rats to be killed.

Rat-catcher's Pay.

Although the charge for ferreting and destroying rats under an order, should be greater than the usual rate, it should not in any way benefit the rat-catcher; but on the contrary, the remuneration to him, should be, if anything, on rather a lower scale. This would not only counteract laxness in private employment, but would make it necessary for a larger number of rats to be destroyed for the ordinary day's wage to be earned under an inspector's order.

Rat-catcher's Expenses.

When fixing the price to be paid to the rat-catcher for rats killed, it ought to be remembered that he has preliminary and working expenses which may be heavy. Dogs have to be procured and fed, ferrets procured and housed, and the requisites for keeping dogs and ferrets obtained; as well as those for ferreting and trapping. The cost of these items might well be onerous to a man without capital.

A rat-catcher employed daily throughout the year must have a number of ferrets. Not only are several required for use each day, as they work hard and want rest from time to time, but one or more ferrets are often severely bitten, and have to be kept from work for some days until their wounds have healed. Ferrets, moreover, often die from these wounds; and frequently it is the best ferrets that get killed, for they have fought the most desperately against heavy odds.

Number of Rat-catcher's Dogs.

With regard to the number of dogs that should be kept, two are essential; but double this number is often required, and even more when ferreting buildings. A rat-catcher should always keep more than two; so that one that has been injured, or is not well, can be left at home without detriment to his master's work.

Licence Injustice to Rat-catcher.

A rat-catcher cannot do his work without dogs, they are as necessary to him as a sheep-dog is to a shepherd;

it is therefore a gross injustice that he should have to pay for a licence for each dog while sheep-dogs remain untaxed.

With rat-catchers under police control, the number of dogs kept could be known and registered; but every inducement should be offered to a rat-catcher to keep a full number of dogs, as it enables his work to be done more thoroughly.

Supervision of Rat-catchers.

It must not be forgotten that the work of some rat-catchers requires supervision, to prevent, as far as possible, rats being deliberately left to re-stock premises and thus provide work in the future.

Reward for Information.

A reward for information as to where rats are to be found, would materially assist in freeing a district from them and preventing the formation of colonies. The fund for this payment might be raised by setting aside for the purpose a percentage of the fines.

Rat-pits.

From time to time the re-introduction of rat-pits is recommended with the object of giving an incentive to the capture of rats; and as an argument in their favour, reference is made to the large number of rats killed by dogs in the various matches.

It is obvious, however, that the re-establishment of rat matches would necessitate the existence of a large number of rats for the contests; and they would have to be obtained in a limited area if they were supplied at a low rate. Matches would then tend to prevent the number of rats in the country being reduced to a minimum, as in this case it would be difficult to procure even a few rats on a given date.

Rat Clubs and Payment for Dead Rats.

At the present time the popular proposal for waging a more or less universal war against these destructive animals is the establishment of rat-clubs; or an arrangement by which public bodies pay a fixed price for each dead rat. It should be obvious that these methods are doomed to failure because they are not based on sound business principles, and are devoid of a perpetual incentive. Although by the expenditure of a corresponding amount of money a large number of rats may be killed, and some areas may be practically freed from rats for a time ; those who earn a living by killing rats will not wish to destroy them utterly.

Not Business Method.

As the destruction of rats is principally an advantage to the owner of the premises harbouring them, an organization which arranges for neighbours, or a public body to pay him or his servant for killing them for his own or his master's benefit, cannot be regarded as an organization to be countenanced by business men.

Mistake to Pay for each Dead Rat.

It will be found, as a general principle, to be a mistake for authorities to pay for each dead rat brought to them, although this plan may be of use in some restricted areas.

Never Pay for a Tail.

Payment should be made only for each rat or rat's head, and never for a rat's tail. It must not be forgotten that tailless rats can produce descendants as readily as those which have not been maimed for reward. Some of those in authority, as well as other individuals, are well aware that payment for each rat killed, may lead to abuses such as the breeding of rats or the importation of dead rats into the district. Instances have come to their knowledge where both these dishonest practices have been employed.

No Incentive to Kill a Few.

The greatest incentive throughout the world to continuous and determined action is self-interest; and this will always be found to be the mainspring of constant work. Therefore, as long as there are a large number of rats to be killed, many men will be active in their destruction and ever ready to take the money for the bodies which they deposit. When the number of rats becomes materially reduced, and a day's work results in only a few rats being obtained; many men will cease killing rats so that the number may again increase and enable them to earn a large day's wage as before.

Rat-Rate Unjust.

A rate levied by a public body to provide funds for rat-destruction would be a gross injustice; and it would, moreover, defeat its object. It would be an injustice, because those who have the intelligence to realize that it is to their advantage to keep their premises free from rats, and who do their utmost to attain this object, would have to contribute in addition for the employment of men engaged to kill their neighbour's rats. The larger their own farm or property, the greater would be their own out-of-pocket expenses; but nevertheless, the rate levied in their case would be heavier than that of many of their neighbours on account of the area which they represent.

Then again those who have no rats on their premises would be called upon to pay for the destruction of rats on the premises of those who ought to pay for them to be killed, for the reason already mentioned. The demand would, therefore, be very strongly resented, and justly so.

Object Defeated.

The object of the rate would be defeated because many, if not most, individuals would not spend money to keep their premises free from rats, when they had already contributed to a fund specially constituted to deal with this matter.

The Rats and Mice (Destruction) Bill, 1919, empowers the authorities to impose fines on those who do not destroy the vermin on their premises. Let the Act be strictly enforced.

A SCHEME FOR THE ORGANIZED DESTRUCTION OF RATS THROUGHOUT GREAT BRITAIN.

It is not suggested that the following scheme should be regarded as final, but only as a skeleton organization, to be clothed and adapted to the various conditions that have to be dealt with and considered.

There is nothing here that conflicts with the purpose of the Rats and Mice (Destruction) Act, 1919. Any additional powers that are necessary might be sought through Parliament to their full extent; indeed, unless the present Act is administered more strictly, it will hardly serve the purposes of its promoters.

Official Control.

The organization, arrangements, and supreme control to be in the hands of a County Official; the Rats Officer for choice, working in conjunction with a Commissioner of Police or the Chief Constable of the county.

The County Official to have one or more assistants if required.

Unless otherwise arranged with the Commissioner of Police or the Chief Constable of the county, the Superintendent of Police of the district to receive orders regarding rat-destruction from the County Official, or his assistant; and to be made responsible for the carrying out of the work in his district.

To enable cities and towns to be efficiently inspected, the usual method of division into areas is recommended.

INSPECTION.

Farms and all premises to be visited; hedgerows, banks, coverts, &c., inspected; and orders issued :—

(1) That all rat-holes are to be flooded, ferreted, or smoked; and afterwards immediately closed.

(2) That all doorways are to have a suitable threshold; and all faulty thresholds, sufficiently worn to give passage to a rat, to be made good.

(3) That any unnecessary hole or aperture through which a rat may enter a house or other building is to be closed.

(4) That every air aperture under flooring near the ground-level, is to be guarded efficiently by a grating.

(5) That a suitable iron grating is to be kept over the aperture through a wall made for a gutter drain, whether from a stable, dairy, laundry or other building.

(6) That the flooring, walls, doors and doorways of barns, granaries and all other places in which grain or other foodstuffs are placed or stored, be inspected once or more often annually. Notice to be given to the Superintendent of Police immediately the barn, granary, &c., is sufficiently empty for inspection. If this is not done, it may be cleared for inspection at the expense of the occupier of the premises who, in addition, will be liable to a fine.

(7) That all fences, banks, ditches, sides of ponds, streams and other collections of water, be cleared annually of superfluous vegetation in places in which such vegetation has harboured or may harbour rats.

(8) That a suitable trap or traps be kept set throughout the year around every pig-sty, and poultry-house and poultry-enclosure.

(9) That staddles be inspected to see that they are of the proper height; and notice be taken as to whether the stack they support is being converted into a cover for implements, &c., which might afford the means of invasion of the stack by rats or mice.

(10) That notice be taken at an inspection as to whether any other requirements have been neglected; and if so, arrange that measures be adopted to ensure their being complied with immediately.

(11) That premises be visited immediately after being ferreted, and especially after being ferreted by order of an official; and a note made of any rat-holes found open, either from not having been closed after the ferreting, or because a rat has opened them in leaving a burrow that has been ferreted. A hole of this latter description clearly indicates that one or more rats have been left in a burrow, for no rat would make a fresh hole into a burrow through which ferrets had lately passed.

All premises to be revisited after an order has been given, and after a reasonable time has been allowed for its execution, to ascertain whether or not the full instruction has been carried out.

Organization.

The Superintendent, or County Rats Officer appointed by the County Council, to receive reports from Constables and others as to where rats are likely to be found, and if satisfied with the correctness of the statements made, to issue a notice that the rats must be destroyed within a given period.

Arrangements to be made with neighbouring districts or counties with regard to the boundary fences, in order that they may be kept free from rats.

The Superintendent or Rats Officer, to report to the rat authority when rat-holes are frequently found unclosed after a particular rat-catcher has ferreted them, or if there are often holes from which rats have escaped from the burrows after he has closed them. The Superintendent, or Rats Officer, must also report when he considers that the rat-catcher has not taken sufficient care to expel as many rats as possible from the burrows.

The maximum fine in all cases should be sufficiently heavy to act as a deterrent; leaving a rat's hole occupied or unclosed ought to be regarded as a specially serious offence.

Fines to be placed to a special account for payment of working expenses; and to provide a fund for rewarding those who give information as to where rats may be found; if in the opinion of the Rats Officer or Superintendent of Police such rats would not otherwise have been discovered. Obviously, supplying information should be encouraged.

Rat-Catchers.

Rat-catchers to be engaged by the Rats Officer, or by the Superintendent of Police of the district, and to be under police control; although a rat-catcher thus engaged is at liberty to accept private work.

All orders by an official for the destruction of rats to take precedence of private employment and engagements.

Each rat-catcher whilst engaged at his work to wear some badge, such as an armlet, which will not hamper his movements. The badge to bear the rat-catcher's official number, and to be issued by the Superintendent of Police.

The badge to be returned to the Superintendent of Police when the official engagement is terminated; or when the badge is worn out and requires renewal.

Each rat-catcher to carry a pocket-book such as is described later, stating the charge he is entitled to make; and giving information as regards rat-destruction for the use of the public.

Each rat-catcher to be allowed to enter into any arrangement he may think fit regarding the remuneration he is to receive in private employment for rat-destruction ; the amount agreed on may be less than the official rate.

The rat-catcher to lay out in a row, or otherwise clearly expose for inspection by the employer or his nominee, all the rats killed, so that they may be counted.

After the employer or his nominee has counted them, the rat-catcher to decapitate all the rats; and to again expose them so that they may be easily counted by the employer or his nominee. Otherwise there is nothing to prevent a rat-catcher bringing rats that have been killed and counted elsewhere, to be counted again with those killed on any premises.

The employer or his nominee, to be entitled to refuse payment for any rat which has been decapitated before the number killed has been counted; and for each one not decapitated afterwards.

Rat-Catcher's Receipt-Book.

The book to be pocket-size and to contain duplicate detachable leaves; each leaf to have printed on it the necessary headings, and to have blanks to be filled in with the amount of money received ; the number of rats

RAT-CATCHER'S NOTE-BOOK.

Received the sum of £..........s......d.

for.............rats killed.

Employer ....

Address............................ ....

Date............Rat-catcher............ ....

The charge for each decapitated rat is...........

[*See Notice at back.*]

NOTICE.

After each day's work the rat-catcher is to place in a row, or otherwise arrange the rats killed so that they can be easily counted by the employer or his nominee. After this has been done the rat-catcher is to decapitate each rat. He is then to again arrange the rats so that they may be easily counted by the employer or his nominee.

The employer or his nominee is to refuse payment for each rat decapitated before the first count or is not decapitated after it.

The authorized charge for each decapitated rat is ....

Any complaint with regard to a rat-catcher, and all communications with reference to rats, to be sent to the Superintendent at the District Police Station.

The Superintendent of Police will advise the Rats Officer, who will send on application an official who may be employed to ferret or poison rats, or block them out of their holes in a house, shop, warehouse, &c. Alternatively he will show how they may be caught by this method, and fix the very simple and inexpensive apparatus necessary. The Superintendent will also furnish, when requested to do so, a list of places in the district at which poisoned meal, smoke-ferrets, and bags suitable for "blocking" can be procured; and a list of rat-catchers who may be employed.

killed; and the date or period of their destruction; also the name and address of the employer. The book to be signed by the rat-catcher on receiving payment, and the detachable leaf left with the employer as the receipt.

With the object of disseminating information as to the available methods for the destruction of rats, each detachable leaf to have the following notices printed on it, either at the bottom or on the back; in the latter case with a notice on the front calling attention to them (for Notice see Note-Book on opposite page).

The books suggested for this purpose are oblong, of a size suitable to go into a pocket; with 100 leaves in duplicate, double numbered with alternate leaves perforated; quarter-bound cloth; marble sides; with rat-catcher's number stamped on the back.

Bye-Laws.

1. Every doorway communicating with the interior of a house or building to be provided with a suitable threshold. The space between the door and threshold to be too small to allow a rat to pass, and not to exceed five-eighths of an inch.

2. Every unnecessary opening into a building to be closed. Every floor-drain, or other passage-way through which a rat may pass into a building to be covered with a suitable grating.

3. Every pig-keeper and poultry-keeper to be registered.

4. Every pig-sty or range of pig-sties and every poultry-house and poultry-enclosure to be provided with one or more traps as ordered. The traps to be kept set and in proper working order throughout the year.

5. Every rat-hole found unclosed to be regarded

officially as "Occupied by Rats," and the existence of the hole after attention has been called to it to be regarded officially as "Harbouring Rats."

6. All stacks, built on the ground, containing corn or other seed-food to be threshed before November 1. In high-lying districts the last day for threshing a stack on the ground to be November 15.

7. No staddle to be allowed which has the projecting unsurmountable rim, or the upper edge of the unclimbable surface, at less than 3 ft. from the ground. The regulation height for the projecting rim or upper edge of the unclimbable surface when a stack is built, to be 3 ft. 6 in.

8. Staddles of an approved pattern to be provided after due notice to do so has been given.

9. Sacking to be placed completely around all stacks which are built on the ground, while they are being threshed, and also around all stacks on staddles which are not of an approved pattern, to prevent the escape of rats and mice.

10. No implement or other article is to be placed under a stack on staddles, thereby affording means for the invasion of the stack by rats or mice.

11. The County Council, after due notice has been given, to order a stack containing rats or mice to be threshed before a fixed date.

12. The floor of a barn, granary, or other building in which food-stuffs are placed or stored, to be concreted. The floor, walls, doors and doorways of such building to be kept in proper repair.

13. Information to be given to the Superintendent of Police when a barn, granary, or other place in which food-stuffs are placed or stored is sufficiently empty for inspection.

14. Work connected with the erection of staddles, or concreting the floor of a barn, granary, etc., for which a Government grant has been obtained, must be completed within the specified time. A fine to be imposed for each week that the work remains unfinished.

15. When premises on which food-stuffs are stored, kept, or prepared for consumption, are infested with rats, the authorities to be empowered to send their own employees to catch the rats before making the premises as rat-proof as possible.

The expense of the rat-catching and rat-proofing the premises to be borne by the occupier in accordance with the provisions of the Rats and Mice (Destruction) Act, 1919.

16. Superfluous vegetation to be removed from a fence, bank, ditch or the edge of a pond, stream or other collection of water, in places in which such vegetation has harboured or may harbour rats. The ground adjacent to the wall of all buildings to be kept free from superfluous vegetation, timber, brushwood, bricks, tiles or articles of any kind.

A scale of fines to be arranged for non-compliance with any Bye-Law.

It must be remembered that fines for non-compliance with laws and regulations relating to the destruction of rats are not so much for the punishment of the individual offender, as for the protection of his neighbours. If these are doing their utmost to keep their premises free from vermin, justice demands that they should receive the assistance they require and deserve.

Office Arrangements.

Book for Name and Address of Rat-Catchers, where Employed, Work Done, &c.

THIS book should have headings at the top of each page for the name and address of the rat-catcher, badge number, date of engagement, date and place of last employment, district in which to be employed, conveyance kept, if any, number of dogs kept, number of ferrets kept, reference to subsequent folio on which his name appears, date of leaving, and be ruled below into columns for: date, where employed, by whom, officially or voluntarily employed, number of rats killed, number of days employed, remarks.

The books recommended for first issue are oblong foolscap of 200 pages, paged with a two-letter index, ruled faint, and whole bound in green cloth. Lettered on side or back, "Register of Rat-catchers," and a distinct number printed on the back for convenience of reference in the future.

A book for entering date of inspection of premises by Rats Officer or other official, and remarks thereon.

A list to be kept of men who can be engaged by the public at a fixed charge per day or hour for placing first bait and then poison in rats' holes; and closing the holes a week after the poison has been laid.

A list of men who will be sent for a fixed charge to show householders, shopkeepers, store-keepers, mill-owners, and others, how to arrange for "blocking" rats; and to fix the necessary screw-eyes or staples to enable this to be done.

A list of shops at which poisoned meal or other vermin poison, smoke-ferrets, and strong canvas bags suitable for "blocking" can be procured. It would be a convenience to the public if a bag and a sufficient length of cord were supplied at a fixed price by the men who make the arrangements for "blocking."

Lengths of 1½ in. canvas hose with unions, similar in construction to fire-brigade unions, to be kept on hire for the use of householders or of rat-catchers, or for the men who show householders how to make arrangements for "blocking." By these means rat-holes in a stable, outhouse, back-yard, or other place which cannot be conveniently ferreted or smoked, may be flooded from a cart, or from a tap in the house if no nearer tap is available.

REGISTER OF RAT-CATCHERS.

Badge number ...	Name	Conveyance kept if any ....
Date of engagement with Police	....	Number of dogs kept......
Date and place of last employment	Address	Number of ferrets kept...
District in which to be employed	.... Folio.	Date of leaving Police ....

Date	Where employed	By whom	Officially or voluntarily employed	Number of rats killed	Number of days employed	Remarks

Total number of rats killed........

Arrangements to be made for the use or hire of a large water-cart with a tap to which canvas hose can be fixed (as described in Section "Flooding") for flooding holes in stables, outbuildings, yards, banks, &c.

All men who work in conjunction with the police to wear a badge or carry a card of identification on which it is stated that they are employed until such and such a date; the card of identification being stamped in advance by the week or month, as may be considered desirable.

As the badge is the property of the police, it should be an offence, punishable by a substantial maximum fine, to wear it when not on the police register.

PART II.

TRAPS.

The "Terrier" Signal Run.

(Patent.)

The Signal Run is a box about 2 ft. in length, 9 in. high, and 7 in. wide across the inside, for a 5-in. trap, with a movable top and without a bottom. It has an entrance at each end 2 in. high, but when there is no likelihood of cats, poultry or rabbits going near the trap, the entrance may be increased to the height of 3½ in. The thresholds B are not essential and may be omitted. The run is fitted with buttresses to compel vermin to pass over the treadle of the trap. The top is narrower than the inside measurements of the run, so that light may be admitted on each side of it.

The buttresses, which should project not less than 1¼ in., nor more than 1½ in., are best placed so that their surface nearest the centre of the Signal Run is 6 in. from the inside of the nearer end. This distance allows a rat to be well inside the Signal Run before it enters the trap.

When making a Signal Run, it is well to cover the inner surface of each buttress with galvanized sheet-iron, as it prevents the buttresses being damaged in the event of a rat not being killed, or in the event of a 4-inch trap being used temporarily; it gives but little additional trouble to affix before the Signal Run is fastened to ether.

The transverse block C below the buttresses strengthens the run; keeps earth, leaves, &c., in position when the trap is buried and ensures the trap being placed so that the jaws cannot strike the buttresses.

To prevent the trap rocking, a piece of wood, tile, or other hard substance may be kept in the Signal Run for one end of the cross-bar of the frame of the trap to rest upon.

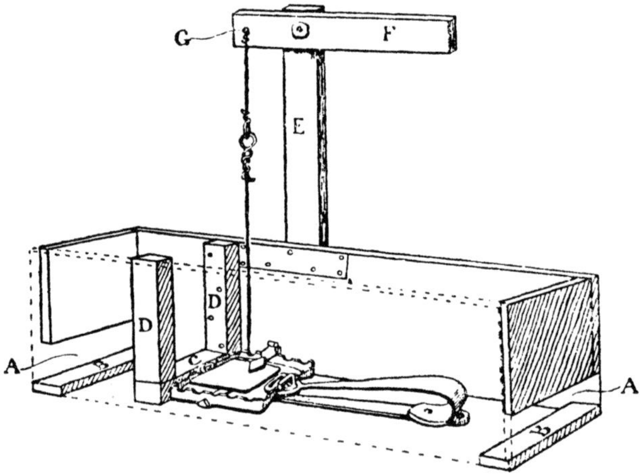

FIG. 3.—[1] The "Terrier" Signal Run (Patent). The cover and one side have been removed to show the interior of the run more clearly. A, entrance; B, threshold; C, transverse block below buttresses; D, buttresses; E, upright to support signal arm; F, signal arm: G, screw to engage wire.

The cover of the Signal Run may be made of a strip of wood $5\frac{1}{2}$ in. wide placed lengthways along the centre, or it may be made of wire-netting. The former is the better, for it darkens the run and prevents the trap being sprung by heavy rain or hail.

[1] Manufactured by Messrs. Boulton and Paul, Norwich, and Messrs. Charles Orfeur and Co., Colne Bank Works, Colchester.

To keep the cover in position, a piece of wood may be nailed to its under surface at each end to key it; a little play being given to enable the cover to be removed and replaced easily.

An arm about a foot long and 2 in. wide painted a different colour from the Signal Run and the upright, is large enough for general use. A white arm shows best, but if the Signal Run is to be placed against a white wall, "Signal red" will be found to be the most suitable colour.

The piece of wire holding the arm in position when the trap is set, is best made of galvanized wire about 12-14 standard wire gauge, bent at the bottom to make a hook about half an inch long; set to rather less than a right angle so that it may catch under the jaw and be retained there. If the angle is too acute, it may be caught by the jaw as it turns when the trap is sprung, and prevent the trap closing.

Obviously the wire must be hooked under the jaw from the outside, otherwise it would be liable to be caught between the jaw and the animal captured, and thus prevent the signal from falling.

The wire which holds the signal in position may be made in two pieces, the upper being about 18 gauge and joined to the lower wire an inch or more above the Run.

Before being placed out of doors, it is advisable to give the Signal Run two or three coats of good paint; care being taken to work the paint well into the joints of the woodwork. Stockholm tar may be used instead of paint. If tar is selected, it is a good plan to add paraffin oil to the tar when it is hot, in the proportion of about half a gallon of paraffin to each gallon of tar, and then stir them well together; the paraffin gives the tar a gloss and greatly improves its appearance.

Signal Runs which will be used only under cover, as in a warehouse, shed, &c., may be made of thinner wood than is necessary for outdoor work.

Combined Rabbit and Vermin Trap.

As shown in fig. 8 the trap is a run-trap and therefore open at both ends, and its peculiarity consists in having the treadle placed parallel with the length of the trap and counter-weighted so that it is kept by the weight in a horizontal position until it is depressed by the weight of the animal which is passing through the trap.

There is a door X at each end, which works in grooves W, each door being raised by a pivoted lever C, the inner end of which is held down when the trap is set, by a lever L passing across it having its free end connected by a cord with a catch D, which when the trap is set rests with its upper end against a block E, fastened to the side of the trap; while its lower end is prevented from rising by the vertical arm of an iron hook F, which is fixed to the treadle G, and passes horizontally through the side of the trap. When the treadle is depressed the hook is depressed with it, and consequently disengages the catch which when freed, allows the levers to rise and the doors to fall simultaneously.

The bottom of the trap is best made of wood not less than one inch in thickness; and its sides of wood about three-quarters of an inch in thickness. For preference the sides should be made of match-boarding, so as to prevent there being cracks through which light will enter the trap; for a rat endeavouring to escape always gnaws at an aperture which admits light.

The outside length of the trap is 42 in.; and its inside

measurement between the doors, 36 in., the remaining 6 in. of the outside measurement being made up by 3 in. at each end as follows: the door 1 in. in thickness, and the outer side of the groove in which it runs about 2 in. in width. The inside width of the trap is 7 in. and the inside height 12 in.

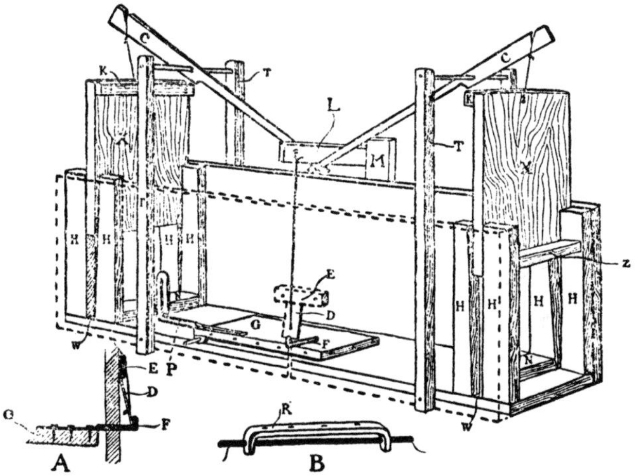

FIG. 8.—[1] Combined Rabbit and Vermin Trap. One side and the top have been removed to show interior. C, pivoted lever; D, catch; E, block for catch to rest against; F, iron hook fastened to treadle; G, treadle; H, sides of groove; K, piece of wood to close aperture between door and top of trap; L, cross lever to secure door levers when trap is set; M, upright for cross lever; N, block across trap immediately inside door; P, counter-weight; R, iron for hinging treadle; S, pivoting bar of treadle; T, uprights to support pivoting bar of lever; W, groove in which door works; X, door; Z, block attached to door to close space between outer sides of groove when the door is raised.

The grooves for the doors are made by nailing two pieces of wood H, about 1 in. in thickness and 2 in. in width, to the sides of the trap; this width giving not only

[1] Manufactured by Messrs. Charles Orfeur and Co., Colne Bank Works, Colchester.

a strong resistance to an animal trying to escape, but also materially strengthening the sides of the trap. The pieces which form the inner sides of the groove on either side must not be nailed quite vertically, but at an angle which will make the groove $\frac{1}{2}$ in. wider at the top than it is at the bottom; where the door should have not more than a $\frac{1}{4}$ in. play to allow for the wood swelling in wet weather.

The treadle, which is 10 in. in length, is best made of stout sheet-iron; the sides being bent at a right-angle after they have been cut to taper to about a $\frac{1}{4}$ in. in front, to give the treadle free movement, and after the pivot-holes have been drilled. The counter-weight P, may be made of iron about $\frac{3}{4}$ in. in thickness, bent at the outer end to reduce length, and to enable it to rest on the floor of the trap or on the top of a flat-headed screw so as to ensure the treadle being always in the horizontal position. The inner end must be flattened and pierced with holes for the rivets. The treadle should be keyed in position by a screw on each side beneath the pivoting rod S. If the treadle is made of wood, it must be covered with galvanized sheet-iron, and may be pivoted through a piece of iron bent down at each end and screwed to it as shown at B.

If the counter-weight P is not sufficiently heavy, iron rings can be dropped over the turned-up portion; or thick iron wire twisted round it until the proper weight is obtained. Lead or other soft material should not be used, lest it be gnawed and the balance thus altered.

The hook F, riveted to an iron treadle, is made of $\frac{1}{4}$ in. or $\frac{5}{16}$ in. rod iron; and projects about 1 in. beyond the side of the trap. The end is turned up at a right angle for about $\frac{1}{2}$ in. to engage the lower end of the catch D, when the trap is set, as shown at A (fig. 8).

The uprights T, which support the levers, are fastened to the sides of the trap, their centre being 7 in. from the end of the trap; and the holes for the pivoting bar being $9\frac{1}{2}$ in. above the top of the trap. This allows the doors to be raised 7 in. when the trap is set.

The top of the trap is formed at each end for about 9 in. by a piece of wood; and the intervening space covered with strong wire-netting with a small mesh fixed to the top of the trap.

The object of the wire-netting is to enable the interior of the trap to be inspected and the animal which has been caught to be seen. Should the trap appear to be empty, the treadle should be depressed in order to make sure that the captive has not crawled underneath it for concealment.

To exclude the light from the wire-netting opening, and thus prevent the captured animal trying to escape through it, a piece of wood the width of the trap and 1 in. or so longer than the opening should be placed over it; the piece of wood being kept in position by buttons fastened to cross-pieces fixed to the top of the trap.

To prevent captured rats gnawing the trap, its inside must be lined with galvanized sheet-iron (24-gauge is a suitable thickness) entirely around the doorways and other apertures, and on the inside of the doors to the height of about 8 in.; special care being taken with the slit in the side, which has been made for the hook of the treadle to pass through, as it is here that the rats will concentrate their efforts to escape. For this reason it is not amiss to place two thicknesses of iron or a special iron plate around the aperture, and to nail a piece of iron also to the floor of the trap at this opening.

FIGURE 4 TRAP.

The size and length of the pieces of wood forming the figure 4 must be regulated by the dimensions and weight

FIG. 9.—Figure 4 trap with treadle. 1, Upright; 2, slanting piece; 3, horizontal piece; 4, treadle; 5, notch for loop which supports the treadle when the trap is set.

of the crushing surface. Width may sometimes be increased with advantage at the expense of thickness. The notch on No. 3 to catch against the back of No. 1 should extend about $\frac{3}{4}$ in. in front of No. 1; as otherwise, the trap will not be sprung readily. None of the other notches should fit tightly the end which is placed in them.

Immediately below the level at which No. 3 crosses No. 1 and on the same side, a notch about $\frac{1}{8}$ in. in depth and $1\frac{1}{2}$ in. in length must be cut in No. 1. This is done so that, if No. 3 gets pulled vertically downwards by the weight of a rat on the treadle, it may slide into this notch and spring the trap. The length and angle of No. 2 should be arranged so that No. 3—the horizontal arm of the trap—will be about 4 in. from the ground.

A surface with a vertical front to hold the loop which supports the treadle, must be cut in the last ½ in. of the upper surface of No. 3, the front of the surface being best about 1½ in. behind the front edge of the treadle.

This treadle must be made of thin and very light wood, and may be strengthened by a narrow cross-piece at each end. Its length should be about two-thirds of the ground length beneath the crushing surface when the trap is set, and about a quarter of its width. Through a hole made near each front corner a piece of string must be passed and the ends tied underneath. Keep the loop formed sufficiently long to rest in the notch on the upper surface of No. 3, while the front of the treadle is raised about 2 in. from the ground.

The loop must slope upwards and backwards, so that the treadle is pressed backwards against the angle formed by the crushing surface with the ground when there is a weight on its upper surface. This keeps it in position.

To prevent the treadle being jerked forward by the loop becoming caught in No. 3 when the trap is sprung, it is well for a hole to be bored in each back corner and a piece of string passed through the holes and tied. Keep the loop sufficiently long to pass under the end of the crushing surface and fasten to a peg behind it.

The treadle may with advantage have one or more thin and narrow cross-pieces fastened to its upper surface for the bait to rest against.

When setting the trap, No. 1 must be slightly tilted forwards to counteract the downward traction on No. 3 caused by the weight of the treadle.

While the loop at the front of the treadle is being slipped over the end of No. 3, No. 1 and No. 3 must be held together to prevent the trap becoming unset. As soon as the crushing surface has been lowered and rests securely on the upper end of No. 2, the trap is set.

To prevent No. 2 slipping off the crushing surface and failing to support it, a slight notch may be cut in the crushing surface to catch against the end of No. 2 and hold it in position. To prevent the crushing surface shifting its position and thus to ensure it always falling on the same area, its back edge should rest against a lath or two screws or pegs projecting about ½ in. from the ground surface.

When wood suitable for a treadle cannot be procured, No. 3 may be made somewhat longer and bait affixed to its free end. A piece of biscuit, or what is very good bait, a very thin slice of cooked meat, may be rolled round the stick and then tied to it. The biscuit or meat should then be rubbed in hot bacon fat, after the ends of the string have been cut off short. Another method of baiting is to rub the end of No. 3 (which may with advantage have some holes bored through it to hold some of the bait) in toasted cheese, or hot beef dripping, to which some meal may be added.

Before the trap is set, it is a good plan to feed the rats underneath and around the crushing surface for several days and nights, the surface being kept up by a strong support at each front corner.

SIGNALS.

IF a trap be set on the further side of a wall from which the inspection will be made, the signal must be pivoted so that it shows well above the wall when disengaged. If a wall has a coping-stone, some arrangement must be devised to prevent the signal catching against it when it rises. For this purpose a piece of wood, rather thicker than the extent to which the coping-stone projects, nailed to the wall for the signal to slide up it, answers very well. The piece of wood should be so placed that the signal end of the lath slides over it and its upper end is immediately below the coping stone.

Another way to form a guide for the signal is to fix a piece of stout galvanized or copper wire to a nail on the other side of the wall, opposite to the signal; and after carrying it over the wall to make it fast to another nail below the level of the pivot for the signal. Further to ensure the signal not catching against the edge of the coping-stone, a piece of wood an inch or more in thickness and about an inch longer than the coping-stone is deep, should be put between the wire and the edge of the coping-stone; as shown on section in diagram, B. This is to allow the wood to project for the distance required above the top of the coping-stone so that when the lower edge of this piece of wood is flush with the lower edge of the coping-stone, a piece of lath or wood nailed to it, and of sufficient width to rest firmly on the top of the coping-stone, will prevent the wood slipping down as the result of alternate wet and hot weather.

The corners of the first piece of wood (D) ought to be sloped off to ensure the signal not catching against it as it rises, and the wire fastened to both pieces of wood with staples.

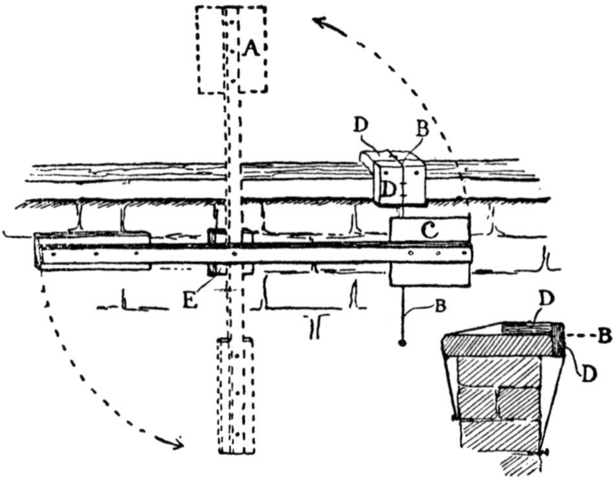

FIG. 11.—Diagram showing the arrangement for a signal to appear over a wall. A, position of signal when trap has been sprung; C, position of signal while trap is set; D, blocks to keep wire away from coping stone; E, block to which signal is pivoted; B, section showing the position of the pieces of wood D on the top and against the edge respectively of the coping stone.

A block of wood not less in thickness than the extent to which the coping-stone projects, must be fastened to the wall so that the signal can be pivoted on to it.

When a trap is set behind a building or wall, the signal may be made to fall into view when the trap is sprung, as shown in fig. 12, a stop (C) holding it in position after it has fallen.

When the wire has to be carried upwards and then at an angle to reach the signal, it is better to turn the corner with a piece of lath pivoted as shown in fig. 12 rather than with a pulley-wheel. The reason is that in course of time the cord which is placed in contact with a pulley becomes moulded to the wheel and does not readily allow

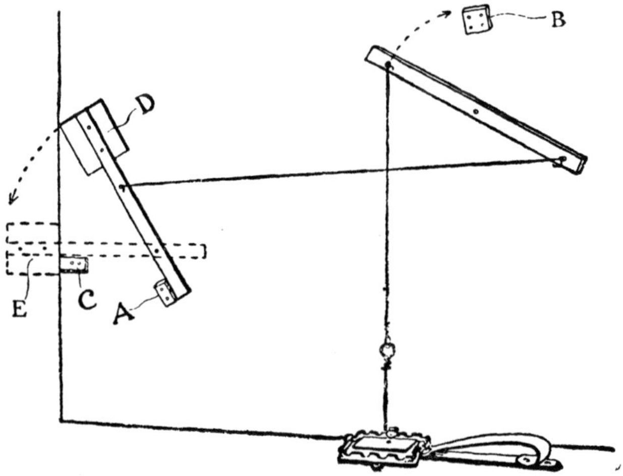

FIG. 12.—Diagram showing the arrangement of a signal for a trap set behind a building. A, block for tail of signal to rest against; B, block to stop pivoted lath; C, block for signal to rest against when trap has been sprung; D, position of signal while trap is set; E, position of signal when trap has been sprung. The trap is shown exposed to make the diagram more clear.

the signal to alter its position. This occurs more frequently if the string becomes alternately damp or wet and then dry.

The movement necessary for the free action of the signal must be regulated by the length of the pivoted lath.

A stop (A) for the tail of the signal to rest against is useful to keep it when set from being displaced by wind.

A stop (B) should also be placed to prevent the pivoted lath swinging too far and being drawn upside down while the signal is being adjusted.

If it is necessary for the signal to be shown at a place in front of that in which the trap is set, as when there are trees with drooping boughs over the trap, this can be arranged easily by placing two pivoted laths on stakes as

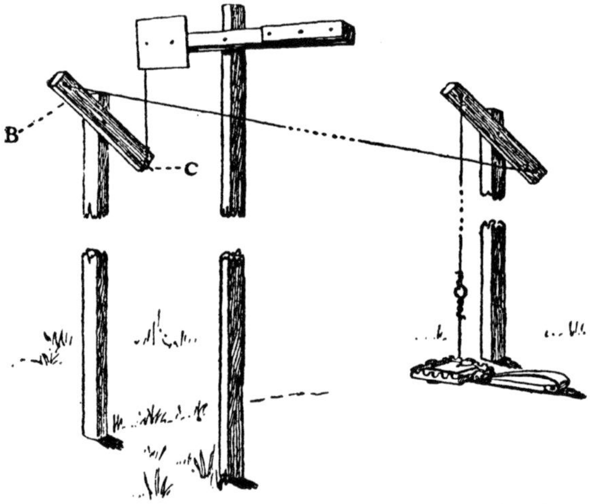

FIG. 13.—Diagram showing the arrangement for the signal to appear at a place in front of that in which a trap is set. A screen has not been placed in front of the signal and the trap has been left exposed to make the diagram more clear.

shown in fig. 13. One is put above the trap and the other in the position where the signal is to be shown. Both laths should be pivoted in the ordinary manner, but the front one (B) should have a nail or screw (C) projecting about an inch from its lower end. The stake which supports the signal must be taller than the post which supports the lath (B) so that the signal is over the end of the lath (B) when the trap is set. It is attached to this by a wire ending in a ring slipped over the projecting nail (C), the signal being pivoted so that it rises to a vertical position when disengaged.

A trap inside a building can be connected with a signal placed outside by means of the simple arrangement shown in fig. 14.

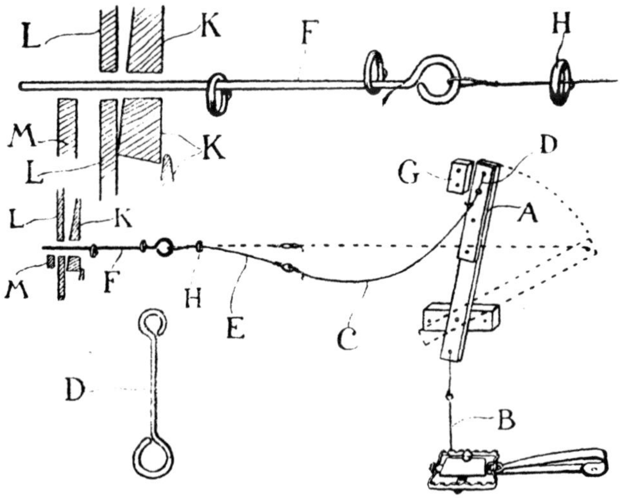

FIG. 14.—Diagram showing an arrangement for connecting a signal outside a building with a trap inside the building. A, pivoted lath above trap: B, wire connected with trap; C, cord; D, wire with ring at each end; E, wire connected with catch-pin; F, catch-pin; G, stop for lath; H, screw-eye to prevent catch-pin being jerked too far away; K, feather-edged boards forming wall of buildings; L, lath for signal to slide on; M, signal. The trap has been left exposed to make the diagram more clear.

As is seen, there is a lath (A) pivoted near one end, and at this end a screw to which is attached a piece of stout binding-wire (B) which is fastened to the looped end of the wire, which hooks under a jaw of the trap when the signal is set. There is a screw, for preference round-headed, at the other end of the lath to which is attached a piece of strong cord (C). The connection is best made with a piece of wire (D) about 14-gauge, bent into a ring at each end; one just large enough to turn easily on the screw fixed to the lath, and the other of sufficient size to allow the cord to be readily attached to it. The total length of the looped wire is about one and a half to two inches. The other end of the cord is fastened to a loop on the wire (E) which is connected with the catch-pin (F). This passes through the wall of the building and supports or holds down the signal until withdrawn, in accordance with the arrangement by which the signal is arranged to fall or rise when the trap is sprung.

The cord should be sufficiently long to allow the lath to fall until the cord is almost on the same level as the connecting wire before it becomes taut; this causes a jerk to the catch-pin. The introduction of the short piece of wire (D) ensures smooth working and keeps the cord from becoming worn.

It must be remembered that the weight of a pivoted lath which is insufficient to release a catch-pin by a direct pull may be quite enough to do so if its weight be applied with a jerk. This is easily arranged by leaving the cord slack, so that the lath must fall some distance before the cord is at its full length. When a jerk is required, it is best to use for the slack portion strong whip-cord or picture-cord, although the remainder of the connection with the catch-pin may be wire.

The lath above the trap is best arranged so that it is almost vertical when the trap is set. This minimizes leverage. It must be pivoted so that it jerks the connecting wire on the level of the catch-pin. The connecting wire must be supported with staples or some other similar arrangement. If this is not done, its weight is liable to withdraw the catch-pin which ought to be always kept well greased.

The pin may be about six or eight inches or more in length, according to the thickness of the wall or the position in which it is placed; it should have a ring at one end; it may be made of round iron or rigid wire, but an iron skewer serves very well in most cases.

To ensure the pin working easily, the hole through the wall of the building must be sufficiently large to allow the pin to pass through without touching its sides; the pin being supported and held in a horizontal position by two screw-eyes or staples placed at different levels. The pin will rest against the top of the outer screw-eye and the bottom of the inner screw-eye, if the signal rises when the trap is sprung; or against the bottom of the outer screw-eye, and the top of the inner screw-eye, if the signal drops.

To prevent the catch-pin being jerked to a distance, the connecting wire may be passed through a screw-eye or staple (H) placed near the catch-pin, that is too small to allow the catch-pin to pass through it. As an alternative, the movement of the catch-pin may be controlled by a piece of whipcord; the former method however is the more durable.

It will be found a convenience when setting the signal, if there is a block (G) on each side of the lath to prevent it turning, or falling too far.

The signal ought to be pivoted so that it presses only lightly against the pin, and it may be concealed when the trap is set. The screen may be nailed along its free vertical end to a narrow piece of wood, somewhat thicker than the signal, previously fastened to the building. Its upper or lower horizontal side may be attached to a piece of wood of similar thickness placed either below or above the stem of the signal, according to whether the signal is to rise or fall.

If the signal is made to rise, a lath (L) nailed to the front of the feather-edged boards for it to slide on, will prevent catching against the lower edge of the boards.

A corner at a right angle can be easily turned by placing over the trap the arrangement previously described and shown in fig. 14, and by having a similar arrangement on the other wall. The lath attached to the long wire or string which jerks the pin from the signal has a ring connected with its lower end for slipping over the pin connected with the pivoted lath on the wall, against which the trap is set.

SNARING.

THE noose is best made of a single piece of fine brass or copper wire, 21 to 23-gauge, about 14 inches long, with a loop neatly formed at one end for the other end of the wire to be passed through before it is fastened to the string. This loop is sometimes made by doubling a piece of very fine wire and then twisting the two ends together to form the noose. This last should be 2½ inches in diameter, and arranged so that the loop is at the top of the noose; otherwise the wire is liable to kink at the loop when the snare is sprung, and so prevent the noose closing quickly and tightly. The lower part of the noose should be about three-quarters of an inch above the ground.

The string (C), which is about a foot in length, must be fastened firmly to the bender, preferably in a notch, to prevent the risk of the weight of the snared rat causing it to slip along the stick. When tying it to the teeler, care must be taken that it is fixed to its upper surface when the snare is set; if this is not done it will tend to rotate the teeler and prevent the pull being directly against the hook on the peg. The string is best attached to the teeler close to the hook; this minimizes the leverage and allows the snare to be most easily sprung. About an inch and a half of string should intervene between teeler and wire.

The bender is best made from a piece of hazel or ash,

the former for choice, about five feet in length, the thinner end being about the thickness of a finger. A stick of this thickness should give a pull of 4 lb. to 5 lb. It is well for the stick to end immediately above the place where one or more twigs have been thrown off, as the enlargement thus caused prevents the string slipping off the end of the stick. Care must be taken to fix the stick

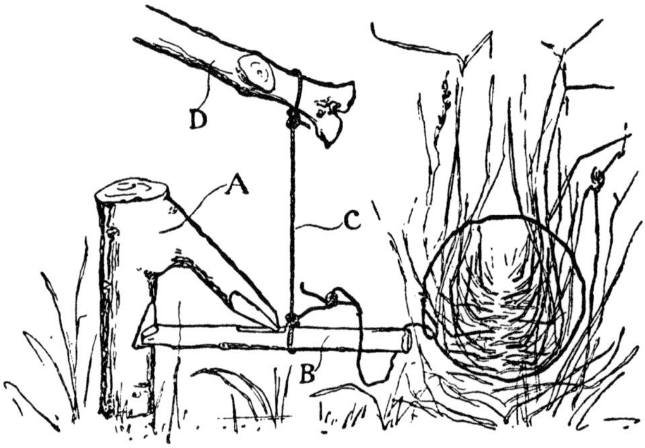

FIG. 15.—Snare for rats. A, peg; B, teeler; C, string attached to bender; D, bender. The herbage which should conceal the noose and other parts of the snare has been omitted in order to leave the drawing clear. The noose is represented by wire much too thick for use, but drawn thus to make the diagram more clear.

firmly into the ground in a position which will ensure the part to which the string is fastened being directly over the attachment of the string to the teeler when the snare is set. It must also be set at an angle that will provide for a rat when caught being lifted well off the ground, yet kept far enough from the stick to prevent it being reached for support.

The teeler (B) is made from a straight twig, about four

inches long and of the thickness of a lead pencil. It is cut flat above and below at one end, so that it may rest firmly on the notch cut in the peg to be presently described. This end may with advantage be cut to a blunt point to enable the teeler to be easily turned to either side, which would not be the case if it were cut square. Its upper surface is also flattened where it rests against the hook when the snare is set. The outer or free end, split vertically, becomes "the grip" to hold the noose in position. It is close to the side of the run when set.

The peg (A) is usually about ten inches long, although this length may have to be altered according to the lightness or heaviness of the soil. It has a downward projection or hook, formed by a fork in the branch, which is inverted for the purpose of the peg. The lower end is pointed to allow it to be driven more easily into the ground. Immediately below the level of the end of the hook a notch is cut in the side of the peg to provide a surface on which the teeler can rest firmly. The depth of the notch is immaterial, provided that its upper part is sufficiently cut away from the surface of the peg to the back of the notch to enable the teeler to be disengaged readily when the snare is sprung. For this purpose the end of the hook may be cut away on four sides until only a flat surface is left, just sufficient for the teeler to securely rest against when the snare is set. All cut surfaces should be rubbed in wet mud to make them less conspicuous.

To set the snare, the peg is driven firmly into the ground, about four and a half inches from one side of the run, until the notch is one inch above the level of the ground, the hook being towards the run. The bender with string, teeler and noose attached, is next fixed firmly into the ground and the noose then spread to the required size, and the wire beyond it placed in the grip.

The bender is then pulled down with one hand while the end of the teeler is slipped into the notch and its upper surface steadied against the flattened end of the hook; the noose across the run being concealed on each side by the vegetation. If the size of the noose is not right, it is best to release the bender so that the noose may be adjusted with both hands.

FERRET-HUTCHES.

FERRET-hutches are usually made with only two compartments, but a third is useful. With lids, 18 in. is a good depth for the front, but 22 in. should not be exceeded. For handling ferrets, lids are more convenient than doors on the front of the hutch; but a movable front to each compartment, best working in a slide from the top, is convenient for cleaning the hutch, and is essential for the nest-compartment.

The holes between the compartments are usually about 3½ in. wide, and about 3 in. above the floor. For the nest-compartment the hole should be as near the front as possible. This leaves the other end warm for the nest. Each hole should be fitted with a vertical sliding door working in a slit, made of a straight piece of wood nearly the width of the lower divisions of the slit, which is wide at the top and divided at the bottom; the hole through the partition of the hutch being midway between the sides of the outer division. The guide between the two divisions of the slit is pointed or rounded at the top, and should not extend upwards more than 2 in. above the top of the hole. The slit should be covered from the top to within about an inch of the upper edge of the hole. This will give sufficient support to the sliding door to render a covering unnecessary on the edges of the lower part of the guides of the two slits. The door should project about 4 in. above the top of the hutch to form a handle, and may be suitably shaped. The lower corners of the door should be rounded to prevent them catching against the edges of the slits. The stop for the door should be fixed about an inch below the hole through the partition.

A piece of wood about 2 or 3 in. wide fastened along the whole length of the front of the top of the hutch flush with the top of the sides and partitions, helps to keep the hutch rigid and prevents the ferrets climbing out directly a lid is opened.

RATS IN THE HOUSE, SHOP, WARE-HOUSE, &c.

FOR trapping a rat that has a run behind a skirting-board, cut a hole in the bottom of the skirting-board about 3 in. square on the outside, and place a "Terrier" Death Run trap or a "Terrier" Signal Run containing a 5-in. rabbit-trap on each side of it, but about two or three yards away. A trail of bait must be laid from the hole to the traps, which if a rabbit-trap, should be placed so that the jaws of the trap face the hole. Should there be any furniture with a solid base between the hole and the trap, it may be moved forward from about 4 to 6 in., so as to leave a clear passage-way behind it for the rat.

The position selected for the hole should be for choice where it will be more or less out of sight. Select a corner, or a place in front of which a piece of furniture usually stands.

A hole should be made with a large gimlet, drill, or small centre-bit at one of the upper corners of the piece of wood which is to be removed, and a fine key-hole saw then introduced through the opening thus made, and the wood cut across the top. When the position is reached where the saw must be turned to cut down the opposite side, another gimlet-hole must be made to enable the saw to be turned.

If the saw is held obliquely, so that the cut at the back of the skirting-board is about ½ in. nearer the centre of the piece to be removed than the cut on the front surface, there will be a firm support for the piece of skirting-board that has been removed to rest against when it is replaced.

It is obvious that the gimlet-holes must be bored downwards, inwards, and backwards, at the angle at which the saw-cut is to be made.

When a rat has been caught, the trap should be left for a few days to make sure that no other rats frequent the run behind the skirting-board. To settle all doubt, lay a trail of bait as before. If the bait is taken and another rat is not caught, and neither the run nor the trap has been touched with the bare hand, it may be suspected that mice have been at work. In this case a trap, or a little finely sifted sand laid on the floor, will decide the question.

Before closing the hole, the cut surface of the skirting-board should be covered with a layer of putty to fill the space made by the saw. Without this, the replaced piece will not be flush with the rest of the skirting-board, and dust will blow through the chinks and make a dirty mark around its outer edges.

The piece is best fixed with a dowel at the bottom, and a short steel pin driven through the top into the skirting-board. If the dowel is short, the piece replaced can be easily levered up and again removed, should a rat at any future time be heard using the run behind the skirting-board. The holes made by the gimlet should be filled with putty, and when all the joints have been smoothed level with the skirting-board, the putty should be painted to match it.

If the gimlet-holes and saw-cuts are properly made, and the puttying finished off and painted carefully, the opening which has been made will be scarcely noticeable, even in an exposed position.

RATS ON A SHIP.

Door for Gangway.

The door, which might be made of galvanized sheet-iron fixed to a wooden frame, ought to be not less than 3 ft. 6 in. in height; and any nails or screws used for fastening should be placed on the edges. The barrier, of which the door forms a portion, ought to project several inches beyond each side of the gangway; and the door should be fitted with a double eccentric hinge. This will ensure it always closing by its own weight from whichever side the slope of the gangway has allowed it to be opened. The usual swing-gate latch which drops into a notch on the edge of a segment of a large circle is also advisable.

The threshold and the two posts should be in one piece. They will then form a frame which—together with the rest of the barrier of which they are a part—can be pivoted at each end, on a strong rounded projection, prolonged from and in the centre line of the threshold; or on a deep transverse groove at each end of the threshold, to be placed on a tongued support fixed to the gangway. The frame must be counter-weighted, so that when the projecting pieces of the threshold, or the grooves on the threshold, are dropped on to their supports, the doorway and the rest of the barrier can swing but will remain vertical, irrespective of the angle at which the gangway is placed. The counter-weights must project on each side beyond the gangway and swing at a level below it. The threshold must be round, and pivoted close to the gangway; otherwise rats will pass beneath it. The posts must be sufficiently high for their tops to be above the level of the upper rail of the gangway at whatever angle it may be placed; and must be kept in position by an iron rod sufficiently long to allow them their full swing. The rod must be bent at a right angle horizontally at each end, and again downwards at a right angle, so as to pass through holes in the centre of the top rail, to be fastened with fly-nuts underneath.

RATS ON A SHOOTING ESTATE AND ON A FARM.

THE desirability of placing all stacks on staddles that will not be threshed almost immediately has been mentioned in a previous Section, and the method about to be described enables either a fixed or movable rick-stand to be erected at a small cost. To make it durable, there must be a sufficient number of upright posts and horizontal supports to carry respectively the weight of the stack and the flooring on which it rests. There must also be sufficient stout horizontal pieces, placed at a right angle to the rest, to brace the frame firmly together. Braces fixed obliquely in both directions from the horizontal supports to the top of posts several feet higher than the other uprights, are useful for keeping the frame rigid when the stack is subjected to wind pressure. When making a stack the higher posts, to the top of which the braces are attached, should not be placed at the corners.

When wood is used for making staddles, any straight smooth piece of sufficient thickness and height is suitable. Perhaps a round piece is preferable; it affords no edge up which a rat can climb; and if the bottom is bedded in concrete carried a few inches above the ground level, it will last for many years without rotting; especially if when the concrete has set, a little pitch is run into the crack between wood and concrete. This is best done by pouring the hot pitch from an iron ladle.

A simple and effective way to make a staddle unclimbable is to drop over it a disused or slightly damaged stone-ware drain-pipe; and to support it immediately below the lower horizontal support of the stack with its upper edge at 3 ft. 6 in. from the ground.

If a sufficient number of farmers were to combine so as to give a substantial order, or if the use of staddles became more general, the manufacturers of drain-pipes might be induced to make specially stout glazed stone-ware pipes to be placed over the upper part of the posts used for staddles. In this case such pipes could be supplied at a small cost.

They should be cylindrical and not less than 1 ft. in length, and might be made with an inside diameter of 6, 6½, 7, 7½ and 8 in. respectively, which would cover posts sufficiently strong to carry even a very large stack. The larger sizes would be used for the corner, centre, and brace posts; and the smaller for the intermediate posts.

The pipe must be supported by some nails driven into the post until their heads are flush with the outer surface of the pipe; and be steadied and kept in a vertical position on the post by a little straw stuffed between it and the post. If in the case of an odd, small post, the space between pipe and post should be sufficient for a rat to crawl through, it could be filled with thin sheet-metal refuse or a piece of old wire-netting crumpled up.

Care must be taken that the stone-ware pipe does not fit the post tightly; for if it did so, it would be liable to be broken should the post swell in consequence of being exposed to rain.

If the use of staddles became general, timber merchants who buy trees when plantations and coverts are thinned, would stock and supply posts suitable for staddles, and wood for the horizontal supports. They would too, for a small additional payment, trim the upper end of the posts to a gauge which would take a stoneware pipe of a given diameter. They would cut the shoulder for the lower horizontal support of the stack frame to rest upon, and a shoulder and flat surface for the upper horizontal support to lie upon and against. Finally, they would bore the holes for the bolts which would be used to fasten the frame together; since they have steam-saws and other machinery on the premises.

When on a farm there are staddles which are too low, they may be raised to the proper height on brickwork, stonework, or blocks of concrete made in wooden moulds; care being taken that no ledge is left on which a rat can stand while making a spring upwards. Staddles may also be made of concrete or reinforced concrete; or circular iron pillars may be used.

Slightly damaged drain-pipes are sometimes used for staddles. They are filled with concrete and their lower end embedded in it; but the objection to this method is that drain-pipes 3 ft. in length are not usually kept in stock in England. With the ordinary length pipes the stack is not raised sufficiently from the ground; and the mass of concrete in which the pipe is bedded gives a surface on which a rat can stand whilst making a spring to get into the stack.

When wood or other material used as a staddle is not made unclimbable by the use of a stone-ware pipe, this may be effected by nailing two pieces of galvanized iron sheeting around the posts, each not less than 6 in. wide. The top edge of the upper piece must not be less than 3 ft., or for preference 3 ft. 6 in., from the ground. The upper piece should overlap the lower about half an inch, and the joint of the two ends of each piece be on opposite sides of the posts, so that a rat cannot climb over both the joints by clinging to the nails. For this purpose the sheet-iron may be from 26 to 30 standard wire gauge.

Another way to prevent the passage of rats into a stack is to have upon the top of each staddle a flat surface projecting horizontally, not less than 4 in., and if 6 in. so much the better; otherwise a large rat may possibly crawl round it. This flat surface may be made of stone, stout sheet-iron, or thick pieces of wood strongly fastened together by cross-pieces on their upper surface. All stacks should be built not less than 6 ft. apart to prevent rats passing from stack to stack.

For making temporary staddles, say for a stack built on the field in which the corn was grown, the posts used should be from 5 ft. 6 in. to 9 ft. in height having regard to the depth to which the lower end is to be placed in the ground; and whether or not the stays are to be fastened to them. The timber used for the longitudinal and transverse horizontal supports, when poles are not used, should be about 5 or 6 in. in width, and $1\frac{1}{4}$ to 2 in. in thickness; they should be placed on edge as joists are beneath a floor.

The dimensions of the stack having been decided upon, a hole for each post must be dug or rammed about a foot or more in depth, according to the nature of the soil. The posts must be 4 to 6 ft. apart, the width varying with the weight they will have to carry.

Each post should rest upon a flat stone or piece of concrete about 12 in. square, to prevent the weight of the stack forcing the post deeper into the ground; and it is advisable to ram the ground until it is hard before laying the stone upon it. It is best not to fill in the hole until the level of all the posts has been adjusted. A post can be steadied if required until its level has been ascertained, by a stick driven into the side of the hole in a slanting direction and fastened to the post with a wire nail.

Each post should be cut to form a shoulder for the upper and lower horizontal supports respectively to rest upon. Above the lower shoulder a hole must be bored in the post, at a level corresponding to the centre of the lower horizontal support; and another hole bored at a right angle to it above the upper shoulder in a similar position for bolting the upper support to the post. The upper supports should rest firmly on the lower ones; the holes both in the posts and in the supports being about 1 in. in diameter, to allow the bolts play.

The four corner posts must be the first to be put into position and bolted together with the two longitudinal and two transverse outside pieces. When the frame thus formed is shown by a spirit-level to be standing true, the holes in which these posts stand may be filled in and the earth well rammed. The correct position and height for each of the other posts are then easily ascertained by shifting each post until the hole through it corresponds with the hole through the longitudinal or transverse support. It is best to place the remainder of the longitudinal supports in position first, as the transverse supports must rest firmly on them; and while the former are being fixed, the end transverse supports may be temporarily removed or loosened. All the transverse pieces should then be bolted on and the frame fixed completely together before the rest of the holes are filled in. When this has been done all the holes must be well rammed.

Before the supports are placed in position all the posts must be rendered unclimbable, as described.

The longitudinal and transverse supports are fastened most strongly to the posts by the intervention of a stout plate for the head of the bolt and the nut respectively to rest against; the hole through them being only sufficiently large to allow the bolt to pass easily. The nut should be large, so as to give good support to its plate.

To ensure the frame being rigid, there must be several braces or stays both longitudinal and transverse. Each brace is fastened to the top of a high post and bolted to another post at the level of the longitudinal or transverse support, according to its direction. Its lower end is best placed on the opposite side of the post to the support, so that one bolt will hold them both in position. In order to obtain sufficient leverage, the upper end of the brace should be attached to the post not less than 2 ft. above the horizontal support; but 3 ft. or even more will be found better.

The transverse support attached to a post to which a longitudinal brace will be bolted, must be fixed on the side of the post opposite to the direction from which the brace will come. If this is not done, the upper edge of the brace will have to be notched to allow it to be fitted to the proper position to receive the bolt.

If the posts and braces are numbered after they have been placed in position, they can subsequently be put into their proper places before the erection of the frame is begun; there will then be no delay due to wrong pieces being bolted together. It is, however, unnecessary to number the longitudinal and transverse supports, provided they are respectively of the same length, and provided all holes have been bored in precisely the same relative position.

The posts and timber, if kept in a dry place when not in use, will last for many years, and the original cost of the material, together with the interest on the money, will be repaid many times over as years pass, by the corn saved.

The bolts should be thoroughly greased before and after use. If the two plates are put on the bolt directly it is withdrawn and are kept there by its nut, they will not be lost or mislaid. By keeping bolts in a covered box the worm of the screw will not get clogged with dirt or dust.

The size of the stand can be enlarged to any extent by placing the required additional longitudinal or transverse pieces on the opposite side of the end-posts to the pieces already affixed and then bolting them on; additional posts and supports being arranged as before described.

With regard to purchasing and erecting staddles, see also Section "Conclusion and Recapitulation."

RATS IN SEWERS.

As may be seen in fig. 50, the entrance to the bag is held open by two expanding oblong frames placed about ten inches apart. These are held upright by the pieces of iron (D) bent at a right angle at each end to drop into the sockets (E) attached respectively to the front and back of the vertical portion (F) of the expanding oblong frames.

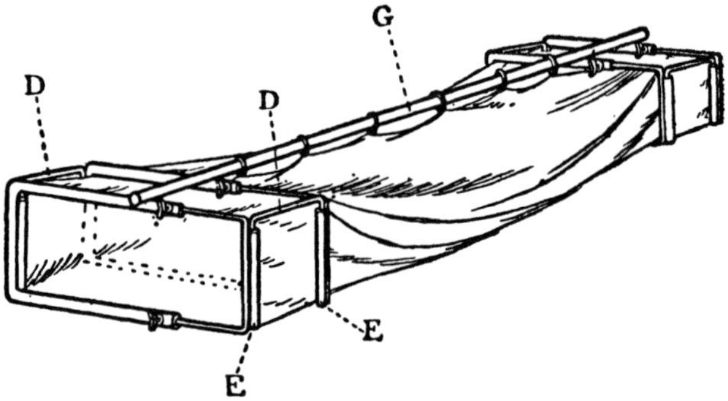

FIG. 37.—Bag attached to expanding ends for capturing rats in sewers.

The end of the bag is furnished with a pair of similar expanding frames so as to form a compartment in which the rats may congregate. The centre of the bag is held up by a rod (G) passing through rings attached to the top of the bag; the ends of the rod rest on the front and back frames respectively as shown in fig. 37.

Each expanding frame, as shown in fig. 50, is composed of a piece of iron rod and a piece of iron tubing, the upper and lower horizontal arm of which—A and B respectively—are about 8 in. apart. As will be seen in fig. 50, the portion of the frame marked A is made of iron rod and it fits into the other portion of the frame B which is made of iron tubing, the diameter of the frame being regulated by the screw C.

A piece of iron tubing (E) is braized on to the posterior and anterior edge of each vertical portion of the front and

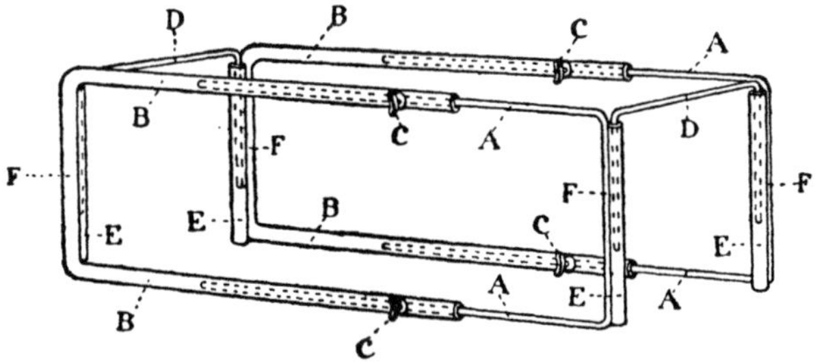

FIG. 50.—Expanding frame to which the bag is attached. A, rod iron; B, iron tubing into which A passes to the required distance where it is fixed by the screw C; D, brace bent at a right angle at each end for dropping into the tubes E affixed to F; E, tube into which the brace D is inserted; F, vertical portion of expanding frame.

back frame respectively (F) so that the front and back frames may be held firmly and vertically together by the descending arm of the brace (D), which is made to slip in and out easily. As an alternative to the movable braces (D), and to make the ends more rigid, a rod may be welded at each end to the top and bottom of the vertical portions (F) of the A and B pieces respectively.

The upper part of the sewer is blocked by a piece of sacking held against the walls of the sewer by the apparatus shown in fig. 51. This apparatus consists of an expanding transverse bar AB, formed by a rod A fitting into a tube B which can be fixed to any length by the screw C. At the free end of the rod and tube there is an end D to which is pivoted the tube DD through which

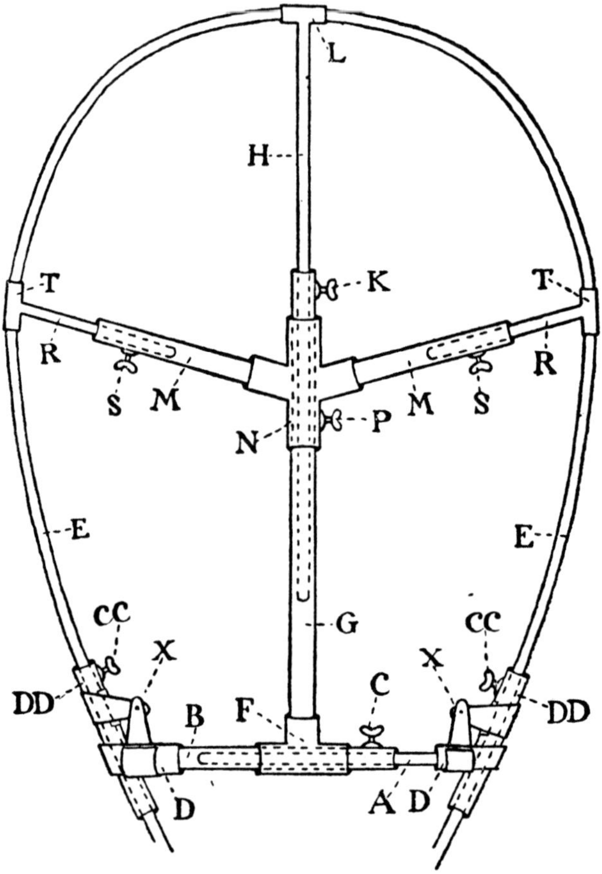

FIG. 51.—Expanding frame for blocking a sewer above a bag.

passes one of the rods E—these last may be made of stout wire wound spirally. Both are kept in contact with the wall of the sewer by the upper part of the apparatus and are bent to fit the roof of the sewer, each meeting in the centre with its fellow of the opposite side, the rod E being fixed in the pivoted tube by the screws CC.

On the centre of the bar is a **T** piece F, its horizontal arm being sufficiently large to slide along the bar AB just described, its vertical end being connected with a tube G about two thirds of the height of the sewer above the canvas bag. Fitting into this vertical tube G is a rod H which can be fixed at any height by a screw K. Its upper end is fitted into a half-pipe L about two inches long for holding the free ends of the curved portions of the rods E which lie in contact with the wall, and fixing them against the roof of the sewer by expanding the vertical portion of the apparatus and fixing it with the screw K in the proper position.

The arms M are attached to the double **T** piece N which can be slid up or down G until fixed to it by the screw P, each arm having a rod R passing inside it which can be fixed in any position by the screw S. The end of this sliding portion is fixed to a half-pipe T, about one inch and a half in length, for fixing the rod E against the wall of the sewer, and thus keeping the sheet of sacking firmly in position so that no rat can pass it.

MICE.

THE COLIN PULLINGER MOUSE-TRAP.

THE sides and the top and bottom at both ends of the trap are made of hard wood about a quarter of an inch thick. The total length of the trap is 13 in. and the width and height 3¼ in.

The trap is divided into three compartments. The central one, about 7½ in. long, is occupied by a balance; and beyond this at each end, between the divisions D and the wires at the end of the trap, is the compartment in which the mice caught are imprisoned. On either side of the trap at its centre, is an aperture F, extending from the top of the trap to within 1¼ in. of the bottom. This aperture at its upper part is 2 in. wide, the top of the trap sloping downwards on each side of the central opening towards the centre of the trap for ⅝ in. at which level it is 1 in. in width and there passes into a circular opening in the side of the trap 1¼ in. in diameter; the top of the trap being deficient between these apertures, so that a mouse can enter the trap from either side or from the top.

The balance (A) consists of a piece of thin sheet-metal 6 in. long and 2⅜ in. wide, pivoted ¾ in. below the centre, with a vertical transverse division (B), about 1¾ in. high across its centre. Each end of the vertical portion has a piece of metal (C) at right angles to it, about ⅝ in. wide in the centre and tapering to the top and bottom. This completely shuts off the entrance from the side of the balance which is resting on the bottom of the trap, while producing as small a projection as possible across the entrance which remains open. The height of the vertical division is arranged so that it just clears the under surface of the top as it is moved to and fro.

At each end of the upper part of the central compartment there is a small space enclosed with perforated metal

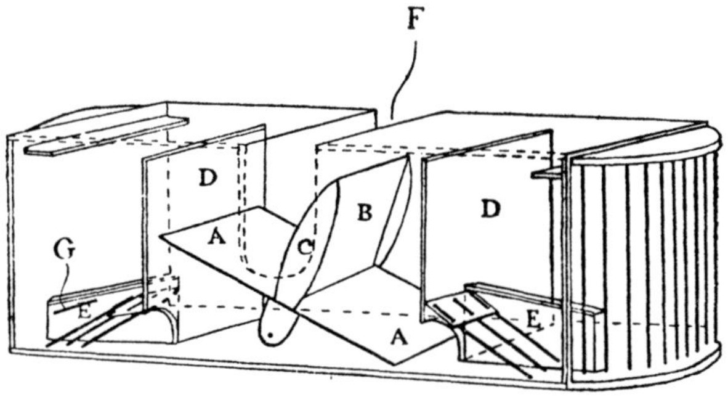

FIG. 47.—Colin Pullinger's Perpetual Mouse-trap. The diagram represents the side of the trap removed so that the arrangement of the balance, &c., can be seen. The receptacle for the food, and the bars at the left hand end of the trap, together with the movable portion of the top to enable the food racks to be reached, have been omitted to make the drawing more clear. A, balance. B, vertical transverse division of balance. C, rectangular end of vertical division. D, end of middle compartment. E, inner wall of passage. F, further side of entrance to trap. G, wire to prevent the door being lifted beyond the horizontal position—omitted for clearness of the diagram at the opposite end.

to form a rack in which grain or other food may be placed as an inducement for mice on entering the trap to go towards this end of the compartment.

The trap works as follows: While one end of the pivoted balance is resting on the bottom of the trap, the central division as a consequence leans in that direction and leaves a clear passage-way through the trap across the opposite end of the balance. A mouse on entering smells the grain, and on turning towards it weighs down the balance and tips it to this side of the trap. The prisoner is unable to escape because the balance cannot be thrown to the opposite side again until a greater weight is upon it. The mouse, however, sees the hole leading into the end compartment and passes through into the passage leading to it, lifting a sloping door $1\frac{1}{2}$ in. in length whilst so doing. This when closed again shuts off retreat.

In Mr. Colin Pullinger's trap the end compartment is entered by a passage-way $\frac{7}{8}$ in. in width, the door being formed by three wires held together at the top. Each passes through two holes in a piece of sheet-metal, bent up at a right-angle at each side and pierced, through which the wire passes upon which the door is hinged.

The outer wall of the passage is formed by the side of the trap, and the inner wall by a division (E) $1\frac{1}{8}$ in. in height. This is continued forward until it is in contact with the vertical bars which shut in the end of the trap. The door cannot be lifted beyond the horizontal position because a wire G (for clearness shown only on one side of the diagram) passes across the upper part of the passage rather beyond the centre.

The free ends of the three wires forming the lower half of the door, which rests in a sloping position, are $\frac{5}{8}$ in. from the vertical bars forming the end of the trap when the door is raised. Thus they leave a space through which the imprisoned mouse can squeeze up into the end compartment. When the mouse has reached the end compartment, the passage cannot be re-entered on account of the smallness of the space and because the end of the door is at a much lower level than the upper edge of the inner wall of the passage. If, however, the trap had been constructed so that the mouse could approach the door from the floor-level, it could be raised and the mouse could re-enter the passage.

Although to the inexperienced an aperture $\frac{5}{8}$ in. in length and $\frac{7}{8}$ in. in width may seem too small to allow a mouse to pass, yet those who are accustomed to the use of the trap are fully aware that it affords sufficient space. Not only can large house-mice pass, but even full-grown, long-tailed field mice and full-grown bank and field voles can enter the end compartment.

In Mr. Colin Pullinger's trap the mice were removed through an aperture created by unfastening a door, hinged at one side, which formed part of the floor of the end compartment and the passage leading to it. The advantage of this arrangement was that the door could be opened while the trap was held horizontally over a pail of water and the mice had no escape.

When the patent expired, several spurious imitations were put on the market and still remain there ; the alterations made being sufficient to do away with the efficiency of the trap for catching and conveniently killing the large number of mice that the Colin Pullinger trap secured.

The chief alteration made in the imitation traps consisted in removing the small door at one side of the end compartment as above described, and placing a door across the entire width of the end compartment. The effect of this alteration is that, although the first mouse caught pushes up the door and reaches the end compartment, the second mouse caught on this side, while entering the end compartment, allows the first one to escape back under the raised door on to the balance, and thus keeps any mouse of less weight from depressing the opposite side of the balance and being also caught. In the case of a small mouse which has escaped back on to the balance, a large mouse entering the trap will throw the balance on to the side he is on and consequently lift the small mouse to the set position of the trap and allow it to escape through the entrance to the trap. With this arrangement it is also impossible for a large number to be caught, because, even supposing several had got into the end compartment, their bodies would prevent the door from being lifted again.

Another stupid alteration consisted in doing away with the doors at the bottom of the trap and making two of the bars of the end compartment removable for the purpose of taking out the mice. Not only is it difficult to get a live mouse to pass through this aperture, but to ensure him falling into the water the trap must be held vertically, and when it is in this position the doors of both end compartments fall open and any mice in these compartments can pass on to the balance and escape through the entrance.

An improvement now made to the Colin Pullinger trap is that the floor of the end compartment is made in one piece, so that, when the floor is removed, all the mice in the compartment can be precipitated simultaneously into a pail of water. There they can be quickly killed by a blow with the back of a table-knife, or drowned by placing another pail inside the one containing them so as to submerge them. A deep pail should be used and the water ought to be not more than 3 to 4 in. in depth or more than is necessary to ensure them being submerged by the pail, as mice sometimes make a spring from the water. Dead mice are best burnt immediately, to prevent the escape of the fleas which infest them.

The trap should be turned upside down while the bottom of the compartment is being replaced to prevent the side door becoming jammed against it.

If a wire is used to keep the piece of glass or metal covering each side of the central compartment and the food racks in position, it ought to be made with a loop at one end, so that it can be easily withdrawn to enable fresh grain or other bait to be put into the racks. Bait requires to be renewed about once a fortnight. A hinged metal cover fastened with wire buttons would be most easily opened and closed.

IF THE PUBLIC WERE TO REFUSE TO PURCHASE BALANCE-TRAPS CONSTRUCTED WITHOUT THE SMALL SIDE-DOOR AND WITHOUT A DOOR ON THE BOTTOM AT EACH END FOR REMOVING THE MICE, MANUFACTURERS WOULD SOON CEASE TO MAKE THE COMPARATIVELY INEFFICIENT ARTICLES NOW ON THE MARKET.

INDEX.

John Bale, Sons and Danielsson, Ltd., 83-91, Great Titchfield Street, London, W. 1.

Lightning Source UK Ltd.
Milton Keynes UK
17 November 2009

146366UK00001B/236/A

9 781846 640261